Geology and Scenery in England and Wales

by

A. E. TRUEMAN

D.SC., F.R.S., F.G.S.

Formerly Professor of Geology in the
University of Glasgow

PENGUIN BOOKS

HARMONDSWORTH · MIDDLESEX

First published by Victor Gollancz Ltd under the title
'The Scenery of England and Wales' in 1938
Published in Pelican Books 1949
Reprinted 1952

*Made and printed in Great Britain
for Penguin Books Ltd
by R. & R. Clark Ltd, Edinburgh*

CONTENTS

CONTENTS

PREFACE TO NEW EDITION

IN recent years there has been a great quickening of interest in town and country planning, in land utilisation, in the scenery of our country and its preservation. The proposals for the creation of national parks and nature reserves are but one aspect of this developing interest. It is the author's hope that this little book in its cheaper form will do something to provide a basis for a wider appreciation of the scenic features of our countryside. Only minor modifications have been made since the original edition.

A. E. T.

1946

PREFACE TO FIRST EDITION

IN this book an attempt is made to describe the scenery of most of England and Wales, and to show how some of the features have come into being. It has been prepared because I believe that there are many people, motorists and walkers as well as students, who desire this kind of information, and because singularly few works on the subject are available. The recent spate of topographical works of one type or another, many of them of surpassing excellence, is evidence of the great interest taken in the English countryside by increasing numbers of people. And yet the scenic background of the village and church has received little attention.

The present volume is written partly though not entirely from the geological standpoint. I have tried to make my account intelligible to all who may be interested. There is no preliminary discussion of principles, and few technical terms are introduced. These are explained simply in the text as they are used, and rather more precisely in the glossary. But in any attempt at popularisation certain risks must arise, and I trust that my efforts at simplification have not led me to be too dogmatic or too general in my statements.

The work was started light-heartedly during a summer vacation; much of the earlier part was written in a quiet bay on the Cardigan coast. As the writing has proceeded I have become more and more conscious that what I have written falls short of what I had planned and I can only hope that the result is not wholly unworthy of the theme.

I hope that the broad ideas on geological history which will be gained from the reading of this book will encourage a wider appreciation of the science. For geology is pre-eminently the layman's science. In it more than in any other science there is opportunity for a beginner to make original observations, to weigh up evidence, to co-ordinate his facts and in general to acquire a truly scientific outlook, whereas a layman can do no more in many sciences than accept ready-made conclusions, often explained by clever but dangerous analogies, without any prospect of understanding the steps by which they have been reached.

Each chapter deals with one area or type of country, and they are so arranged that the more complex areas are described last. The more serious student will find it advantageous to read the chapters in order, but I think that the general reader will be more interested if he first turns to the areas with which he is familiar. It should be made clear, however, that the accounts of the various districts are not always complete in themselves, as certain features are best dealt with when other regions are being considered.

A. E. TRUEMAN

December, 1937

CHAPTER I

THE FOUNDATIONS OF SCENERY

IN England and Wales we are singularly placed to appreciate the relationship of scenery and structure, for few other parts of the earth's surface show in a similar small area so great a diversity of rock types and of landscape features. " Britain is a world by itself "; its mountains are not high, nor its rivers long, but within a few hundred miles of travel from east to west an Englishman may see more varieties of scenery than are to be found in many bigger countries.

There are hill-forms of every type; smooth-contoured Chalk downs in a great belt encircling the London basin, the long line of the Cotswold Edge, even-topped plateaux in Wales and Devon, bleak granite moorlands and craggy volcanic cliffs. All these types reflect their underlying structure and their origin is apparent in their shape.

In many of these different regions the native stone has given character and fitness to the buildings; the wide variety of stones, together with the frequent use of wood and brick and thatch, especially in the stoneless areas, has added a charm to English villages and towns, and has made the dwellings, particularly the smaller cottages (for stones for churches and large houses were carried for many miles even in early times) ideally suited to their surroundings. With the improvement of transport during the nineteenth century, building materials were more frequently carried over greater distances, and soon after the opening of railways houses began to lose that harmony with the countryside so characteristic of the older cottages. The towns which thus sprang up at some railway centres are dreadful examples of the way in which individuality was lost, but lately the housing estate has spread a new uniformity even more widely over the country.

It may be suggested that a traveller can appreciate these aspects of landscape without knowing anything of their anatomy, and that a geologist who must spend much of his time searching the ground is no fit guide for those who seek to know the countryside. It must be urged, however, that many never know an area until something of its meaning becomes clear to them, just as some may never feel comfortable in a strange town until they have seen a map of its streets. For a country is not just a jumble of hills and valleys; the features have a plan, a system underlying their distribution, and once this is understood the region is seen more clearly and its variety more readily appreciated. The geologist acquires an eye for country and an understanding of nature not excelled by that of the artist or the poet.

The areas described in the following chapters are chosen to illustrate the diversity in form and colour of different parts of England and Wales. The Cotswolds and comparable areas are dealt with first because they present a simplicity of structure which is not found in any other large region; the chalklands have some features in common with the Cotswolds, but their distribution introduces new problems of structure, which lead to a discussion of the London basin and the Weald, each bounded by Chalk regions, and of the south coast where the Hampshire basin may be likened to the London basin partly sunk beneath the sea. The areas of the west of England and of Wales are taken later, as they introduce greater complexity of structure.

In the description of these areas some reference is made to their geological history. Most of them are made up of sheets of sedimentary rock laid down on the floor of some ancient sea, but in some there are also sheets of lava and other rocks of igneous character. In general the scenery is controlled by the nature and form of these various beds, many of which have been bent, crumpled and broken at different times owing to the great movements in the earth's crust, the edges of the sheets thus reaching the surface at various angles.

These sediments were laid down in the seas which at different times have covered the area which is now Britain. Of the antiquity of the rocks there is no doubt, but it is not sufficient merely to think of all these rocks as having been formed millions of years ago. They represent a sequence of events, and their histories can be related to a time scale. An Irish railwayman, seeing the writer examining the crumpled rocks by Waterford station, ventured the observation that he supposed nobody living now saw those rocks bend! He was right, but he could not realise how right he was, for the appearance of the first men on the earth, a few million years ago, was but yesterday compared with the age of those folds. But there is no need to worry about putting our time-scale into years; it is sufficient to realise that an area composed of very ancient rocks may have undergone many changes since the rocks were first formed and though the surface features are built up by the old bed-rocks many of them may be of comparatively recent origin. Most of the river valleys of England and Wales have been formed within periods which from a geological point of view are comparatively recent—perhaps ten or twenty million years at most. Almost at the end of that time, and finishing not more than a few thousand years ago, the great Ice Age led to important modifications in the surface of many parts of Britain.

In the description of most areas little reference is made to this question of a time-scale, but in order that the more scientifically inclined reader may get a more precise knowledge of the relations of the various episodes which are touched upon here and there, a brief account of the chronology is added as a final chapter, and frequent reference to the diagrams on pages 311 and 316 may help to indicate more clearly the sequence of events. And if there are readers who would say that scientists have no right to talk in terms of those inconceivably long periods we may point out that the geologist is as well able to appreciate the hundreds of millions of years representing the age of the earth as the Chancellor of the Exchequer is able to appreciate the total of his budget.

CHAPTER II

THE COTSWOLD STONE BELT

THE Cotswold Hills, stretching north-eastwards from near Bath and merging, sixty miles away, into the uplands of Northamptonshire, form an area of essentially similar characters. In this area the land rises in few places above 1000 feet, but the general altitude is between 400 and 800 feet. Rising gradually from the low vales of Oxford, the greatest heights are near the western boundary, where the hills fall away rapidly to the Midland plain and the Vale of Severn. This steep scarp face is indeed the most impressive feature of the Cotswolds and forms a boundary of unmistakable distinctness.

Travelling westwards by coach, Sydney Smith was impressed by this contrast, and his forceful description emphasises at least one essential fact: "The sudden variation from the hill country of Gloucestershire to the Vale of Severn, as observed from Birdlip or Frowcester Hill, is strikingly sublime. You travel for twenty or five-and-twenty miles over one of the most unfortunate desolate counties under heaven, divided by stone walls, and abandoned to the screaming kites and larcenous crows: after travelling really twenty and to appearance ninety miles over this region of stone and sorrow, life begins to be a burden, and you wish to perish. At the very moment when you are taking this melancholy view of human affairs and hating the postilion and blaming the horses, there bursts upon your view, with all its towers, forests and streams, the deep and shaded Vale of Severn."

We need not say that Smith was unkind to the Cotswolds in this account, but he doubtless shared with many of his time a dislike for upland country. It is not necessary, however, to defend the Cotswolds against his charges. This is an area of stone though not of sorrow ; indeed, in illustration of the change of attitude to such uplands, we may note that a more recent traveller (J. B. Priestley) has felt that the Cotswold walls know " the trick of keeping the lost sunlight of centuries glimmering upon them."

The Cotswold Hills as well as their villages are built of stone, mostly of the light-coloured limestone which weathers to rich and varied tints of brown and yellow. Often these rocks are near the surface, and the light-brown soils in the fields are thin and made up of a rubble of pale limestone fragments. In many areas the fields are divided by dry-stone walls, dug long since from long shallow quarries which often extend along the roadside. The buildings likewise are almost universally of stone, and the whole area has a fitness of colour and pattern that cannot but be a delight to modern eyes. A single building of brick here becomes an eyesore.

It is clear then that the essential characters of this area are determined by the rocks. These limestones are to be seen in innumerable small quarries, and in the stone walls themselves. In many parts they are full of shells of various types, together with corals in some cases. They certainly represent deposits laid down on an ancient sea floor, and it is apparent that a wide area of such a sea floor has been elevated into these hills, for rocks of similar type (and in fact of equivalent age) cover the hill-tops over the whole region. Where quarries make the arrangement of the rocks visible, it is seen that they occur in beds lying more or less horizontally : actually the beds are tilted very slightly, and if they are examined over a sufficiently wide area they will be found to tilt gently towards the east, although locally they may be inclined westwards : when they were upraised from beneath the sea they were lifted higher on the west than on the east, the minor rolls resulting from irregularities in the original uplift or from slight changes at subsequent times.

Many of the limestones possess a structure which is known as oolitic, and these rocks are frequently spoken of as the oolites. Such oolitic limestones consist mainly of minute rounded spheres of calcium carbonate, massed together and resembling the roe of a fish, from which they derive their name (Fig. 1). Many such limestones show

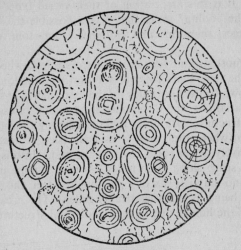

Figure 1.—Thin section of oolite from
Leckhampton, Cheltenham.
Magnified ten times.

an oblique lamination, indicating that the rounded grains have been arranged by strong currents in shallow water, and it may be taken as generally true that the limestones of this area are of shallow water origin. But not all are oolites: it is obvious that some are composed of shells or shell fragments. The nature of the stone, as well as the thickness of the beds, has controlled its use for building. The shelly limestones break irregularly and in general can only be used for rough walling, while some of the thicker oolite beds are much more readily dressed into blocks of any required shape. The quarrymen thus recognise ' freestones ' (which can be so dressed) and ' ragstones '. Many of the freestones can be cut easily when freshly quarried, but harden on exposure. The thinner beds of limestone are used largely for roofing purposes, and are locally known as ' slates ', though of course they differ greatly from the true slates of Wales. It is this association of such varied types of rock within the ' oolite ' series that makes possible the building of cottages, mansions and churches from stone of local origin.

The most striking feature in the Cotswolds is the general form; the steep scarp slope on the west, and the long gentle slope down to the clay vales on the east. Notwithstanding minor variations, the Cotswolds are a region of essentially simple structure, with older rocks occupying the surface in the west (where the newer ones have been removed) and progressively newer rocks towards the east. In this upland area the scarp slope often takes less than a mile, in which the ground may rise six or eight hundred feet, the slope to the east being as much as twenty miles. The great asymmetry of the hills is due to their geological structure, being

Figure 2.—A receding escarpment.

controlled by the dip or tilt of the limestone beds. The simplified section shown in Figure 2 will best help to make this clear. The limestones, which are tilted eastwards or south-eastwards, meet the surface in the top of the steep face on the west, where they are seen to be underlain by other rocks among which clays are most abundant. Many other hill ridges in central and southern England are of this character, a hard bed of sandstone or limestone between softer beds producing such an unsymmetrical hill.

The attack of the weather along the steep slope wears away the softer clays more rapidly than the limestones; moreover, the rain which falls on the limestone mostly sinks underground, scarcely affecting the limestone surface, while that which falls on the clay, and that which rises in springs along the junction of the two, flows over the clay and carries some of it continuously downhill. This steep slope therefore tends to be always concave, the clay being to some extent hollowed from underneath the limestone. Those who drive or cycle up the face of such a hill will be familiar with this type of change of slope, at any rate on old roads, for many newer roads are more carefully graded.

The continuation of these processes leads to the limestone being so far undermined that in time portions may slip down the slope, to be broken up gradually while the weather attacks a new surface of clay and again produces the concave form of hill. In short, any position of the edge is only temporary, and, although very slowly, the effects of rain and weather have caused it to recede to positions farther east than those it once occupied. It will be apparent, therefore, that when speaking of the Cotswold limestones as representing a former sea floor which has been upraised, it must not be thought that the present border of the Cotswolds marks the limit either of the sea floor or of the uplift. The possible extent of the Cotswolds at an earlier stage need not be discussed, but clearly if the Cotswold uplands extended far to the west, there was at that time no Vale of Gloucester, a point to which reference may suitably be made later.

The fact that the Cotswolds formerly extended farther to the west is shown by the existence of a number of detached outliers of the main ridge. One of the most notable of these is Dundry Hill, an elongated hill about four miles south of Bristol, which is separated by six miles from the present limestone edge on the north-west of Bath. This outlier of Dundry shows that the whole of the area between

Bristol and Bath must once have been covered by the oolite limestones: moreover, Dundry shows the characteristic scenery and building stones of a Cotswold area though it is cut off by the other types which surround it. From the Dundry quarries was obtained stone for the beautiful church of St. Mary Redcliffe, in Bristol. Scenically and agriculturally as well as geologically, Dundry is an outlier of the Cotswolds.

Smaller outliers, though even more striking, rise sharply out of the plain near Gloucester to form Robin's Wood

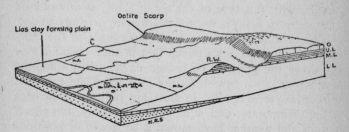

Figure 3.—The Cotswolds and outliers at Gloucester.
O., Oolite; L.L., M.L., U.L., Lower, Middle and Upper Lias; N.R.S., New Red Sandstone.

Hill, to the south of Gloucester, and Churchdown, between Gloucester and Cheltenham (Fig. 3), while farther north again the larger mass of Bredon Hill, between Evesham and Tewkesbury, is still more conspicuous.

It will be useful to speak of the Cotswold ridge as an escarpment, a ridge controlled by the occurrence of a hard band between softer bands, the worn edge giving rise to a steep slope while the exposed upper surface of the hard band forms a gentle slope, the amount of slope being determined by the dip or amount of tilt of the beds; in each such ridge there is thus a scarp slope and a dip slope. The Cotswold area is a typical scarpland, for not only may the whole mass be regarded as a great escarpment, but within the mass itself all the minor features resulting from the occurrence of clays between the limestones similarly exhibit steep westward-facing slopes and gentle eastward-facing slopes.

William Smith, one of the founders of geological science, likened this type of structure to slices of bread and butter arranged on a plate, a helpful comparison which must not be carried too far, for there is nothing different or permanent about the crust of the slices. The cyclist crossing the country used to be well aware of these different slopes: going from west to east he had short but steep slopes to climb, with long easy runs down the dip slopes, while on his return he had long dreary climbs, with steep descents that were often too sharp to be ridden in safety. True, improved roads have to some extent eased out many of these gradients, but the asymmetry of the hills is still marked enough to impress itself on the motorist, the stiff gradients of the Cotswold edge, notably at Birdlip, being well known. In south Gloucestershire the scarp is still used for the game of cheese-rolling.

The view from the Cotswold edge across the valley to the west is always impressive. From Frocester Hill near Stroud and from Leckhampton Hill near Cheltenham the view embraces the wide clay plain, with its outlying oolitic hills, with the Severn widening out into its estuary, and beyond, the irregular crest of Malvern and the round mass of May Hill with its crown of trees, marking the real boundary of the English plain.

The front of the ridge is often wooded: beech is the commonest tree on these dry soils, but pines have also been planted in some areas. Cranham Woods north of Painswick, traversed by the road from Cheltenham to Stroud, afford many beautiful glimpses over the plain. But though the scarp is steep, it varies greatly in pattern. From Old Sodbury for some eight miles it extends due north in almost a straight line, but thence to Dursley and Stroud the upland is deeply curved and its edge is fretted into long winding valleys of striking beauty. Here too the edge is complicated by the presence of a low narrow terrace, corresponding to the position of a hard band of ferruginous limestone (Marlstone) which occurs among the Lias clays underlying the oolites (Fig. 4). Near Gloucester and Cheltenham the scarp is rather simple in pattern, but as Worcestershire is approached it is cut by the wide embayment of ·the Vale of Moreton. There is little marsh hereabouts but Moreton-in-Marsh aptly suggests the great

Figure 4.—The Cotswold Edge, north of Wotton-under-Edge.
The lower terrace is formed by a hard band (the Marlstone of the Lias).

southward extension of the clays which floor the Vale of Gloucester and the Vale of Evesham.

Along the whole of this tract, no river flowing from west to east crosses the Cotswold edge. On the upland, however, the bulk of the rivers flow from west to east, or from northwest to south-east. All these streams follow the general direction of the dip of the beds, and some would call them dip streams or consequent streams, since their direction may be a consequence of the inclination of the beds on which they flow. Chief among these rivers is the Thames itself, though which of several streams is the real source is open to discussion. These dip streams occupy wide and generally shallow valleys on the upland surface. Indeed they introduce the chief diversity into the uplands, for along many of them extend belts of woodland and in them are situated many of the villages, for the availability of water supply was a prime factor in determining the location of many of the early settlements. Many valleys are dry, but nevertheless water may be obtained in them by wells of smaller depth than are required in the main part of the upland.

The origin of the Cotswold dry valleys has been variously explained. It is certain that they have been cut by water and in most cases the problem is to explain the disappearance of the stream. In some cases it is possible that the solubility of the limestone in water has allowed the stream to make for itself a deeper course, leaving the valley dry, but it has been suggested that many of these dry valleys were cut by melt waters flowing from snow or ice caps which were situated on the higher uplands during the Ice Age. This part of England was not covered by glaciers, as were areas farther north, but during the more intensely cold periods snow may have accumulated on the higher ground, giving rise when it melted to temporary but powerful streams. This explanation of the drying of some of these valleys is supported by the fact that they ' hang ' above the stream-bearing valleys to which they are tributary ; these valleys, watered from springs which have continued to flow, have been progressively deepened since the ice disappeared, leaving the springless tributary valleys in disharmonious junction with the main stream.

Within this upland region there are no large towns : on its flanks lie Bath and Gloucester to the west, and Chippenham and Swindon to the east, but these belong rather to the vales than to the upland, except in so far as they have formed markets for the exchange of the produce of the adjoining regions with their differing products. The towns of the Cotswolds themselves are smaller and most of them have grown very little for many years. Few are situated in the highest part of the upland, Minchinhampton and Stow-on-the-Wold being almost alone in their hill-top situations. The other Cotswold market towns have lower sites, usually where old routes cross the valleys. Cirencester, Tetbury, Malmesbury, Northleach, Chipping Norton and others are spaced at intervals of ten or twenty miles, that is at such a distance that market centres were within suitable reach of all parts.

Many of these warm brown towns were more important in mediaeval times, when they were centres of the wool industry; then the value of Cotswold fleeces was widely recognised, and from these market towns wool was exported to the Continent. In many cases the towns were beautified by the merchants who prospered during the fourteenth century, and who built or extended churches and wool-markets, and they have been little changed in recent years, although their importance declined when the wool was no longer exported for weaving.

Many of them are spacious towns: their streets are wide, for the main street has served as market-place. The better houses are built from large well-dressed stones, with windows of fine masonry. Many have steeply pitched gabled roofs formed of Cotswold slates. Generally the larger slates are hung at the eaves, and they get smaller towards the ridge; mostly they are hung dry with oak or deal pegs, or, more recently, with nails. One notable feature is the arrangement of the slates where roofs of different angles adjoin, for in these ' valleys ' the slates form one wide sweep, with no sharp line of demarcation between one roof and the next. The churches and more important buildings have derived their stones from well-known beds in large quarries: some stones of Malmesbury and Lacock Abbeys were from Box. But the materials for smaller buildings were not carried for any great distances, and they were usually dug in the neighbourhood of the town itself. Even in the smallest cottages, however, the stone-work of he chimneys and of the windows is carefully dressed, though it may be placed side by side with rough walling. Some of the towns which are built on flatter ground, so that the view does not include a massing of buildings, are much less pleasing; this is the case at Marshfield, which has some fine houses but in the absence of trees is one of the dreariest towns on the hills.

The villages of this area share these same characteristics as regards buildings (Fig. 8). But they show greater variety in arrangement and in scenic features. Many of the cottages date from the sixteenth century but few have conspicuous architectural dating.

THE VALLEYS OF THE COTSWOLD EDGE

The towns and villages of some valleys nearer the Cotswold edge have more individual characteristics. They are situated in valleys which are far deeper and narrower than those of the main part of the upland. This results in part from the fact that the rivers of this area are flowing along a steep path to the sea in the Bristol Channel rather than into the Thames, and have been enabled to cut down their beds more rapidly. The two most important of these west-flowing streams are the Bristol Avon and that Frome which traverses the Stroud valley (for each of these names is shared by several rivers). These two rivers, with some smaller streams in the same area, and with their various tributaries, have cut valleys which extend for miles into the upland area.

The Avon commences above Malmesbury as a stream essentially similar to the dip streams of the upland area, but shortly it turns almost at right angles, to follow a wide open valley through Chippenham (where a temporarily narrow valley makes possible an easy crossing) to the picturesque town of Bradford-on-Avon, whence by a deep gorge the river winds its way through the oolite uplands to Bath. The rest of its course to the sea is equally anomalous. The Frome, if it does not commence as a dip stream, intercepts such streams above Miserden, and then likewise flows south to Sapperton where it also turns sharply west and cuts a deep narrow valley from which it escapes at Stroud.

The cutting of deep gorges by these streams has produced

quite a different type of relief in these areas compared with that of the main part of the uplands. The upland surface is more broken up or dissected than farther east, for whereas in that area the valleys often form mere channels in a moderately even surface, the valleys here cut the surface into narrow and irregular strips, pieces of the upland surface being frequently cut off from the main mass.

Examples are well seen in Cam Long Down, which when seen from the hill above Dursley is clearly recognisable as a detached portion of the neighbouring upland which has been isolated by the efforts of the little stream flowing into

Figure 5.—Cam Long Down and other outliers of the Cotswolds, north of Dursley, Glos. The Severn plain is to the left.

the Dursley valley (Fig. 5). The long irregular tongue of upland culminating in Stinchcombe Hill is only connected with the main area of high ground by a ridge a few hundred yards wide between Waterley Bottom and the Dursley valley; it is interesting to notice how the only good road on to this tract makes use of the 'isthmus'. Obviously a little further erosion by these streams, carrying their sources farther back into the plateau, will separate this also as an outlier. From a consideration of these instances, it is apparent that the rivers have produced much of the present topography, and an examination of this area shows also how such outlying hills as Robin's Wood Hill and Dundry have been cut off from the Cotswolds.

It is, however, by no means easy to explain the anomalous courses of these streams. It is clear that streams flowing down the scarp face, from near the scarp summit to the plain a short distance away, must have a very steep gradient and must therefore flow almost as torrents : their average gradient is in many cases as much as 1 in 10. They reach an elevation of 200 feet above sea-level after flowing possibly mile, whereas the streams flowing on the dip slope may flow some scores of miles before they reach an equivalent level. Thus the scarp streams have much greater cutting power than the dip streams, and they not only deepen their valleys but simultaneously carry back their sources, extending their valleys into the upland.

This tendency of swiftly flowing streams to push back their sources into the upland frequently results in such a stream intercepting the drainage of another valley. Such extension of west-flowing streams and capture of dip streams may perhaps explain the development of the west-flowing portions of the Frome and the Avon.

These valleys around Stroud and Bath have other peculiarities. Their towns and villages are hemmed in by the steep hills, and houses are ranged in picturesque fashion along the tree-clad slopes. The Avon valley about Limpley Stoke is well known : the Frome valley (better known as the Stroud valley and aptly named the Golden Valley) is not less attractive : it is glimpsed from the Great Western Railway line into Gloucester, but it merits closer inspection. The tributary valleys are more beautiful than those of the main streams, just as their villages are more unspoiled than such towns as Stroud which shows too much modern expansion to allow of comparison with the older Cotswold towns, or even with Bath. This latter is best admired from a distance, as from the road running north along the Cotswold Edge or from Combe Down : then the silver grey of its terraces, its beautiful bridges and the sombre Abbey emphasise the delight of its situation in the hollow of the hills.

The valleys tributary to the Avon both on the north and

Figure 6.—Castle Combe.

south have been deepened for many miles. One of the most interesting is the By Brook which joins the Avon at Bathford after intercepting numerous dip streams on its right bank. So deep is the valley carved by this brook that the Fosse Way from Bath to Cirencester was kept to the west of it and turned abruptly at its head. The most interesting village in this valley is Castle Combe, perhaps the most perfect village of the Cotswolds (Fig. 6). Some will hold that other villages are as beautiful but certainly none are more unspoilt. In this village every cottage is a picture, every view is delightful. The brook runs for some way through the village street, and the irregular grouping of the houses around the market cross, with the thickly wooded hill slopes, makes a scene in which no touch of modernity, unless it is a visiting car, seems to intrude. Farther down the same valley is the smaller and similar but less-known village of Slaughterford, while in close proximity are such upland villages as Biddestone, which differ in having had greater room to grow, and spread themselves casually around the extensive village greens.

In the valleys of the Stroud area are many larger villages, which grew to importance with the growth of the home woollen industry. The waters of this area proved well suited to dyeing, and hand looms were formerly found in nearly every cottage. Later the mills have supplied water power, and small modern factories are to be found in most of these valleys, but they do not detract greatly from their picturesqueness. This area became the great broad-cloth region, while towns of the uplands, handicapped in many cases by lack of water (and of water power), lost their wool trade, or, as in the case of Tetbury, took up such branches of the industry as wool-combing and spinning. But many of these little towns, though situated in the deep hollows within the Cotswold belt, are rather of the vale than of the upland, and places like Nailsworth show a mixture of building materials, brick and tile being used side by side with stone in a way

quite unlike that of the real stone area, but here without any
loss of attractiveness.

Southwards from Bath and Frome the stone belt forms
a much less impressive feature, but it may be traced through
Somerset and Dorset, forming wooded scarps rarely over
five hundred feet high. Several distinct ridges are present
in places, running more or less parallel to one another.
The more prominent overlooks the Somerset plain near
Bruton and Castle Cary, extending south to beyond Sher-
borne. To the east these ridges slope down into the clay
country, in part the Vale of Blackmoor so well described
in Hardy's *Tess of the d'Urbervilles*.

THE CLAY COUNTRY EAST OF COTSWOLD

All along its extent the stone belt sinks gently to the east,
to the area where the limestones pass beneath the clays
which floor the vale stretching with small intermediate
elevations almost to the foot of the Chalk hills. Where the
Cotswolds join this belt of clays a line of towns and settlements occurs, some prospering, as we have noted, as market
or exchange towns between the adjacent regions, most of
them benefiting by the more abundant water supply which
becomes available when the clay belt is reached. Along
this border-line more varied agriculture is possible, for
whereas the limestone soils are light and dry, some soils of
the adjoining region are heavy. On these clays the beech
woods of the limestone tract are replaced by denser woods
of oak, while great areas are devoted to meadowland, the
chief activities being cattle rearing and dairy farming.

This clay belt stretches through Trowbridge to Oxford
and Bedford. It is interrupted by a discontinuous ridge
which is well seen in the neighbourhood of Oxford, where
the Corallian limestones (often similar in general character
to the coral limestones of the Cotswolds, but of somewhat
more recent age) give rise to an escarpment quite comparable
to that of the Cotswolds but of smaller elevation. This

ridge, with its concave scarp facing to the west and its dip slope to the east, rarely exceeds 300 feet in height, but in this wide flat vale it makes a conspicuous line of hills which are rather too emphatically known as the Oxford Heights. To the west of this the clays are known as the Oxford Clay, to the east as the Kimmeridge Clay, but both are grey-blue clays and for our present purpose further distinction is unnecessary.

In the clays the rivers are able to cut down their beds

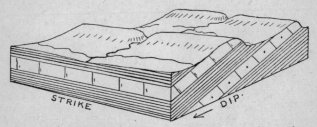

Figure 7.—Diagram to show strike and dip features in a series of limestones and shales.
A dip stream cuts through the escarpments, and subsequent tributaries flow in the strike valleys.

more rapidly than on the limestones: as these outcrops are lowered they tend to form valleys and the dip streams from the Cotswold slope frequently turn at right angles to flow along the clay belt. They thus follow the strike of the rocks, as in the case of the Thames in the Vale of the White Horse south-west of Oxford. Subsequently the Thames turns once more to follow the dip and cuts through the little escarpment o Corallian limestone. The situation of Oxford was determined by this gap in the miniature ridge which provided a dry land route in a clay district where formerly there were extensive marshes.

The tendency of rivers in this region to form systems with a more or less rectangular pattern illustrates a fundamental feature in river evolution. Dip streams or consequents determined by the inclination of the original slope on which drainage was initiated represent the first stage in river development, but where softer beds occur, tributaries presently begin to develop at right angles to them along the outcrop of the softer rocks, and where rapid erosion is possible these streams (known by many as subsequents because they are only formed after the dip streams, or as strike streams because they follow the trend or strike of the beds) become the more important in the river system. But

Figure 8.—A Cotswold farm, Slaughterford.

for long the pattern of tributaries at right angles to the main streams persists, and in country of simple structure, controlled by gently dipping beds as in the case of the Cotswolds, this pattern is almost always characteristic (Fig. 7).

In this clay-belt, stone has been used only for churches and larger houses, and of course for the Oxford colleges: for almost all of these the Cotswold quarries have provided the materials. But the city of grey towers is rapidly becoming a city of red roofs, while the cottages in this tract are mostly of brick and there are extensive clay pits in many areas, especially at Peterborough. So we find that in travelling from the stone belt towards the east we pass from towns that are almost wholly of stone, such as Bradford-on-Avon, to Trowbridge, where a moderate proportion of stone houses is still found but where red brick is plentiful, or to Lacock, where stone, half-timbered and red brick houses are side by side, and so to Westbury where stone is rare, as it is also in most of the villages of the clay area. The suddenness of the change in domestic building materials in passing from one area to another suitably emphasises the local source of most of the materials; equally noticeable in its scenic effect is the replacement of stone walls by hedges.

CHAPTER III

THE NORTHERN EXTENSION
OF THE STONE BELT

FOLLOWING the Cotswold belt to the north-east, the Northampton Uplands and their extension into Leicestershire next call for brief comment. Essentially the structure is quite similar to that of the Cotswold area. From the crest of a steep escarpment facing westwards there is a wide view across the plain of the English Midlands, while to the south-east the surface slopes gently down to the clay plain, its dip face showing irregular steps owing to successive hard bands coming to the surface. The north-western face of the ridge in this area is made by a group of ironstones, the Middle Lias ironstone or Marlstone: the equivalent of this rock was mentioned in describing the Dursley area, where it forms a low platform or terrace along the face of the main scarp (Fig. 4). Northwards this rock becomes thicker and stronger and itself forms the front of the upland for many miles. The oolite limestones form more or less distinct and parallel ridges. This upland has less altitude than that of the Cotswolds, its height being little over 500 feet, but it has been deeply dissected by several rivers, as by the Cherwell and its tributaries at Banbury and the Nen at Northampton. These valleys compare in character with those of the Stroud area but they are generally wider and more open.

This area has also its famous building stones, the quarries at Barnack in north Northamptonshire having yielded stones which were in constant use in mediaeval England, supplying stones for Peterborough and Boston and for many churches in the Fen country and for other areas where they could be carried by water. Ketton in Rutland likewise supplied the stone used not only locally but in some of the Cambridge colleges. Stamford is a most delightful town of stone buildings.

On through Leicestershire a similar type of country continues, the Middle Lias ironstone forming the sharp ridge on which Belvoir Castle stands, overlooking the Vale of Belvoir on its north-west. Throughout much of its outcrop this ironstone is a deep brown or orange colour, and imparts a richness to the colour of the fields; it has been used in many of the walls, which appear quite distinct from those of the oolite tracts. The ironstone is extensively quarried at many places along its outcrop. This is a bedded ore quite different from many iron ores, which occupy irregular veins traversing other rocks; the ironstone of workable quality here forms a bed some ten feet or more in thickness which extends for many miles along the outcrop, and south-eastwards passes underneath the newer rocks which occur above it. The quarries are shallow and extensive, the thin soil being removed to an area already worked as the ore is quarried, the fields from which the ore is dug being thus lowered by some ten or more feet below the level of the roads or of any unworkable areas, and the country presents a curiously uneven appearance.

THE LINCOLNSHIRE STONE BELT

The Lincoln Cliff is the most striking feature in the county. Running almost due north and south it rises very steeply on the west from the extension of the Midland plain. It has no great elevation, for it rarely rises more than 150 feet above the low ground to the west, but its straightness and sharpness make up for its lack of height, and facing such a wide expanse of flat and often marshy country, its scarp is no less impressive than that of the Cotswolds. East of the edge is a dip slope some four or five miles in width, known as the Heath, an area which is commonly treeless and almost devoid of surface streams:

it has a few dry shallow valleys, and in this feature, and in its dry-stone walls, it greatly resembles portions of the Cotswold stone belt. For long, however, it remained almost uncultivated, and much of it was heathland until the Napoleonic wars : as a consequence it has few villages and it lacks much of the attractiveness of that area.

East of the Heath is a wide clay vale, and as is the case further south, where the limestone tract meets the clay there is a chain of settlements. Here also the clay has been readily eroded, and several streams follow the outcrop in strike valleys, the Ancholme to the Humber, and the Langworth, rising near the Ancholme within the clay vale itself, to the Witham and so to the Wash.

Along the western face of the Cliff are numerous small villages, their sites determined by the spring line at the junction of the limestone and the underlying clays, for much of the rainfall of the limestone area passes underground to flow out where the clays prevent further downward percolation. These villages are at almost regular intervals of one mile, and as in the case of Coleby and Boothby Graffoe, their parish boundaries extend for a greater distance east and west than from north to south : in this way each parish includes below the village an area of low meadowland, and above it a portion of the drier Heath, an arrangement which is frequently found along the junction of two areas of different type.

As has already been pointed out, the most impressive feature of the Cliff is its simplicity and regularity. From just north of Grantham to the Humber the scarp forms an almost unbroken line, scarcely crossed by any rivers. In about fifty miles it is only cut by one gap of any importance, that at Lincoln. Here the Witham has cut through the Cliff a narrow gorge, on the north of which stands Lincoln : the castle guarding the crossing of the river by the old route which naturally followed the crest of the scarp, above the swampy lowlands. The cathedral now dominates the city, and the view from the west, with the old town clustered along the steep hill slopes above the river, is one of the happiest in England. But like other similar gaps, whether through escarpments or mountain ranges, the Lincoln Gap has also affected more recent transport development, save that the railway uses the gap to escape the high ground whereas the old roads were forced to descend at the gap: the result, however, is similar, for Lincoln has extended rather awkwardly over the plain in response to its development as a railway and engineering centre.

The Lincoln Gap affords a clear illustration of the tendency for rivers to follow the strike of the soft beds rather than to flow with the dip, which involves crossing the outcrops of soft and hard beds alike. For formerly much of the Trent drainage which now reaches the sea by the Humber flowed through the Lincoln Gap, and there is still an almost open path for Trent water along this course, so that even in recent times flood water from the Trent has found its way through the gap into the Wash. But the lower Trent has cut down its valley along the soft clays to the Humber and has left only a diminutive Witham in possession of its original gap.

THE MOORS OF NORTH-EAST YORKSHIRE

In Yorkshire the stone belt is only represented in a very modified form. The moors of north-east Yorkshire may be regarded as its continuation, but they differ greatly in many ways. For much of this extensive upland tract, some thirty miles wide and fifteen miles from north to south, is beautiful heather moorland over 1000 feet high, cut by deep steep-sided dales. Generally the upland surface is smooth or gently undulating, and the dales are narrow. The chief roads therefore avoid the valleys and afford wonderful views over the moors; those from Whitby to Pickering and Scarborough are well known for their beautiful scenery.

Limestones are here much thinner than in the Cotswolds

or even in Lincolnshire, and these moors are made up of a varied series of rocks—shales, ironstones, grits and limestones—ranging in age from the Lias to the Corallian. The region thus lacks some of the essential characters of the simpler parts of the stone belt, and there is more variety of soil and land form. There are no such characteristically limestone soils as in the Cotswolds, and while grey stone is much used in building, red tiles are also very abundant.

The highest parts of the moors are mostly to be found along the east-west line running from Goathland through Glaisdale Moor and Westerdale Moor; from this line the dales generally run north and south, the streams flowing north being tributary to the Esk while those going south enter the Vale of Pickering.

In view of this arrangement of the streams it is not surprising that they have cut no through route across the area: each valley normally ends up among the moors, though Bilsdale extends so far to the north that it almost reaches the scarp edge, and provides one valley route across the area.

Within the moors themselves there are no towns and few villages, for on account of the elevated position, little ground is cultivated. Many villages are to be found around the borders of the area, however, and especially along the southern edge, where the dales open out into the Vale of Pickering; here are situated the old market towns of Pickering and Helmsley, and a dozen smaller places. The dales, however, have always been quiet, and Rievaulx Abbey in Rye Dale, not far from Helmsley, has a very lonely site, hemmed in between the river and green hills, scarcely rivalled in its beauty of setting by any ecclesiastical ruin except possibly that of Tintern.

The northern and western borders of the moors are very distinct. On the west they rise sharply from the Vale of Mowbray where the scarp, terraced owing to the harder bands among the shales, rises in a few steps to over 1200 feet in the Hambledon Hills. This scarp is somewhat fretted, but only by swift scarp streams flowing into the Vale. Further to the north-west and north there are some outliers of the moors beyond Guisborough Moor, of which Roseberry Topping is perhaps most conspicuous, capped by a bed of hard grit, with terraced slopes owing to the alternation of harder and softer beds. In places the grits have weathered into strange forms; the Bride Stones near Pickering are best known among these.

Along the northern border of the moors, that is particularly along the Cleveland Hills, the ironstone bands of the Middle Lias, which are mined in Northamptonshire, are again of workable quality. Although they were known and dug more than a century ago, it was only about 1850 that they led to the development of the important iron industry which now centres on Middlesbrough, a town which grew from a population of 154 in 1831 to over 7000 in 1851.

The only really continuous channel across the moors from north to south is Newtondale, the winding route by which the railway traverses the moors from Pickering to Whitby. It lies just west of the main road which follows a more direct path over the moors. For the greater part of its length this is not a river valley; Newtondale is in fact an old glacial spill-way or overflow valley, which originated during the Ice Age at a time when ice along the coast and in Eskdale held up the drainage from the northern slopes of the moors, forming lakes in each of the dales. The waters rose in these lakes, held up by the ice in front and the hills behind, until they overflowed from one valley into the next, and then these waters reached such a height that they were able to pour over the water-parting at its lowest point and to flow into the Vale of Pickering. This condition is illustrated in Figure 9, where the solid black area represents the lakes which overflowed at the eastern end. This rush of water led to the carving of the dale, which with the opening of drainage channels to the north on the disappearance of the ice, has been left without any

streams proportional to its size. Like other overflows of
its kind, it is characterised by its steep sides and its wide
and nearly flat floor: unlike the other dales which are
generally wider on the softer rocks, its form is little affected
by the rocks which it traverses, and the small supply of
water using it is inadequate for complete drainage so that

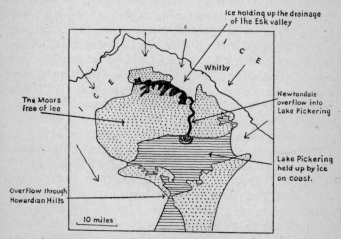

Figure 9.—Ice-dammed lakes in north-east Yorkshire.

*Ice-covered regions unshaded, arrows showing direction of ice move-
ment; land, dotted. The Eskdale lakes shown black together with
their spillway, Newtondale. Lake Pickering and its overflow shown
by lines.*

peat bogs develop (as at Fen Bog). Where the waters left
the hills at Pickering they laid down a deltaic deposit
shown by concentric lines on Figure 9.

THE YORKSHIRE COAST

The coast of this area exhibits very clearly its main
structures. The high cliffs show a sequence of almost
horizontal or slightly undulating beds, grey shales and
clays, or brown sandstone and limestones predominating

in different parts. Owing to the strong joints which cross the beds almost at right angles, and along which the rocks break away under the action of the waves, the cliffs are often vertical, but the clays tend to wear down into smoother slopes more quickly than the sandstones and limestones, so that the variation of rock types introduces a fascinating diversity of cliff form and colour. The changing dip brings first one bed then another to form the curved reefs which

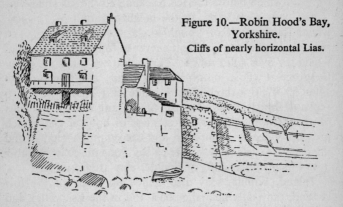

Figure 10.—Robin Hood's Bay, Yorkshire.
Cliffs of nearly horizontal Lias.

are exposed on the foreshore at low water. Where the softer clays of the lower part of the Lias are brought up into the cliff by gentle folds the coast has been cut back to form bays, such as Robin Hood's Bay (Fig. 10). And in these are placed delightful villages of red-tiled cottages which are perched irregularly on the steep hillsides. Around the coast there are in fact more settlements than in the moors themselves, and Whitby and Scarborough are the largest towns in the area, although these have a life which is almost independent of the moors.

At intervals along this coast quite another element enters into the construction of the cliffs, and produces a strongly contrasted type of coast scenery. This consists of the deposits formed by the glaciers to which reference was made above (Fig. 9) As these melted they left behind a vast irregular mass of material which they had gathered from the rocks over which they had passed, and which included boulders of all sizes and many kinds, together with finer material resulting partly from the grinding together of these larger blocks : this mixture of coarse and fine débris was dumped in unsorted heaps showing no trace of bedding when the ice melted away. This occurred in the valley of the Esk, which before the Ice Age entered the sea some way to the west of Whitby, in the neighbourhood of Upgang, where this deposit of ' boulder clay ' completely blocked the original mouth, forcing the river to follow a lower outlet which lay over solid rocks. Through these it has lately cut the gorge at whose mouth Whitby stands, and thus on both sides of Whitby the cliffs are made of regularly stratified rocks of Jurassic age, whereas at Upgang the cliffs consist of an unstratified structureless mass of boulder clay which presents a deeply channelled and exceedingly irregular and unattractive surface. At other places along the coast, notably near Filey, similar cliffs of boulder clay are found.

Inland, boulder clay also builds up much of the low ground, especially near the coast and in the Esk valley and its tributary dales. Egton Low Moor, west of Whitby, is based on such clay deposits.

THE VALE OF PICKERING

At this stage some reference may appropriately be made to the Vale of Pickering which lies on the southern border of the moors and which extends for some thirty miles from the coast at Scarborough and Filey as far west as Helmsley. The Vale is shut in between the moors on the north and the wolds on the south, and immediately impresses by its remarkable flatness. Writing of it over 150 years ago in his *Rural Economy of Yorkshire*, Marshal said that " Nature, perhaps, never went so near to form a lake without finishing the design ", but in fact the lake had been formed and the

Vale represents a lake which has been drained rather than one incompletely formed.

The unusual nature of the Vale is strikingly shown by the amazing course of the river Derwent which drains it. Rising in the moors not far from the coast, and joined by the Hertford River which rises almost on the shores of Filey Bay, it flows for many miles westwards away from the coast, turning south near New Malton to leave the Vale by a path through the Howardian Hills in a gorge some 200 feet deep, yet so narrow that it seems a small landslip might block it. The explanation of this anomalous course is to be found in the coastal area near Scarborough and Filey where as we have already noticed mounds of glacial deposits tell of an ice sheet which filled the North Sea and impinged on the coast (bringing with it material from Scandinavia whose source can be traced with such certainty that the direction of the ice flow is beyond dispute); as in the case of the Esk valley, the ice held up the drainage which until then had passed from west to east along the Vale. The dip streams from the moors at that time joined a strike stream flowing east along the wide outcrop of the Kimmeridge Clay which underlies the Vale, and a wide area of low relief had already been carved out in the soft rocks. The ice dam at the valley mouth led to the flooding of this valley and the formation of a wide lake, into which the streams from the dales continued to flow, joined by the waters from the Esk valley, via the spillways of Newtondale, as already indicated. With this abundant inflow of water the floods rapidly rose and the lake expanded until the waters reached the level of the lowest available outlet: this happened to be on the southern edge, at the position of the present Kirkham Gorge, south of New Malton, other areas where the land was lower being then blocked by ice (Fig. 9). Thus an important spillway was established, carrying the melt waters from the whole Cleveland area into the Ouse basin to the south. Naturally such a vast flow of water possessed considerable erosive powers, and the shallow col by which it at first escaped was deepened to form the deep gorge in which Kirkham Abbey is situated. With the deepening of the gorge the level of the water in the lake was lowered, and eventually the whole was drained, but not before the floor had been covered by wide layers of clay and silt, and deltaic deposits had accumulated at the mouths of the dale rivers.

With the disappearance of the ice it might have been expected that the drainage would be re-established in something of its original condition, but the mounds of boulder clay left near the seaward end of the Vale were just high enough to prevent the flow of streams to the coast.

So the peculiar characters of the Vale may be explained. The present Derwent, flowing for so many miles with so little slope to the sea, is exceedingly sluggish, and this, together with the nature of the alluvial deposits over most of its area, has made much of the Vale a marshy area, parts of which have only been drained in recent years. In the centre of the Vale are damp cattle pastures of richest green, but around its fringes, and especially where the ancient deltas have provided slightly higher and drier ground, there is some cultivation. Most of the towns and villages, as we have seen, are to be found along this fringe, but small and low ' islands ' within the marsh have provided sites for Kirkby Misperton, Edston and Normanby.

CHAPTER IV

THE CHALKLANDS

THE chalk areas of England, which Huxley thought so suggestive of mutton and pleasantness, are perhaps the most easily recognised, for the wide expanses of grassy downland and the smooth rounded curves of the hills are as characteristic of Salisbury Plain as of the Chilterns or the Downs. Although the Wolds of Yorkshire may differ somewhat in contour, they show some features characteristic of all Chalk country. In many parts the short grass barely covers the white rock, for the soil is extremely thin, and the white gashes of chalk pits on the hillsides and the pale cream of the rough flinty tracks give to these areas a lightness, a delicacy of colouring, which is unlike that of any other type of hill country. The wide extent of a chalkland view is seen at its best in the clear lights between the broken storm clouds, when the swiftly moving shadows throw into relief the contours of the hills.

On these rolling hills clumps of beech crown many summits, but great areas are given up to sheep pastures, and there are wide stretches of open tillage. Farms are few, and often are so placed in the valleys that in a view over miles of country scarcely any are in sight. Most villages are dotted along the valley bottoms, while such few towns as occur in the Chalk tracts are to be found on water-courses: of these Salisbury is a notable example, being situated near the confluence of several rivers.

It will at once be apparent that the distribution of the Chalk is not so simple as that of the stone belt just described (Fig. 11), for whereas the oolites are practically confined to an almost continuous belt from Dorset to Yorkshire, the Chalk not only forms a belt parallel to this and a short distance to the east of it, extending through the

Chilterns to the Yorkshire Wolds, but it spreads in a wide expanse in Salisbury Plain, from which stretch eastwards the North and South Downs, while a further narrow belt extends from Dorset eastwards through the Isle of Wight. This more complicated pattern in its outcrop has resulted from the crumpling of the Chalk into a series of folds in

Figure 11.—The distribution of the Chalk.

Chalk areas shown black; rocks younger than the Chalk, dotted: rocks older, unshaded.

south-eastern England. The nature of these folds will be more fully described in later chapters, but it may be remarked that these radiating tracts are all parts of one bedded series which formerly consisted of flat sheets lying nearly horizontally on the sea floor. For the present, attention may most usefully be directed to the fact that nearly everywhere along the western edge the Chalk is dipping to the east or south-east, resting on a varied series of sands, clays and limestones which lie between the Kimmeridge Clay and the Chalk. In short, the Chalk is a newer rock than the oolites, and in many places a sufficiently deep well sunk through the

Chalk would, after passing through the clays, reach the oolites which underlie the Chalk (Fig. 12).

Along this western edge a steep scarp of Chalk overlooks the clay vales. The scarp has not the same form as that of the oolites, for owing to the general uniformity of much of the Chalk it makes more rounded slopes, generally convex instead of partly concave. In parts the scarp is steep, almost cliff-like, as at Clyffe Pypard, north-east of Marlborough, while elsewhere it shows irregularities due to landslips. The Chalk is not so homogeneous as it appears at first sight, and certain parts are better able to resist erosion

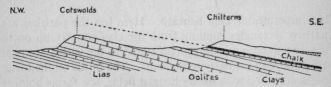

Figure 12.—Section through the Cotswolds and Chilterns with the clay vale between.
Broken line shows former extension of Chalk.

than others, so that subsidiary scarps within the Chalk area are sometimes as prominent as those which bound it.

The scarps are usually steepest where the dip of the rocks is gentle, and here too outliers are most frequent: when the dip steepens the escarpment is low and straight, and the whole outcrop is narrow. This is well illustrated in the Chalk scarp along the northern edge of the Vale of Pewsey, for in the neighbourhood of Savernake Station the beds are inclined to the north at about forty-five degrees, giving a narrow and unimpressive escarpment, whereas to the west, near Adam's Grave, there are bold spurs rising sharply from the vale to over 900 feet (Figs. 13, 14).

Like the Cotswold scarp, the Chalk is rarely crossed by valleys from the west: the chief exception is Goring Gap by which the Thames finds its way into the London basin.

Along this scarp also, farms and villages have been located at regular intervals near the spring line where the waters of the Chalk or of the sands (Greensand) are thrown out by

N.   All Cannings Down   Mill Hill   Alton Priors   S.

Figure 13.—Section across the Chalk scarp on the northern edge of the Vale of Pewsey: rocks dipping gently.
Black, Gault Clay; dots, Greensands; other shading, the Lower, Middle and Upper Chalk. (See also Fig. 11.)

the impermeable clay beneath. Here too the parishes are narrow rectangles running from the clay country up on to the downland, an arrangement suited to the varied needs of agriculture in the early settlements. The farms on the lower parts are small with neatly hedged fields, few farms holding more than 150 acres, whereas some farms on the Chalk have as much as 1000 acres.

At many places on the scarp are the familiar white horses, testifying to the thin soil above the white Chalk. Not all of these are of any antiquity, for that above Calne was cut

N.   Savernake Forest   S.

Figure 14.—Section across the Chalk scarp on the northern edge of the Vale of Pewsey: rocks dipping steeply.
Shading as in Fig. 11.

only near the end of the eighteenth century. There are others in the Pewsey Vale as well as further south: those facing to the west can be seen for many miles, that at Westbury, " a very modern well set cob ", being visible from many points on the Mendips. That on the Berkshire

Downs, supposed to commemorate the victory of Alfred over the Danes at Ashdown, though possibly of much greater antiquity, is a more interesting example.

Wherever these Chalk hills reach the coast they give rise to steep cliffs and headlands. The " white chalk of Dover " formerly appeared in many school books, but similar and even more impressive Chalk cliffs at Beachy Head and on the Brighton coast, and the points at the Needles in the Isle of Wight are not less familiar (see Fig. 30). The smooth Chalk breaks along joint planes to form almost vertical cliffs, exposing continuous sections revealing its great thickness and comparative homogeneity.

The characters of this rock are so familiar, and its marine origin so well known, that a very brief account of its nature will suffice here. It is actually a soft white limestone, often of great purity, so that all but a hundredth part will dissolve in dilute acid. The Chalk is partly made up of small shells belonging to microscopic organisms known as Foraminifera, but it is not correct to interpret the Chalk as dominantly composed of such remains, as is frequently suggested ; the Foraminifera rarely make up more than ten per cent of the deposit. The presence of fragments of larger shells, together with the fact that nearly a half of the Chalk consists of very fine-grained calcium carbonate (possibly derived from the disintegration of other large shells) suggests that it does not represent a deposit formed at great depths on the ocean floor, as many have supposed from the exaggerated importance attached to the Foraminifera. Although the Chalk appears to be uniform in character, some beds are much harder than others, while the lower part in some places is particularly marly and soft.

In some parts of the Chalk, and especially in the upper part, nodules of flint are abundant. They chiefly occur as isolated nodules a few inches or more across which are generally arranged along the bedding. The flints are black or brown, the outsides being white where they merge into the Chalk. They are composed of silica, a hard insoluble material, and consequently the disintegration or solution of the Chalk in which they occur leaves the flint nodules behind. Thus flint boulders originally derived from the Chalk may be met with over wide areas from which much or all of the Chalk has been removed, forming flint gravels in river valleys and flint shingle beaches along many coasts.

The silica comprising the flints has probably been derived in the main from the skeletons of sponges which lived in the seas where the Chalk was deposited. Occasionally a flint encloses a fossil sponge, and preserves its characters, but quite frequently flints surround shells or sea-urchins, the ' lime ' or calcium carbonate of their skeletons being so replaced by the silica that all the minute details of their structure are retained in the flint. From such evidence it is apparent that the flints are not original deposits of silica formed as such on the sea-floor : they represent ' concretions ' of secondary origin, the silica having been disseminated widely in small particles through the whole mass of the Chalk until some time after its deposition ; when the Chalk was finally elevated from beneath the sea, the silica was concentrated by solution and precipitation in rhythmically arranged layers more or less following the beds of the Chalk.

Flint has exercised more influence on early human history than almost any other rock in Europe. For early man discovered that by breaking flint he could obtain sharp-edged tools suited to his many simple needs. And for tens of thousands of years, even after he had acquired considerable skill in the making of implements, he continued to use flint, chipping and flaking it to form a wide variety of tools and weapons. For this reason, as for others, the Chalk areas attracted great prehistoric populations, and the mining of flint became an important industry, for example, at Grime's Graves, near Brandon, near the border of Norfolk and Suffolk.

Among the inhabited regions of prehistoric England

none was more important than Salisbury Plain. The reasons for this are not far to seek; among the lowlands and vales of southern England the Chalk ridges formed natural causeways, especially after the climate became mild at the close of the Ice Age, when the clay vales became marshy and so densely wooded as to be impassable to primitive man, the woods of the vales being chiefly of oak and therefore less easy to penetrate than such beech woods as existed on the Chalk, which would be free of undergrowth. To Salisbury Plain such routes led from several parts of the south and east coasts, on account of the almost radial arrangement of the Chalk outcrops to which we have already referred. The Plain thus became a focus of routes each following the dry and comparatively open uplands, and it is not surprising that this region shows more signs of early occupation of different dates than almost any other area, with its ancient track-ways, its hill-top camps, its tumuli, and its stone monuments.

This great central expanse of Chalk includes Salisbury Plain itself and extends eastwards into much of north Hampshire, an area almost fifty miles across, and if the Marlborough and Berkshire Downs are included, is about thirty miles from north to south. The Marlborough Downs are partly cut off from the Plain by the Vale of Pewsey, a narrow inlet running eastwards from Devizes into the Chalk upland.

These wide uplands with their sparse population and often shallow valleys, with their large fields and occasional clumps of beech woods, show important diversity in agriculture when a superficial cover of any other kind of material is present. Thus in parts of Salisbury Plain are tracts with a rougher pasture, sometimes with gorse, developed on stretches of gravel, usually ancient river deposits laid down before the valleys were carved to their present depths. Still more common in many Chalk regions are patches of damp oak wood often with hornbeam, frequently on hill-tops, but not to be confused with the more usual dry woodland; an excellent example is the Savernake Forest, south-east of Marlborough. In places such woodlands have been cleared and afford damp cattle pastures of a richer green than the dry sheep pastures ordinarily met with on the Chalk. Such areas overlie deposits of clay-with-flints, a superficial accumulation chiefly found capping hills on the uplands. This consists generally of a brown clay with abundant flints, which has in part been left behind on account of its insolubility while the calcium carbonate of the Chalk has been removed in solution; it therefore represents a great thickness of vanished Chalk; the clay-with-flints also includes material from rocks which formerly covered the Chalk. The clay-with-flints gives rise to a soil quite different from that of the Chalk itself, for whereas that is naturally rich in lime the clay-with-flints gives rise to a heavier clay soil.

Although so much of the Chalk is occupied by springy turf and the short grass of sheep pastures, this condition is only maintained because the pasturage prevents the growth of trees. Professor A. G. Tansley has recently suggested that the great bulk of the Chalk grassland would pass once more into woodland if sheep were withdrawn. It is by no means unlikely that the earliest settlers in these areas found dense woods, perhaps of beech and pine, and that many of the small clumps of woodland now on the hill-tops have never been cleared.

CHALKLAND VALLEYS

On Chalk areas there are generally few rivers. On Salisbury Plain and neighbouring regions there are several streams flowing generally towards the south-east, such as the Salisbury Avon, but there are many more valleys than there are rivers. These dry valleys are a characteristic feature of the Chalk, and while their dryness is readily explained as resulting from the porosity of the Chalk, into which almost all the rain falling on the surface immediately sinks, the origin of the valleys themselves presents a more difficult problem (Fig. 15). They are so similar both in form and arrangement to the few stream-bearing valleys

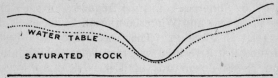

Figure 15.—Section showing form of water-table in Chalk valley.

that there can be no doubt that they were carved by streams when surface water was more abundant: in many of them deposits of alluvium and gravel swept down by the rivers still cover the floors. It has been suggested that they were carved at a time when rainfall was heavier than at present, while others believe with the late Clement Reid that during periods of colder climate, especially during the Ice Age, the surface soils were frozen (at least for certain parts of every year) with the result that there was much less percolation of rain water and more activity by surface streams. Recently Mr. C. C. Fagg has also emphasised the fact that the erosion of the clay vales and the recession of the Chalk scarp has

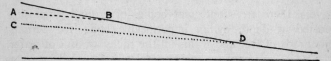

Figure 16.—Section along the valley of a Chalk stream showing positions of the source (B, D) at different positions of the water-table (A B, C D).

progressively lowered the water-level in the Chalk, thus bringing it in many cases below the floor of the valleys (Fig. 17). When the clay vales were about a hundred feet higher than at present many of the valleys were probably occupied by streams, which disappeared as the water-level was lowered.

At the present time many otherwise dry valleys on the Chalk are occupied by streams during or after very wet seasons. Such temporary streams are known as ' nailbournes ' or ' bournes ', and the frequency of such placenames as Bourne and Winterbourne on Chalk areas illustrates their distribution. Their occurrence will best be understood if it is realised that rain water sinking into the ground passes downwards until it is held up by some impervious layer, or until it joins another body of water similarly held up. In the Chalk, which has few impervious

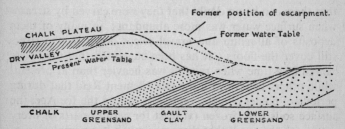

Figure 17.—Section of the Chalk scarp showing a dry valley on the dip slope: the position of the water-table before the Gault Clay was lowered led to the presence of a stream in the valley. *After C. C. Fagg.*

layers, there are often great bodies of ground water supported at depth by an impermeable bed; for perhaps hundreds of feet above this all the rocks are full of water, the pores and crevices being completely occupied by water which is able to percolate through the whole in the direction of any outflow, such as a spring. Above this water-saturated zone there is usually a dry zone, in which the only water is recent rainfall on its way to join the main mass. Between these two zones is a more or less definite plane of demarcation which is known as the ' water-table '; below this the rocks are normally saturated, above it they are essentially dry (Fig. 15). The level of the water-table at any place varies according to the supply. During or after wet spells it rises, while dry spells may cause it to sink. After a time of heavy rainfall the water-table may thus rise sufficiently to bring water into a normally dry valley. The bourne is then ' up '.

Owing to the time taken by water in passing through the minute pores of these rocks, there is frequently a great lag between the time of maximum rainfall and the rising of the bourne. Thus in the case of the celebrated Hertfordshire Bourne, near Berkhampstead, there was heavier rain during the period from October 1911 to March 1912 than during any six months for the previous sixty years, yet the bourne did not flow during these heavy rains; after a month of drought, however, the bourne was at its height. In this river as in others, the source varies in position, a high level of the water-table making the source further upstream (see Fig. 16). Although the water-table is not level, it is usually nearer the surface under the valleys than under the hills, and so water can be obtained by wells at smaller depths along the valleys than elsewhere, a fact which is of considerable importance in the location of settlements, bringing farms and villages down into the valleys even when they are quite devoid of streams.

This difficulty of obtaining water supplies on the uplands, especially for the sheep pastured there, has frequently been met by the construction of dew-ponds, shallow excavations lined with cement or clay in which both rain and dew collect, though there is a widely held view that they are supplied only from dew, and that if a stream is allowed to flow into a dew-pond, it will certainly fail. Kipling aptly described these chalklands :

> We have no water to delight
>   Our broad and brookless vales—
> Only the dew-pond on the height,
>   Unfed, that never fails.

It may be useful to point out here the main reason why Chalk gives rise to uplands ; Chalk is not ordinarily a hard rock, though some bands are moderately tough and the presence of abundant flint in some places adds to the resistance. On account of its porosity, however, and the scarcity of surface streams, Chalk escapes most of the effects of river erosion and its surface is not lowered to anything like the same extent as the clays which lie along its borders: the Chalk thus stands out in ridges as surely as if it were a harder rock.

GREY WETHERS OR SARSENS

On many parts of the Chalk are isolated and irregular blocks of hard sandstone known variously as sarsens, grey wethers, Druid stones or bridestones. Frequently they are covered with lichen, and lie half buried. They are nowhere so common as on the downs near Marlborough, and especially in valley bottoms in the neighbourhood of Fyfield Down, where hundreds are to be seen, as in the " Valley of the Rocks ". South of the Kennet they are less abundant, but similar stones are found beyond the limits of the Chalk country as far as Swindon. They are believed to represent remnants of a former sandstone bed which covered the area, a bed in which certain irregular masses were tougher than others owing to a subsequent deposit of silica which bound the grains together. Many of the larger blocks are of great size, but these have generally been used by the prehistoric inhabitants, particularly for the building of the great circles for which these areas are famous.

Stonehenge is the best known of these, but while its larger stones are derived from sarsens of local origin others have been brought from the Prescelly Hills of Pembrokeshire. It is much more recent than the circle at Avebury, the stones at Stonehenge being dressed and sized while those at Avebury are rough and unhewn. Among them are sarsens over twenty feet in length which must weigh more than sixty tons but which have probably been transported for miles and arranged to form one of the most imposing prehistoric monuments in Europe. The circle itself, covering an area of twenty-nine acres, is the largest known to exist, and is surrounded by a rampart and fosse, evidently not for defensive purposes, since the fosse is inside the wall. Few of the stones remain in position, for inside the circle has grown up a picturesque village, occupying what is surely the most remarkable site in England. It is interesting to note that the church has been built just outside the pagan circle: many stones have been taken from the circle to form parts of houses and barns.

The whole area is obviously an early centre of great importance. About a mile to the south, by the side of the Marlborough–Calne road, stands Silbury Hill whose regular mass represents the largest artificial mound in Europe, while also quite near, besides many tumuli, are the Kennet Barrows, the largest long barrows in Britain. It is clear that in prehistoric times this was a centre of early tribal and religious activity, a focus which owed its importance largely to its position near the meeting-place of lines of movement. The Chalk areas were amongst the most densely populated parts of Britain for thousands of years, for these various remains date from periods as far apart as the Neolithic and the early Iron Age.

It is very remarkable that this part of the Chalk should have yielded, in the sarsens, masses of durable stone in a state which may be described as ready quarried, for the Chalk as a whole is singularly deficient in building materials. And it is doubtful whether stone circles as early as that of Avebury would have been built on Salisbury Plain but for the presence of the sarsens. In some parts of the area harder bands of Chalk have been used for buildings, but in many districts flint nodules have been adopted, a rather unusual material for many purposes, since the small size of most of the pebbles, the difficulty of dressing and the impossibility of carving have led to the development of peculiar and localised architectural styles. The ruins of the Benedic-

tine Abbey in Reading and some cottages near Marlborough
illustrate an early method of using flints, with plentiful
mortar, but it is in East Anglia that the use of flint is seen in
its best forms. In most Chalk districts wood has also been
largely used and the large wooden barns and farm buildings
are often very attractive.

THE VALE OF PEWSEY

Within this central area the greatest diversity is introduced by the deep inlet of the Vale of Pewsey, which extends
eastwards from Devizes for almost twenty miles, carrying
into the Chalk upland a narrow belt of lower country which
is flanked on both north and south by the Chalk escarpment.
The Vale of Pewsey is not a real valley, for no river flows
through its length; it has a hillocky floor of Greensand,
and many villages with large and beautiful houses of brick
and half-timber, but the River Avon which enters at its
western end turns south about half-way along its length and
cuts through the Chalk scarp at Upavon, to become an
ordinary dip stream as far as Salisbury. It is not likely that
any river ever flowed continuously along the vale, for there
are signs that formerly several dip streams comparable with
the Avon flowed across it from north to south, valleys in
the Chalk north of Huish, Alton Priors and Bishop's
Cannings, on the northern edge of the Vale, according to
Mr. H. J. O. White, representing three such dipward streams.
The Vale has been produced by the expansion of the tributaries of such streams along an east-west belt where the
Chalk is thrown into a gentle anticline or upfold, which has
proved weaker than the undisturbed Chalk. Accordingly
tributaries developed rapidly and cut through the Chalk,
exposing the older rocks underneath, and since the Avon
held some advantage its tributaries succeeded in taking over
the drainage of neighbouring streams, parts of whose valleys
are therefore left dry.

The Vale of Wardour further south (north of Shaftesbury) is a somewhat similar inlet into the Chalk developed along a comparable weak anticlinal belt, but the removal of the Chalk has here exposed a varied series of rocks including sands, clays and limestones which, enriched from downwash from the Chalk scarp, have given rise to varied soils and to an agricultural area of great beauty. This differs further from the Vale of Pewsey since the river Nadder flows through it from west to east, joining the Avon at Salisbury.

GAPS IN THE CHALK SCARP

Between the Berkshire Downs and the Chilterns the Goring Gap affords a passage for the Thames, which after flowing through a wide and indefinite clay vale is there confined to a deep wooded valley for some six miles before it enters the London basin. The valley sides are steep even though the flat floor is about a mile wide, and the river curves from side to side, here and there cutting into the Chalk hills as it swings. Through this gap the Great Western Railway now runs to Swindon and the west, and the importance of this and other gaps in the Chalk ridges, especially those north and south of London, has been such a common topic of school geography as to need no emphasis here. But the origin and characteristics of the gaps call for further consideration.

The Goring Gap has been cut by the Thames itself. It traverses the Chalk where there is no structural weakness, and the Chalk beds on one side of the gap are in line with those on the other, so that there seems to be no escape from the conclusion that the beds formerly extended across it. At first some difficulty in understanding the cutting of the gap may be aroused when the district is viewed from the west. The wide clay plain is overlooked by the steep face of the Berkshire Downs and the Chilterns, and it may seem surprising that a river should leave a belt of low ground to cut even a narrow gorge through this higher region. In all such cases it is well to remember first that when a river commenced to cut a gorge it must have been flowing approximately on a level with the top of the ridge through which the gorge is cut; it then follows that the portion of the stream above the gorge must have been at a still higher level. In other words, the Goring Gap was initiated when the area of the Oxford Clay plain was higher than the Chalk scarp. Viewed in this way, one is less impressed by the work done by the river in carving its gorge than by the work done higher up-stream in carrying away the much vaster quantities of material where so great an area has been lowered. The gorge impresses by its narrowness, but the narrowness is only a proof that the river has moved far less material than in the places where its valley is wide.

The Goring Gap is therefore to be thought of as a place along the Thames where erosion has been less effective, and where the valley has failed to grow in width. So may also be explained most of the gaps in the North Downs, as will be shown later (p. 104), and many gorges in other areas.

Other gaps along the Chilterns have been produced in different ways. Among the most striking are those which breach the Chalk ridge south of Aylesbury, at Wendover and Tring. These gaps are followed by railways and roads to London; they differ from the Goring Gap in being dry. The Goring Gap is sometimes called a water gap while these are spoken of as wind gaps. Moreover, they do not lie at the level of the clay plain to the north, but some way up the scarp face. Like the Goring Gap, however, they have been cut by running water, through the escarpment at points where there is no structural weakness. According to Dr. R. L. Sherlock, these trenches were formed in a manner somewhat similar to the spillways described in the Yorkshire Moors (p. 39), for at one stage the northern ice sheet reached as far as the Chilterns. During its retreat the melting ice yielded great volumes of water which were held up between the ice and the escarpment, so that a lake was formed, with the ice as its northern shore and the Chiltern scarp as its southern. Here again the waters rose until they reached the level of the lowest available outflows, which were at these points along the scarp.

THE CHALK OF LINCOLNSHIRE AND YORKSHIRE

The Chalk once more gives rise to an upland area in Lincolnshire, its western escarpment bounding the clay vale while its eastern edge is marked by an ancient cliff overlooking the wide coastal tract of marsh and clay. The scenery of this area presents some features comparable with those of the Chilterns and southern areas. In the south the scarp is deeply fretted, but farther north near Claxby and Caistor, although the Wolds are not so high, they present a sharper face to the west; in this area, too, there are few surface streams, but such villages as occur are small and are mostly found in the dry valleys. On the uplands, as in most Chalk areas, the farms are large, with extensive yards and granaries. Farther south the Wolds show a different type of scenery, the Chalk being covered in many places by deposits of boulder clay, sand and gravel: these give rise to conditions of soil and agriculture quite unlike those of the bare Chalk. These differences have been brought about by deposits left by the ice which formerly covered the whole of this tract; since the ice melted the material it had deposited has been removed from some parts by rivers, but sufficient time has not elapsed since the Ice Age to allow all these deposits, which though they vary in thickness are only superficial, to be carried away.

The Chalk is widely breached by the great gap of the Humber, but the Yorkshire Wolds represent its further continuation. The Wolds, however, differ greatly from other Chalk areas in England, for the slopes are more abrupt and the lower parts are more widely cultivated than in the downlands. These characters result chiefly from the fact that the Chalk of Yorkshire is harder than that of the south of England, many beds being more like ordinary limestones: thus they stand out as more impressive cliffs and lack the rolling hills of the south Chalk country.

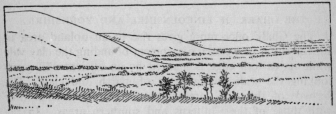

Figure 18 —The Chalk escarpment on the north of Pewsey Vale.

CHAPTER V

THE HEART OF ENGLAND

THE great triangular area of low country which forms the centre of England is bounded on the west by the north-south line which marks the Welsh borders and on the east by the northern extensions of the Cotswold belt; the most southerly part of the plain tapers along the Severn valley to Gloucester. From this broadly triangular tract there are northerly projections stretching along both east and west sides of the Pennines.

While most of this region is of low elevation it neverthe-less shows much variety in relief. Its hills rarely exceed 500 feet in height, but they are of several different types, and the area as a whole is very diversified. Within it there are places of unspoiled loveliness, the woodlands of Sherwood Forest and the soft green lands of the Vale of Gloucester, contrasting with industrial areas of unmatched ugliness where not an acre of the original surface remains unscarred by diggings or by refuse. The Midlands cannot be summed up in a word; one speaks of " the Midlands, that are sodden and unkind ", another of " these most beloved of English lands ", and both perhaps are right.

THE VALE OF GLOUCESTER

This tract is simplest in its southern part, in the Severn valley north of Gloucester. Here on the west the Malvern Hills form a cliff-like boundary rising impressively from the vale, while on the east the more irregular but no less conspicuous scarp of the Cotswolds makes a definite boundary (Fig. 3). The intervening area is almost uni-formly low, but through it runs a somewhat indefinite wooded ridge rising in places about 200 feet above the level of the valley. For the most part this higher ground lies over on the left bank of the river, but it is so weak a feature that the Severn several times crosses it south of Tewkesbury.

Seen from the hills on either side, the Vale of Gloucester presents a wide expanse of fertile lowland, with flat riverside meadows situated on the level tracts of alluvium laid down by the river, and liable to frequent floods. Stretching away from the river for miles, the fields, bounded by high hedgerows, still retain their rich green. From many directions the Vale appears to be well wooded, but this results mainly from the numerous tall trees which form part of the hedges and border the lanes, elms being especially common in many areas while oak is also locally abundant. Orchards are also common, especially in the west.

Dotted over this area are many villages, mostly small and placed at intervals of only a mile or two, much closer than those of the Cotswolds or the Chilterns. The southern part of the Vale is dominated by the great tower of Gloucester Cathedral situated near the centre of the old but rapidly expanding town, and just above the alluvial tract of the Severn. Tewkesbury, with its abbey of solid Norman simplicity, is similarly placed some ten miles upstream, and retains more of its original character, with its streets of Elizabethan houses, half-timbered and gabled, and narrow lanes affording glimpses of river and meadows from the main street. Whatever the charms of Cheltenham, it has much that is alien to the Vale, for it was little more than a village until the early eighteenth century, when its waters were accidentally discovered, and its subsequent progress has been that of a successful spa.

Many of the villages are scattered and irregular in form, sometimes straggling along the several roads leading from the centre. As in the old towns, so to an even greater extent in the villages, stone is rarely used in building, and cottages of brick or half-timber, thatched or tiled, are characteristic of the whole area, though in many cases stone from further afield (and often from the Cotswolds) has been used in building the churches. It is at once obvious that this is not a stone district, almost the only stone being in the villages along the low ridge referred to above. Apart from this, the whole area is underlain by marls and clays, which normally give rise to a heavy soil. This clay belt was originally densely wooded, and it was only gradually that parts of it were cleared for cultivation, long after the tracts of lighter soil (for instance on the Cotswolds) had been developed. On such clay ground the dominant natural vegetation was probably oak woodland, and the dense forests together with the marshy nature of this low clayey country rendered passage through the area difficult. It is probable that, in such country, clearances were made at a number of spots, many of which later became the sites of settlements. Thus numerous small villages are now found irregularly scattered through the area, which has never developed the large concentrated villages to be found in the areas of lighter soil. Moreover, in the clay areas water supplies, at least of surface water suitable for early settlements, were so frequent as to cause no difficulty.

The clays were dug for brickmaking, in the absence of suitable stone, and small brickworks formerly existed in very many of the villages in this belt, supplying also tiles and, later, drain-pipes for agricultural land. The clays are of two types: in the west of the area they are deep red in colour, and give rise to fields of characteristic appearance, while east of the Severn and extending to the slopes of the Cotswolds they are generally blue or grey-blue, turning to a dirty yellow at the surface. The latter clays give heavier and stickier soils than the red marls of the west, but when used for brickmaking both yield bricks of a red colour. The difference in colour of the clays is due to a difference in the iron compounds which are present, and the baking of the blue clay brings about a change which turns the bluish colouring matter to red.

C

The clays or marls of red colour belong to the rocks known as Keuper Marl, a part of the group named the New Red Sandstone: the blue clay represents the lowest part of the Lias, the bottom group of the Jurassic. Both groups are dipping to the east and pass under rocks which form the scarp of the Cotswolds (Fig. 3). The base of the Lias includes some beds of blue limestone (the Blue Lias) which give rise to the low ridge mentioned above. On the western edge sandstones are present amongst the red rocks, and as these rise on to the shoulders of the Malverns they form a small area of lighter soils and rougher country in the area around Bromsberrow Heath.

It must not be thought that the course of the Severn through this tract of green lowland has been determined by the presence of higher ground to west and east, for in all probability the Vale was not markedly lower when the Severn started on its work of erosion. In other words, the Vale has been carved out by the river and by weathering agents; it is only when this conception of its origin is grasped that the real significance of river work can be appreciated. Standing either on the Malverns or on some viewpoint on the Cotswold edge, such as Leckhampton Hill, the immensity of the valley is so impressive that it may be hard to realise that the rivers almost unaided have been able to carry away the vast amount of material which formerly filled it. Such a contemplation of a great valley affords a demonstration of the length of geological time, for the carving of this valley (although it has taken some millions of years) is but a recent feature of the landscape when viewed in relation to the time during which the rocks underlying it were formed.

Many students of river development have thought that when the English rivers began their work of carving the present landscape, not only was there no Vale of Gloucester and perhaps no Severn, but the drainage from part of Wales passed over the elevated ground which then occupied this part of the Severn valley and so down the Cotswold slope into the Thames. Later, streams beginning on the outcrop of these soft beds have been able to cut down rapidly and to capture the waters of their less fortunately placed neighbours. In this way the Midland region has become pre-eminently the land of the great English rivers, for apart from the Thames, all the larger rivers flow across it for considerable parts of their courses.

THE MIDLAND PLAIN

North of the Vale of Gloucester the Midland plain is wider, chiefly because the red rocks become thicker and occupy a greater expanse of country, the red marls covering a tract which in Warwickshire and Worcestershire is roughly forty miles from west to east. Here is the red English plain in its finest development, extending along the valleys of the Severn and the Stratford Avon, the England of Shakespeare's country, with its roads fringed with great trees, with its red ploughed fields making the green of the hedges seem a deeper tint, with innumerable villages of red brick or black and white thatched cottages set along twisting roads, the narrow gardens fronting the road bright with common flowers. Where nearly every village is ' typical ' of the area, it is useless to name examples, but none is more charming than Harvington, where every turn in the road brings a new picture into view.

The market towns of this area are nearly all delightful ; Warwick, Evesham, Pershore and Worcester all have their half-timbered houses, and when stone comes into use, it is frequently, as in Warwick Castle, from some of the red or grey sandstones which occur below the red marls. In spite of its temptations, Stratford-on-Avon has so far contrived to keep something of its own quality, and few of these old towns have been touched by large-scale industries, for there are no coalfields in the southern tract. Along the Severn itself, no coal-bearing rocks are exposed until the Forest of

Wyre coalfield is reached near Bewdley, where, as at Coalbrookdale, the navigable river led to early exploitation of coal and iron deposits. The amount of material available was not comparable with that in the larger coalfields, however, and this trade gave rise to no important industrial developments in the lower Severn valley.

Throughout the more northerly part of the plain, however, wide areas have been industrialised, and the whole

Figure 19.—Evesham.

region has changed its character during the last 150 years. Few of the older towns remain unaffected, and most of them are completely overgrown by the products of this later period. In parts of these north Midlands it is impossible to imagine the beauty that once existed, but the ugliness which has replaced it is just as surely a result of the geological structure, for it is the distribution of materials which has determined the areas which have become rich and populous. Here in the north Midlands are the coalfields of north and south Staffordshire, Warwickshire, Leicestershire, Derbyshire and Nottinghamshire, too varied in activity and scenery to be described as a whole.

It is a wide area chiefly based on sandstones and clays. As compared with the Vale of Gloucester, sandstones are more important, but the clays and marls continue to occupy wide areas and to attract to their outcrops the greater rivers. So the sandy areas are rather more elevated with drier soils and different vegetation. Perhaps the most suitable point at which to commence the examination of this region is the north-east corner, in the neighbourhood of Nottingham and Leicester, where the Trent valley makes its sweeping curve from Burton past Newark to the Humber, keeping to the outcrop of the red marls.

One of the most characteristic rocks in this area near Nottingham is the Bunter Sandstone, on which the city was founded. It forms the steep crag on which the castle stands, and extends thence northwards through Bulwell Forest to the area east of Mansfield and Worksop. The Bunter yields a light thin soil and although many areas are cultivated there are still great expanses of heathland with gorse, ling and broom, while in the north Sherwood Forest with its oaks and dense bracken remains as a vast expanse of primitive woodland, left unworked because of the poor soil; its former extensions southwards to the borders of the city, however, have slowly yielded to the advance of cultivation.

This Bunter area consists of rolling hills about 400 feet high and of unusually rounded shape, rarely showing simple scarp topography and more frequently yielding convex than concave slopes, a result of the uniformity of the thick soft sandstones. In this they resemble the Chalk, and also in their porosity, for most of the valleys on the Bunter Sandstone are streamless, practically all the rainfall sinking into the ground. The water-table rarely reaches the surface; in many places it is at great depth, and within the Bunter outcrop very deep wells are necessary if underground supplies are to be obtained. Such wells afford water nowadays for large undertakings, but the difficulties of water supply precluded any considerable early settlement in the area except along the rare streams. It has therefore long remained sparsely populated. In the valley of the Maun are Clipstone, Ollerton and Edwinstowe, but elsewhere there are scarcely any old villages.

Recently, however, there has been a tendency for new mining towns to spread on to this part of the red sandstone country, as is also the case elsewhere. Early coal mining was mainly confined to places where coal outcrops at the surface or where it can be mined at little depth. The belt of small coalfield towns which grew, particularly in the last century, on the uneven country extending from Ilkeston to Chesterfield, marks the outcrop of the Coal Measures, the ' exposed ' coalfield of east Derbyshire. But the need for large supplies has gradually led to coal mining being carried further east, under the newer rocks, where the Coal Measures can be reached only at greater depths : recent development has thus tended to the exploitation of the ' concealed ' coalfield. But while the former pits were often small, the deeper and more scientifically planned pits can only be economically worked if they deal with large areas underground, so that the collieries which are being sunk on the rural areas are fortunately few in number though they carry with them on to these areas vast new populations.

Mostly these Bunter Sandstones are soft and are very easily excavated : in the Nottingham district are great numbers of caves which have been dug out, and which generally remain dry owing to the porosity of the sandstone and the fact that they are situated far above the water-table, so that any water rapidly percolates downwards. These excavations have been used as dwellings, and the famous " Trip to Jerusalem " inn, beneath Nottingham Castle, extends into the rock itself, while the dungeons and " Mortimer's Hole " are also hewn in the solid rock beneath the castle.

A few miles to the north of Nottingham, on a hillside near Bramcote, stands the remarkable pillar known as the Hemlock Stone, always an object of interest to those who live in the city (Fig. 20). Its occurrence has been attributed to Druids, and of course to the Devil, who is believed to have thrown it at a good Abbot of Lenton, and to have fallen a few miles short in his aim. But whatever the stories may say, this stone was not transported here either by Devil or by ice (which has done much work in dropping huge blocks into unexpected places), for it belongs where it is found, and is effectively rooted on the hill. It stands out,

Figure 20.—The Hemlock Stone, Nottingham.
A wind-eroded pillar of Bunter Sandstone.

as on a larger scale do many mountains, because the material around it has been worn away; it is, in short, like a small outlier, which has resisted erosion because it is a little harder than the rock round about. In this case the hardness is due to the fact that the sand grains are held together by a cement of barium sulphate, small quantities of which are irregularly distributed in the Bunter Sandstones. This insoluble cementing material has enabled this mass of rock, as well as the larger cappings of neighbouring hills, to resist disintegration. Possibly the wind, carrying sand grains in greater quantity near the ground than higher up, has also helped to cut away the lower part of the pillar, as in the case of the Yorkshire Bridestones.

The Keuper Sandstones give rise to quite a different type of scenery from that of the Bunter, for they mostly occur in thin beds among the marls, especially near the base of the group, and form sharp escarpments with steep or alternately convex and concave faces quite unlike the generally convex hills of the more uniform Bunter. The high ground to which they give rise runs north-eastwards from Mapperley, and on account of the dip the scarps fall away sharply to the west, and more gently to the east into the Trent valley.

These sandstones thus occupy an interesting position between the Bunter Sandstones on the one hand, with practically no surface water or shallow wells, and the red marls on the other which are so generally impermeable that almost all the rainfall flows away in surface streams, and scarcely any water at all is available from shallow wells. In this intervening tract there are numerous springs and shallow wells, and this group of rocks is known locally as the 'Waterstones'. It is not surprising, therefore, that along this outcrop and just below it are many villages, Arnold, Calverton, Woodborough, while others are situated along the steep-sided little valleys or 'dumbles' which are cut into the surface, as at Gedling, Lambley, Lowdham. Farther north, the old towns of Southwell and Retford are situated in this same belt.

A far wider area is occupied by the outcrop of the red marls, which form a belt miles in width. East of the Trent this is occupied by low country, ill-drained and peaty in some parts, as near Gotham, broken by small ridges where sandstone bands produce minor scarps. This wide clay plain has much in it that recalls the western part of the Vale of Gloucester, and its arable fields show the same deep red. But although the villages are fairly numerous they are not always so picturesque in their setting as those of Gloucestershire, nor are the cottages individually so attractive; they are almost universally built of red bricks made from the clays, rarely thatched, and usually tiled. Timbered cottages are not so common as in the south and west, but in strong sunlight or at sunset the rich glow of the red cottages in such villages as Orston and Cotgrave is very pleasing. Generally the churches are of stone, grey or brown or yellow according to its derivation, and tall spires are characteristic, but brick has been used in church-building in a few cases, the diapered tower of Edwalton being a noteworthy example (although little of it can be seen for the covering of ivy).

Across this area to the east there rises the low but distinct wooded ridge formed by the limestones of the " Blue Lias ", running irregularly across the low ground, in the well-known Bunny Hill and passing through Elton and Kilvington to beyond Newark. East of it the Lias Clays form even ground scarcely broken by any feature until the Lincoln Cliff, or further south, the boundary of the Vale of Belvoir, is reached.

Before leaving the description of the rocks of this part of the Midland plain it may be useful to tabulate those which are represented, so that their relative positions may be clear. In the table the oldest rocks are placed at the bottom, and it will be recalled that these are missing in the Gloucester area.

Lias		Lias Clays (with Marlstone forming escarpment)
		Blue Lias (Limestone forming small ridge)
New Red Sandstone	Trias	Keuper	Keuper Marl
			Keuper Sandstone
		Bunter Sandstone	
	Permian	Magnesian Limestone (forming an escarpment which increases in importance in Yorkshire)	

As we have already pointed out, many of the New Red Sandstones are deep red in colour, and the others are generally but not always reddish. They form a great series, some thousands of feet in total thickness. As a whole the marls actually occupy a much greater area at the surface than the sandstones : this is particularly true, as we have seen, in the lower part of the Severn valley, but it is also generally true in the north Midlands where the sandy beds are thicker. It is necessary, therefore, to regard the term New Red Sandstone as a convenient label for a group of rocks of similar age, but to realise that all the rocks contained in it are not sandstones and that some are not even red ; the geologists' habit of using such descriptive names in a chronological sense is sometimes misleading to a beginner. These rocks are called ' New ' to distinguish them from the Old Red Sandstones, a group of somewhat similar character, which also is often red, but likewise is not wholly a sandy series. The newer group appear above the Carboniferous rocks (including the Coal Measures) while the older group in places forms their floor, and so the distinction was a matter of great importance in the early efforts to understand the distribution of coal.

The redness of these rocks is ascribed to their having been deposited under ' continental ' conditions : in few cases have any of these beds been laid down in the sea, where the iron compounds are generally reduced and give to the deposits a blue or grey colour (as in the Lias Clays or the Oxford Clays, which are typical marine muds) : the state of oxidation of the iron in the New Red Sandstone leading to the red colour, implies deposition under non-marine conditions. There are reasons to believe that some at least of the New Red Sandstone rocks were laid down when Britain was practically a desert.

THE TRENT VALLEY

For many miles the Trent meanders in its wide flood plain, its alluvial tract being nearly two miles wide. Much of this area is liable to flood, save that at many points raised banks or levées line its course. Near Trent Bridge in the south of Nottingham the alluvial area, still known as the ' Meadows ', was not built over until late in the nineteenth century, and has only been rendered free from floods by the erection of considerable embankments. Naturally there are few villages within this damp alluvial tract, which is given over to meadowland, willows fringing the river in many parts. In this low land the river meanders in the broad curves characteristic of rivers which have reached their maturity. The gradient of the river is low throughout this stretch and as the water is so little above sea-level it is

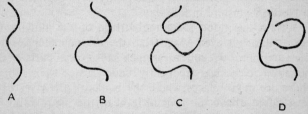

A   B   C   D

Figure 21.—Stages in the development of meanders (A to C) and the formation of an ox-bow lake (D).

unable to do much further work in deepening its valley, and like all mature rivers it flows slowly, swinging from side to side and widening its valley and building up its alluvial plain.

In the course of time each bend of the river tends to become more and more a complete loop, until ultimately, during some time of flood, the meander is cut off, the river shortening its course and leaving the old bed as an ox-bow lake, much in the way that modern straightened roads leave portions of the former bends derelict, in time to become grass-grown and lost : so the old bed becomes in time silted up and curved shallow depressions on the flood plain mark some of the former positions of the river (Fig. 21).

Stages in the cutting of some of these meanders have been traced from old records by Dr. Bernard Smith.

There are places further down the river where near the end of the eighteenth century it was said that a boatman might have thrown his hat over the bank, and after sailing two miles have taken it up again. But where the river formerly bent back so completely on itself, it now takes a direct course. This cutting across meanders has of course resulted in transferring some areas within the meander from one side of the river to the other, and where county and parish boundaries have been drawn along the former positions of the river a portion of a parish has frequently been transferred to the further side of the river: in the neighbourhood of Gainsborough portions of Lincolnshire have been attached to Nottinghamshire in this way.

Within this flood plain the surface of the alluvium is almost flat, but even apart from the meander depressions there are minor irregularities which cause some parts of the meadows to be less frequently under water than others. There are many places where the banks of the river have been raised above the general level of the plain owing to the greater amount of sediment dropped there during times of flood, and so tributaries find some difficulty, once they are on the flood plain, in reaching the main river, which in building up its banks tends to pond back its tributaries. One stream near South Muskham flows for about five miles more or less parallel to the Trent before effecting a confluence. Other small streams draining the flood plain actually rise within the raised belt and flow away from the river for some distance.

From time to time the river in its meanders impinges against the higher ground formed by the solid rocks fringing the flood plain; the rocks are generally red marls, and locally the river is cutting into them to form steep cliffs; the red tree-covered cliffs below Radcliffe-on-Trent afford one of the best examples of this erosion of the solid rocks, showing how the river is extending its flood plain laterally, and illustrating the way in which valleys are gradually widened. The steep wooded bank below Clifton Grove, formerly one of the beauty spots of the region, shows similar features, with the Trent again hugging the right side of its valley.

Where the Trent comes so close to the higher ground afforded by the solid rocks, it has been possible for villages to grow up near the river. But most of the villages of the river area are situated not on solid rocks but on patches of gravel which are slightly raised above the river plain, and which gain proximity to the fertile meadows while they themselves have dry situations. Such villages occur at short intervals along the valley, at Shelford, Gunthorpe, Hoveringham and Bleasby, while Beeston had a similar position, but has outgrown both the site and its village character. Some of these gravel terraces represent earlier flood plains of the river, which had an expanse even wider than that of the present alluvium. In this feature also the Trent is typical of most big English rivers; it reached base levels at which it built up wide plains, but changed conditions have enabled it to cut down through those plains and by its meanders to reduce them to more or less isolated remnants situated at intervals along the valley tract, sufficiently far above the river to escape its floods. Further details of the formation of such terraces are given with reference to the Thames (p. 91).

Neither of the other two large towns of this region, Derby and Leicester, is situated on the Trent, but both are on its tributaries at some distance from the main valley and just on the edge of a wide area of low country which is subject to extensive floods. Both of these places are built on the red marls, and as in Nottingham, red brick forms the main part of their buildings.

CHARNWOOD FOREST

Rising unexpectedly from the clay plain about six miles north-west of Leicester are the surprising hills of Charn-

wood Forest. Craggy summits of bare rock and bracken-
covered slopes above wide expanses of woodland introduce
into the gentle fertility of the Midland plain a type of
scenery of so unusual a nature that the hills appear to be
more elevated than their 800 or 900 feet would suggest.
The barren soils of these hills and the surprising character of their summits at once proclaim that different
types of rocks are introduced among the red rocks of the
plain and by their hardness stand out to form the high
ground. Various types of rock are here. Granite-like rocks
of igneous origin, formed by the consolidation of molten
magmas at great depths, are quarried at Markfield and
further north at Mountsorrel, chiefly for road stones. In
Swithland and other parts, slates of similar general nature
to those of Wales were formerly extensively quarried, while
other hills show rocks representing hardened deposits of
ash and débris from ancient volcanoes : it must not be
supposed that these are volcanic peaks, for they have no
relation to the unknown craters from which the material
was derived, and the hills owe their form primarily to the
hardness of the rocks.

These rocks are obviously more closely comparable with
those of many parts of Wales than with anything ordinarily
met with in central or eastern England. They represent,
in fact, some of the oldest rocks known anywhere in England. Similar rocks may underlie much of the Midland
area at varying depths, but here they have been exposed by
the wearing away of the red marls from round about them.
They form a number of ' islands ' or inliers in the great
stretch of marl (Fig. 22). They can best be visualised as
a series of related and neighbouring mountain-tops which
were buried by the red marl as it accumulated ; the red
marl was formed under desert conditions, part of it probably
in drying up salt lakes comparable with those of south-
western Asia, and the Charnwood Hills stood high above
these for ages, until the accumulating sediments slowly en-

gulfed them. These red sediments were themselves buried under the Lias and later rocks when the whole region sank beneath the sea, but with its uplifting, long afterwards, the overlying beds have slowly been stripped off by rivers and atmosphere. At the present time just enough of the red marl has been taken from the area to expose the old mountain peaks. But as the red marl is so much softer than the old slates and granites, very little change has been effected in the form of these harder rocks during the removal of the marl.

As Professor W. W. Watts has suggested therefore, Charnwood Forest presents us with an old landscape of

Figure 22.—Charnwood Forest.
Diagram to show the relations of the red marl to the
peaks of ancient rock.

hills and valleys which existed when the New Red Sandstone was formed, a landscape long buried and just being re-exposed as the red beds are removed. In the old surface there were several valleys between ridges running in a north-west to south-easterly direction. These old trenches have to some extent been re-excavated, and are followed by the main roads through the area, such as that from Shepshed up the Shortcliffe valley, and down Lingdale to Swithland, and that along the Blackbrook valley. The main streams of the area flow along parts of these ancient valleys, but in parts of their courses they pass across the old ridges of hard rocks; the valleys then show striking contrasts, the streams having cut deep picturesque gorges in the older rocks; the best examples are the Ingleberry gorge on the Shortcliffe brook, in the north of the forest, the Brand gorge about a mile south of Woodhouse Eaves and the Bradgate

Park gorge near Newtown Linford, at the southern end of the area.

To understand the development of these gorges and their relation to the wide valleys where the streams flow on the softer red marls, it must be remembered that the drainage of the area was initiated when the harder rocks were still completely buried. Streams running on the softer rocks in cutting down their valleys here and there came across projecting ridges of the old rocks, into which they continued to cut downwards. But they were unable to widen their valleys in these harder beds as they could in the marls, nor could they cut downwards so quickly, so that the streams flowing on the marls filling the old valleys gained an advantage over those which had to contend with slates and granites; hence the main streams came increasingly to follow the original channels in the old rock surface.

THE WEST MIDLANDS

The remainder of the Midland plain is largely made up by the outcrops of the various divisions of the New Red Sandstone together with extensive areas of Coal Measures. These latter are mainly areas of clay and shale, giving rise in many parts to a dull grey soil associated with the familiar evidences of coal mining, though red rocks are very widespread in the Warwickshire coalfield. The coalfield areas of both Warwickshire and South Staffordshire are rather more elevated than the surrounding plain, and the chief valleys therefore lie outside these regions, frequently on the red Keuper Marls, the Tame uniting with the Anker at Tamworth where the castle guards the passage of the united rivers.

The borders of the coalfield plateaux are sometimes marked by a definite edge, especially at Nuneaton, on the north-east of the Warwickshire coalfield. Here ancient rocks, including some of volcanic origin not very different from those of Charnwood, make up a sharp ridge facing across the marl and clay country which stretches through the west of Leicestershire as far as Charnwood Forest. Similar ancient rocks give rise to the Lickey Hills some ten miles south-west of Birmingham.

But apart from these occasional inliers within the Midland plain, the greater part of the area is made up by the New Red Sandstone, which gives rise to low marly country or to rather more elevated and drier tracts according to the distribution of the marls and sandstones. Extensive outcrops of sandstone stretch north and south of Birmingham, where the country has characters similar to those already described at Nottingham. Dry sandy soils formed by the Bunter Sandstone were among the last to be cultivated, and much heath and natural woodland may still be found in Sutton Park and Cannock Chase. On the Keuper Sandstones the soils have neither the heaviness of the marl regions nor the dryness of the Bunter, and give rise to a fertile belt which attracted early settlements at Bromsgrove and Sutton Coldfield. Here the grey and red sandstones have been used in building, but over much of the area red brick predominates, and many newer towns are characterised by those rows of dull brick houses which are the mark of industrial progress in most parts of the Midlands.

THE CHESHIRE PLAIN

The red marl country covers much of Cheshire, though this plain is also fringed by outcrops of the sandstone beds. In its main features the scenery is thus closely comparable with that of the Midland plain. The dull red town of Crewe, grown up as a railway centre where not even a village existed before, may be contrasted with old Chester, with its timber and stone ; Chester Cathedral is a notable example of the use of the warm-toned Keuper stones. At a few places such as Marton and Warburton, however, even churches are half-timbered.

One other feature of the scenery of Cheshire may be

noticed in the existence of wide lakes, formed as a result of salt working. In the red marls salt occurs in beds with an average thickness of about 100 feet, formed by the evaporation of the salt lake in which much of the Keuper Marl was deposited. The extraction of these thick beds has caused the surface to subside to a considerable extent. Subsidence is of course frequent in coal-mining areas, but it must be remembered that coal seams are usually no more than a few feet thick, and that supporting pillars and packing prevent collapse to a certain extent, while in working salt by pumping it out in solution the whole of the bed is removed and no support is left. So in many parts of the salt-mining area, between Nantwich and Northwich, great meres or flashes are common, and are constantly extending.

But these conditions are peculiar to the Cheshire plain and to the west Midlands, for salt does not occur in quantity in the red marls of other areas. All these areas agree, however, in the quietly undulating country, with many streams flowing gently in wide valleys, in the warm colouring of the buildings and in the pleasant patterns of red and green.

CHAPTER VI

THE LONDON BASIN

IN the expanse of low ground within the Thames basin below Reading many types of scenery are represented. The wide green meadows where " the silent river glides by flowering banks ", the low marshes along the estuary, rich agricultural lands and dry heaths are all in sharp contrast with the open uplands of Chalk which bound the area both to north and south. The centre of the basin is occupied by the great expanse of the city and its suburbs, spreading its usually hideous outgrowths along all the main routes. The description of these miles of brick and stone is no part of the present purpose. Its building materials have been drawn from a wide area, but much of London is built of dull yellow bricks which supply the dominant tint to many parts : many of these bricks were made from the London Clay which occupies more of the basin than any other rock. But if the clay has been primarily responsible for the drabness of many London streets, the inadequate foundations which it affords have prevented the erection of skyscrapers on the scale of some cities. Thus even in London, where man's effort has been most concentrated, the physical background has controlled the changes he has been able to make, and has largely determined the form and colour of the city

In Essex the London Clay also makes up large areas, and here brick has long been the dominant building material, this county being particularly noteworthy for the use of brick in church building from an early date. For bricks were not frequently used in churches in other areas until the last few centuries, even in those areas which are comparatively stoneless. These clay tracts were formerly heavily wooded, and wood has also been used in Essex churches more than elsewhere, the wooden spires (for instance at Blackmore) being very characteristic.

The area to be described in this chapter, however, is essentially the basin of the Thames, which, eastwards from Reading, is bounded on both sides by Chalk hills. Here the river receives dip streams from the Chilterns where the Chalk is dipping to the south, while on the other bank it is joined by rivers which rise not on the North Downs but still farther south on the hills of the Weald in Kent and Sussex. The drainage thus links these two areas, already closely tied together in other ways. It will be recalled that

Figure 23.—The London basin and the Weald. Section to show the folded rocks. Tertiary in the London basin; Gault, Greensands and Wealden beds beneath Chalk in Weald.

from the great stretch of Chalk around Salisbury Plain three main ridges extend to the east, the Chilterns, the North Downs and the South Downs, formed by the bending of the Chalk in south-eastern England; the folds of the London basin and the Weald are closely related and complementary, for the North Downs not only form the southern limit of the London basin but also the northern part of the Wealden fold (Fig. 23).

Into the London basin the Chalk dips generally southwards from the Chiltern scarp, while on the other hand the same rocks in the North Downs dip to the north. It has been amply proved by many deep wells sunk in the London district that the Chalk extends under the basin. Thus it may be said to form a continuous sheet, cropping north and south of the basin but underlying all the intervening area where it is covered by newer rocks. This great downfold or syncline extends for many miles east and west. On the other hand the Weald represents an upfold or anticline in which the dips on the north are to the north and on the south to the south. The rocks in the London basin rest on the Chalk, and are therefore newer than the Chalk. These relations will be clear from Figure 23, from which it may also be seen that the Chalk which formerly extended continuously over the Weald has been removed, exposing older rocks in this area. It will be apparent, therefore, that the geological conditions are quite different in these two areas, but it should be noticed that the pressure which produced an anticline in the one area also gave rise to the syncline in the other. This pressure affected southern and south-eastern England very markedly, but it had little recognisable effect on the Midland and Cotswold areas, although the rocks of those areas, being older than the Chalk, were in existence at that time.

Thus the London basin is not merely a physical basin, an area of low ground surrounded on several sides by higher, but it is also structurally a basin. The rocks above the Chalk may be spoken of as Tertiary beds : they consist chiefly of clays and sands, the clays being soft and very widespread so that over large areas they have been worn down to form low country. The Thames flows from west to east along the syncline and though its course does not always coincide exactly with the structural basin it is difficult to escape the conclusion that the course of the lower Thames has been determined by the fold, and that the river began to flow along this wide channel soon after it was formed (Fig. 24). The early part of the Thames, as we have seen, is a dip stream on the Cotswolds, and with many other dip streams to which attention has been drawn it doubtless originated on the gentle surface of beds which sloped to the east and south-east; in that direction, however, the beds had been folded, so that while the general slope continued the waters were collected in the bottom of a trough, resembling a wide shallow gutter tilted to the east, where they received dip streams flowing down the sides of the trough from north and south, that is, from the Chilterns and the Weald. Possibly the courses of many of these tributaries were also determined by minor folds subsidiary to the main syncline.

In its obvious relation to its basin the Thames is unique among the larger British rivers, which as we have noticed mostly follow the outcrop of some soft bed (frequently the

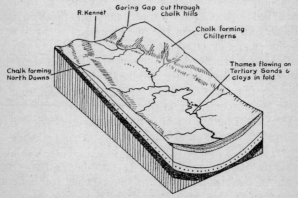

Figure 24.—Block diagram of the London basin, looking west.

Keuper Marls) and occupy valleys which cannot in any way be regarded as structural basins. On either side of the valleys of the Trent and the Severn the hills are different in structure and rock type, whereas in the Thames basin a general symmetry of rock distribution and scenic character is determined by the folding.

The Thames is not flowing precisely along the bottom of the synclinal trough, however, and there are many ways in which the drainage system is more complex than the above account suggests. As regards the larger scenic effects the most striking anomalies are in the west, where the Thames enters the basin through the Goring Gap,

already described (p. 59). This gap is situated some distance
to the north of the deepest part of the trough, the Kennet
valley here approximating more nearly to the line of the
syncline (Fig. 24). For some distance below Reading the
Thames keeps near the junction of the Chalk and the Tertiary
rocks, the former extending over wide areas north of the
river, the latter making up most of the area to the south.

Although the Thames crosses the Chalk at Pangbourne
it turns north again towards Henley and again passes on
to that rock, its higher and drier banks affording sites for
riverside towns. Still further east, the Thames encounters
another small area of Chalk at Windsor, where a subsidiary
anticline or dome brings it to the surface among the Tertiaries. This Chalk forms a prominent feature in Windsor
Castle Hill, and the river has cut into it to form a low but
sharp cliff (Fig. 26). This Chalk bluff is probably significant
in delaying the sharp swing to the south which the Thames
makes between Windsor and Chertsey.

THE ROCKS OF THE LONDON BASIN

But apart from these areas of Chalk the greater part of
the Thames basin below Reading is occupied by Tertiary
rocks and also by superficial deposits of river gravel and
boulder clay. The arrangements of these various clays,
sands and gravels appear at first sight very irregular, and
while the London Clay occupies the widest area, the other
rocks seem to be sporadically scattered about the surface.
It is essential to realise that they belong to two series, the
Tertiary rocks having been folded to form the trough along
which the Thames flows, the superficial rocks having been
laid down at various times after the channel was further
excavated. There is thus a symmetry in the Tertiary rocks,
resulting from the folding, which is absent from the more
recent deposits.

The London Clay occupies wide areas of the low country
in the basin, stretching from Regent's Park and Wembley

northwards into south Hertfordshire, while it also underlies much of the south and east of Essex, besides a wide strip along the south of the river reaching almost to Croydon. The London Clay gives rise to low-lying country with heavy soil. It was formerly well wooded, oaks and elms being the chief trees. In Essex parts of Epping Forest, formerly a royal hunting ground, still survive on it, but in Middlesex most of the woodland has been cleared, though St. John's Wood, Enfield Chase and Wormwood Scrubs all testify to the former extent of the woodland. As the trees were cleared the London Clay became used increasingly for pastureland, but on the clay itself settlements were few except where overlying gravels and sands provided drier sites with supplies of water from springs and wells. Even in the neighbourhood of London it was long before dwellings spread over to the clay tracts, which were mostly uninhabited until the beginning of the nineteenth century: modern drainage has made many areas habitable but they are rarely selected for better types of houses, and it is only along the main railway lines that they are completely built over.

The Tertiary sands in the basin occur in beds both above and below the London Clay. Their distribution is best understood when it is remembered that they were folded into the syncline, so that the lower beds occur chiefly in a narrow belt adjoining the Chalk outcrop on both sides of the basin, in some places forming a low ridge, while the upper form a more extensive spread near the middle of the basin, for instance north of Aldershot (see Fig. 23), and also cap many small hills in the middle of the basin further east. The distribution of Tertiary clay and sand is thus not accidental but depends on the stage reached in the denudation of the folded series.

The lower sandy beds occurring along the Chalk borders of the basin are often associated with clays and give rise to various soils of considerable fertility so that their area is well cultivated, especially in the districts within easy reach of London, where there are extensive orchards and market gardens. Along this belt, too, settlements were above the marshy London Clay country and had readily accessible water supplies, in contrast to the Chalk slopes immediately above them : for these and other reasons a line of important market towns approximately coincides with it, from Canterbury to Croydon and Guildford.

The country north of Aldershot is in marked contrast to the clay district nearer Windsor. The Great Park with its woodlands and meadows and half-timbered houses stretches southwards from Windsor, but as the ground rises the scenery changes to wide heaths, often uncultivated for great distances, covered with bracken and heather, or in places with pine woods. Here the Bagshot sands occupy the middle of the basin, followed by other sandy and loamy beds.

Nearer London only small detached patches of these sands remain as outliers standing slightly up above the plain of London Clay, the last remnants of a bed which must formerly have been continuous with that near Aldershot. Many of the favoured drier uplands are based on these outliers; Hampstead Heath, Highgate and Harrow are the most notable hills which though reaching no great elevation yet stand sufficiently high to afford wide views over the clay plain.

THE TERRACED FEATURES AND DEPOSITS

The features we have described are those to be expected within a synclinal basin, the newest rocks occupying a small area in the deepest part and progressively older rocks occurring in more or less regular concentric belts towards the flanks. In these respects the scenic features of the London basin are fairly regular; the traveller entering the basin from the north, south or west must first cross the Chalk hills, then the rather varied lower group of sands and clays, then a wide stretch of London Clay and may lastly reach the drier outcrop of the Bagshot sands : coming from the north the distance to be crossed is wider than from the south, owing to the gentler dip. Generally the land forms are related to these rock types and this arrangement of the rocks forms the fundamental basis of the scenery. But in the basin the land forms have also been to some extent controlled by the conditions under which the rocks have been denuded, while in many parts there are also newer and often quite thin superficial deposits which change the character of the soil and lead to important differences in the scenery.

It will be more convenient first to notice the general character of these superficial deposits. By the riverside are great expanses of alluvium, similar to those of the Trent (p. 75), the tract near Woolwich and Barking being three miles wide. In these flat areas the Thames meanders freely, for its gradient is slight ; much of the Thames water rises at only 400 feet above the sea, and though the source may be some 400 feet higher, the fall is rapid (about seven feet per mile) for the first twenty miles. From Lechlade to Teddington the river bed only falls some eighteen or twenty inches per mile, below Teddington the gradient is lower still. With such a gentle fall there is practically no vertical erosion below the Cotswold tract, but the river, as in the case of the Trent, expends its energy in widening its valley : it is a mature river, and reaches maturity early in its course.

Occasionally in its meanders the river comes near to the solid rocks on either side of the flood plain, and early settlements frequently grew up at such points, notably Gravesend and Greenwich. In many places the flood plain was formerly a marshy waste, but it has usually been drained to form meadowland, though in the Lea valley there are still considerable areas of marsh. Embankments along the shores in the tidal portion of the river have made this utilisation possible, but great areas such as the Isle of Dogs remained as marsh until they were used for dock construction in the last century. In some places east of London the surface of the drained marshlands is several feet below the level of the highest tides, the surface level having fallen, according to the late W. Whitaker, owing to the shrinkage of the peat and clay which compose them. In early times many of these marshes must have been impassable, and it is probable that their occurrence on one side of the river or the other for so great a distance from the mouth made it necessary to go upstream as far as the site of London before a suitable place for a ford or bridge could be found : thus while the solid rocks are near the river at Gravesend, marshes extend on the opposite side, and when at Grays the north bank could be approached the Swanscombe Marshes made the south bank unsuitable for a crossing.

Going northwards or southwards from the river at London, the ground tends to rise in a series of small steps, rather than gradually, each step being relatively level. Thus from the Thames side at Westminster there is a rise to Hyde Park, where the ground is level over wide areas, though further north there are other well-marked steps to higher levels. These steps represent river terraces comparable with those already noticed in the Trent valley. The lowest terrace stands about fifty feet above river-level, and thus marks a stage when the land stood some fifty feet lower in reference to the sea than it is now. At this stage the river excavated for itself a wide valley and spread its flood plain deposits over a great area. These deposits, cut through by the Thames in more recent times when a raising of the land gave the river power to cut vertically once more, have been removed along the area near the river but form a distinct terrace rising sharply from the flood plain ; they give rise to a ledge on which Hyde Park stands, an area where the ground is better drained than in the flood plain or in the clay areas (Fig. 25). This terrace extends as a wide flat area from Paddington to Holborn, where it is cut by the deep trench of the Turnmill Brook or the Fleet River ; thence from St. Paul's it spreads eastwards through Bethnal

Green to the banks of the Lea.   This terrace is known as the
Taplow Terrace.

About an equal distance above this terrace is another,
the so-called Hundred Foot or Boyn Hill Terrace, which
represents a still earlier base-level of the Thames when an
even wider spread of gravel was laid down at a level corresponding to the land being about 100 feet lower than it
is now (Fig. 31).   Since its formation much of this higher
terrace has been destroyed (during the formation of the
Taplow Terrace, and subsequently), so that it is mostly
represented by fragments of the original level tract, often
situated some miles from the river, and in some cases merely

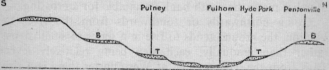

Figure 25.—The terrace levels of the London area.
Terraces dotted : solid rocks unshaded.

forming cappings of small hills.   Near London itself,
Clapham Common and Pentonville owe their elevation and
dry situation to their position on this terrace, which raises
them above the London Clay underlying both areas.

While both these terraces indicate an elevation of the
land during the time since the Thames valley has been
substantially of the present form, there is also evidence of
a not very distant period of submergence, for the river
alluvium under the present flood plain extends down beneath
the sea-level, filling a channel which can only have been cut
when the land stood higher than at present.   This deeper
occurrence of the alluvium has of course no effect on the
surface scenery, but the subsidence of the land which has
caused it has produced other features in the area of the
London basin and elsewhere; these will be dealt with more fully
later, but the drowning of the valley mouths and the formation of narrow inlets on the Essex shore may be mentioned.

All the movements both of elevation and subsidence, and the formation of the deposits which comprise river terraces and river alluvium, have taken place since the Ice Age. They are in a way only minor features within the basin, almost flat tracts at varying intervals above river-level, but they produce regions of distinctive character especially where patches of the gravel terraces rest upon a clay foundation. The Ice Age which preceded the formation of the deposits chiefly affected the north-east of the basin (for example above Colchester) where wide expanses of boulder clay cover the Chalk dip slopes and the Tertiaries. The boulder clay, brought by ice which invaded this area from the north, and which crossed the Chalk outcrop, itself contains much Chalk; for this reason it is a much lighter and more fertile clay than is frequently found in glacial deposits, and where it rests on Chalk the normal characters of that rock are completely transformed by the blanket, which supports some excellent arable land.

Before the boulder clay was deposited, however, the Thames valley had already attained essentially its present form: it has since been deepened by more than 100 feet, but its general characters had already been determined. Some evidence of the stages in the development of this pre-glacial valley can be gained from a study of the land forms on its slopes. It is clear, of course, that all land lying at less than about 100 feet over sea-level has been cut since the time when the Boyn Hill Terrace was formed, since this represented the base-level of erosion at that time; indeed, much of the land above that terrace must have undergone subsequent erosion. But there are features in the higher ground, such as level platforms on hillsides, and small hills all reaching the same general height, which are held to be fragments of former base-levels attained during pre-glacial erosion. The details of these features need not be discussed here, but attention may be drawn to the fact that the hills in and around the London basin frequently

reach either to about 200 feet or to about 400 feet above sea-
level. The 400-foot level is well marked on the hills to the
north and south of London, while many of the small outliers
reach to a height near 200 feet: the hill at Minster in the
Isle of Sheppey is thus about equal in height to the Rayleigh
Hills in south Essex, which rise conspicuously from the
Thames marshes and present a noticeably flat top. The
same wide extent of heights between 200 feet and 300 feet
has been demonstrated in another way by Dr. S. W. Wool-
dridge who has plotted a 'hypsometric curve' showing the
percentage of the area above certain heights: the flattening
of the curve at this particular interval emphasises the fact
that an unusually large area of the higher ground stands at
about this level. These levels are thought to correspond
approximately to former positions of sea-level and it is
believed that they are the result of weathering and river
erosion, which produced a fairly level plain near sea-level.

The Thames basin is therefore by no means a simple
area of low land. Differences in soil and in relief have been
brought about by the various rock types represented in the
Tertiary, while the gently terraced topography reflects stages
in the erosion of the basin. Lacking any striking elevations,
such small hills as are left by the dissection of more extensive
platforms have exercised great influence on the settlements
of the area and largely control those modifications of the
scenery which are associated with the making of London.

Figure 26.—Windsor Castle.

CHAPTER VII

THE WEALD OF KENT
AND SUSSEX

THE densely forested area to which the name Weald was originally given still has much woodland in many parts, but most of it is now used for agriculture. Its hop fields and orchards, wide meadows and breezy commons, are almost completely surrounded by the Chalk downland which forms part of the same structural unit, and in this description, therefore, the North and South Downs may be conveniently included. Crossing this area from north to south, scarp is succeeded by dip slope, which in turn is followed by another ridge running parallel to the first. While most of the vales are floored by heavy clays in which the rivers have made wide spreading valleys, the ridges vary greatly in character and in their outlines show striking contrasts to the Downs themselves. With such diversity of rock foundation, there are not only differences in soil and agricultural development, but many types of building materials, and the simple thatched cottages of brick and timber found in some areas give place in others to stone buildings. And over the whole area lies the ugly shadow of the expanding metropolis, so that its character has already been changed completely in the more accessible parts, and its individuality is threatened in many others. Yet even the popularised beauty spots of London's playground, with their outlook towers and other ' amenities ', retain many features of interest which not even development can obliterate, while there are still considerable areas whose natural loveliness remains. But here, as in much of south-eastern England, it is necessary to get away from main roads to see any unspoiled country.

THE SYMMETRY OF THE WEALD

The Weald of Kent and Sussex presents a symmetry of structure and a variety of scenery which are in some ways comparable with those of the London basin, for it is traversed by hill ridges running east and west, those of the north of the area matching those of the south. And yet the structure is really the opposite to that of the London basin, for whereas in that area the scarps face outwards, in the Wealden area they fall inwards to the centre; the dips are therefore outwards and the Weald is a worn-down anticline (Fig. 23).

The view southwards from almost any point on the edge of the North Downs shows the general character of much of the area. For instance from Colley Hill, north of Reigate, the Chalk scarp falls abruptly into a vale formed by Gault and Upper Greensand, mostly occupied by permanent pasture but with many oak trees in the hedgerows. Beyond this the land rises slightly to form another scarp, corresponding to the outcrop of the Lower Greensand, an area of arable land, but with much heath and parkland, which extends south-westwards to the more imposing heights of Leith Hill. South of this Greensand ridge another clay plain, more monotonous than the last, stretches for many miles, but out of it the land rises again in another dip slope, to culminate in the High Weald, the core of the region. And far beyond, forming the distant sky-line, the clear curves of the South Downs complete the pattern of the area.

THE ROCKS OF THE WEALD

The rocks of the middle of the Weald are older than the Chalk, but they are newer than the oolites and the clays of the Oxford and Kimmeridge groups. It may occur to the reader to wonder why these beds, occupying so wide an area in the Weald, have received so little attention in the description of other regions. Some of the beds have been mentioned casually, as the Greensands occurring under the Chalk scarp (p. 48); in the Vale of Pewsey, which in a small way repeats the structure of the Wealden area, these Greensands form much of the floor (Fig. 14). But in Kent and Sussex a much bigger variety of rocks is present, especially underneath the Greensands, and these rocks are not much represented in areas farther north in England, for they consist of sands and clays laid down in a lake which extended only over the south-east, a lake of fresh water in which non-marine shell-fish were living.

The sequence of events to be visualised begins with the marine conditions under which the Lias, the oolites and the succeeding clays were deposited, followed by a shallowing of the sea and eventually its disappearance from England; 'Wealden' deposits of sand and clay were then accumulated in a restricted area of fresh water until, with the deposition of the Greensands, the sea once more re-entered the area, the land sinking still further to allow the sea to cover the greater part of England and to extend, when the Chalk was deposited, over areas which had long been land. The rocks included in the Wealden area may thus be tabulated:

Chalk	
Gault Clay and Upper Greensand	} marine
Lower Greensand	
Weald Clay	} laid down in
Weald or Hastings Sands	} freshwater
(including the Wadhurst Clay)	} lake

The Wealden Sands occupy the centre of the area and the newer rocks form more or less regular bands around it, the harder Lower Greensand and Chalk standing out as ridges while the Weald Clay and the Gault Clay form low ground: variations in the thickness of these formations and

D

in the nature of some of the rocks lead to differences in the heights of the ridges and the breadths of the valleys and interfere with that complete regularity of scenic pattern which might otherwise be expected.

Although the sea may have washed over much of this region since its denudation began, its present form has mainly resulted from the work of the rivers, aided by frost and rain. These agencies have been able to cut down the outcrops of the softer rocks, leaving the ridges upstanding; these have gradually been undercut and their scarps have slowly retreated to north and south.

The Weald Sands occupy the High Weald, the area stretching from Hastings to Horsham, a broken upland rising in places to 800 feet above sea-level. This region, sometimes called the Forest Ridges, is mainly an area of sandy soil, once densely wooded. Although the lower slopes are generally of poor grassland, in the valleys there are richer soils. Most of the trees were cut down either for ship-building or in connection with the local iron industry, the ironstone beds in this area being similar to those occurring in the Lias (see p. 35); for many centuries charcoal was used for smelting the ore. Ashdown Forest is situated on this tract, an upland area of woods and commons, but over much of the area only the place-names and the scattered clumps of trees suggest the former extent of the woodlands, while other names like Furnace Pond and Hammer Mill recall the iron industry which helped in the deforesting of the area. In the sixteenth century there were thirty-two furnaces and thirty-eight forges in Sussex alone, but from this area the iron workers moved to other parts of the country, including South Wales, where their activities also led to great tracts of woodland being cut down.

The open commons along the belt through Tunbridge Wells are situated on these sands; in this area the rivers have cut deep valleys. The strong sandstones have been

deeply weathered along the prominent vertical joints, and curiously shaped masses stand out from the hillsides, as for example along the valley at Rocks Wood, near West Hoathly; here one mass, "Great-upon-Little", has been almost completely undermined along a thin bed of clay, a layer only about a quarter of an inch thick but sufficient to hold up the water percolating through the sandstone. Other masses in the same district have been quite undercut

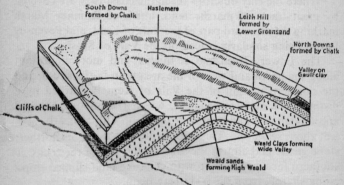

Figure 27.—The western end of the Weald.
Shading as in Figure 23.

and have tumbled over. Similar irregularity is noticeable at High Rocks near Tunbridge Wells and on Rusthall Common, where the Toad Rock is a relic of a block isolated by weathering along joint planes and shaped by wind action.

The Weald Clay vales, or the Low Weald, including the Vale of Kent and the Vale of Sussex, almost completely surround the High Weald (Fig. 27). The clays, like those of the Lias and of Oxford, give rise to heavy sodden soils, and the landscape is featureless. Here and there, where the railways cross the vales, villages are growing up around the stations, but generally there are few settlements in this clay region, and few good roads, although since the land has been drained or cleared of the oak woods which formerly

covered it, it has been converted into neatly hedged cattle
pastures or orchards. Trees are still abundant in many
parts. Formerly the roads in this clay country were exceedingly bad, and near the end of the eighteenth century
oxen were used to draw coaches in some parts because no
horse could move in the stiff clay. In this area much clay
has been used in making red bricks and tiles, and timber has
also been used in building.

Where the clay outcrops reach the coast they are covered
by great tracts of marshy land, much of Romney Marsh
marking the sea-ward part of the Vale of Kent, and Pevensey
Levels being similarly placed on the Vale of Sussex.

The Lower Greensand is thicker and more important
along the north and west of the area than in the south, and
the northern margin of the Vale of Kent is marked by a
distinct and steep escarpment, which rises above Ashford
and Godalming and culminates in Leith Hill at nearly 1000
feet above sea-level. This is an impressive ridge, its northern
slope gentle and almost the same as the dip of the rocks, its
southern face a real scarp with concave land-slipped slopes
rising sharply from the wide clay plain.

These sandy beds give rise to well-drained upland country
with abundant water supplies, and though the soil is sometimes poor, extensive tracts being given over to heathland,
there are some fertile belts. Westwards around Haslemere
and Hindhead these beds give rise to wider upland areas,
with much heathland and pine wood, but the valleys are
often more fertile, though the slopes are often steep.

The Devil's Punchbowl, Hindhead, is one of the best-
known valleys in Surrey. It has been eroded by a stream
flowing northwards which has cut a valley through the
sandy rocks, and the springs along the junction of these
with the clay beneath (the Atherfield Clay) have given rise
to the steep slopes of the valley. By the undermining action
of the springs the valley head has tended to become larger
and wider than the remainder of the valley, producing the

' Punchbowl '. In the Leith Hill district are similar steep-sided valleys in which it is easy to trace the spring line and to note the difference in the character of the vegetation where the sands join the clays.

The local variations in this Lower Greensand group lead to differences in scenery along the outcrop. In the Leith Hill area the Greensand contains exceedingly hard beds of a highly siliceous rock known as chert, a rock very similar in its characters to flint. This very resistant material is responsible for the unusual height of these hills. Near Guildford these cherts are less in evidence, and the crest of St. Martha's Hill is made up by rather soft sands with masses of ferruginous sandstone (the Carstone), the presence of which has controlled the erosion of these beds, and has here retarded denudation.

Over this Greensand country the picturesque tracks are often deeply cut, in places to a depth of twelve feet or more below the adjoining fields. This sinking of the tracks is still going on, for where the vegetation is destroyed by making a new track over the hill, wind and rain quickly remove the surface soils, and wind action still further deepens the channel as dry débris is produced by the continued disintegration of the rocks at the surface.

The Lower Greensand includes many stones which have been used in building, the Kentish Rag in particular being important in the eastern part of the Weald, though it has also been carried over a large area, as to Canterbury and to Dover, especially for windows and doorways. But almost everywhere along the outcrop of the Greensand from Maidstone to Hindhead some stone houses are to be seen, while the tall towers of the ragstone churches are also characteristic.

As the Greensand ridge dips northwards into the clay Vale of Holmesdale the scenery again changes, the blue Gault Clay being a stiff blue marine mud similar in its characteristics to the clays of the Lias. Much of the soil is too heavy for cultivation, save where the admixture of down-washed sand from the Greensand outcrops which flank it have produced a lighter soil; elsewhere there are extensive green pastures. On the south of the Weald the outcrop of the Gault Clay is so narrow that it gives rise to no very important feature (Fig. 27).

THE DOWNS

Above the Gault Clay the Upper Greensand is usually so thin as to be unimportant in relation to our present discussion, occurring as a narrow belt merely on the scarp formed by the Chalk. This latter formation is quite normal in this area, and in its rolling downlands, its dry valleys, its beech woodlands, its ancient routes (especially along the North Downs) it is closely comparable with the Chalk country of other parts of England. The Chalk is less used in building even than in most areas in England, but flint has been fairly extensively used in Kent from very early times, as at Margate and Sandwich.

The form of the Downs varies in relation to the amount of dip, much as does the form of the escarpment in the Vale of Pewsey (Figs. 13 and 14). From the coast to near Guildford the scarp of the North Downs is steep, rising sharply from the clay vale to a height of over 600 feet, the whole Chalk belt here measuring six or eight miles from south to north, the dip slope to the London basin being long and gentle. On the other hand, between Farnham and Guildford the scarp is much less prominent; the outcrop, moreover, is very narrow on account of the steepness with which the beds here plunge down, while the steep dip gives rise to a steeply inclined dip slope. In this part of the Chalk outcrop, therefore, the north and south slopes are almost equal, and the narrow ridge is suitably known as the Hog's Back; the way in which it differs from the ordinary escarpment produced in gently dipping rocks is worthy of notice, for while such gently dipping beds are characteristic of the areas with which we have dealt already (that is, for example, the Midlands, and south and east of England), in the west of Britain the rocks have often been more affected by pressure and they lie more steeply tilted : in such cases ridges are frequently not so wide and are less asymmetrical than those of the more undisturbed regions.

The North Downs are more extensive and more varied than the South Downs. In the former there are large areas of clay-with-flints, which are mainly occupied by woodland or coppice, while wheat is grown on the lower slopes, but on the South Downs sheep farming is almost universal, for there is much less cover of superficial deposits.

Even the large rivers lose much water under ground where they cross the Chalk, and on both these Chalk tracts are many dry valleys, generally running with the dip of the rocks and cutting deeply into the uplands. As a result there are no important routes east and west along the plateau, the old roads following the lower part of the scarp or the bottom of the dip slope (where Watling Street runs along the lower Tertiary beds) thus avoiding the deep trenches in the uplands.

THE RIVERS OF THE WEALD

Among the most interesting features of this area are the gaps by which the Weald rivers escape northwards through the Greensand and Chalk ridges into the London basin, and southwards through the Chalk into the sea. At each of these gaps is a town, the sites being somewhat similar to that of Lincoln, marking the places where the east-west routes were compelled to descend to cross the rivers, and where modern routes following the valleys now cross the ridges. Guildford on the Wey, Leatherhead and Dorking on the Mole, Maidstone and Rochester on the Medway, Lewes on the Ouse and Arundel on the Arun, all owe their sites to similar conditions : many of them have old castles guarding the ancient routes. Lewes, which Defoe described

as " in the most romantic situation I ever saw " is at a confluence where a minor fold more or less detaches the upland
of harder Middle and Upper Chalk on which the town
stands. Arundel is also striking as a meeting place of routes;
here the Chalk gives rise to steep river cliffs. Guildford is
situated in the Hog's Back area where the Chalk outcrop is
very narrow, and in consequence it stretches through the
Wey Gap, really uniting two earlier settlements, one to the
north and one to the south of the Chalk.

The origin of these gaps probably calls for little comment, since they are in many respects so similar to those at
Lincoln (p. 37) and at Goring (p. 59). The rivers flowing
northwards from the High Weald rise on the sandstone hills
and cross a clay belt before cutting their gaps in the Greensand ridge, after which they cross another clay vale before
cutting gaps in the Chalk. Throughout the greater part of
their courses they are flowing with the dip, and though they
are joined by strike streams flowing along the clay belts of
the Vales of Kent or Holmesdale, where some themselves
become meandering strike streams, their essential character
is clearly related to the dip of the beds, and they may be
called consequent streams. The cutting of the gaps was
obviously begun before the clay belts had been reduced
below the level of the uplands, when the rivers flowed along
a dipping surface inclined to the north, and the present
relief has been produced while the gaps have been steadily
lowered, by the more rapid removal of the soft beds along
the length of their outcrop, assisted by the growth of subsequent streams.

As these changes have taken place there have been many
minor readjustments of drainage owing to some rivers
having been able, by virtue of more advantageous positions
or of greater cutting power, to erode more quickly than their
neighbours; so their tributaries have cut back in the clay
belts in a way that enabled them to capture the headwaters
of their neighbours. Thus the Medway has been able to

behead the Stour and Darent, the water from the High Weald formerly flowing into these being now transferred to the Medway by east and west tributaries flowing in the Vale of Kent. Similarly the Wey has grown at the expense of the Blackwater, which formerly rose to the south of the Chalk; the headwaters of the present Wey really belong to the Blackwater but are carried along the Gault Clay outcrop eastwards from Alton and Farnham to Guildford. The strengthened Wey has thus cut for itself a deep gorge-like valley near Godalming but the reduced Blackwater now has a valley too large for such a stream, which may be called a ' misfit '. All these changes, however, have tended to make the clay vales lower and wider, and to bring the harder outcrops into stronger relief, while making the more extensive clay tracts increasingly monotonous.

But if the rivers of the northern part of this area originated on an inclined surface sloping to the north, it is equally true that the rivers of the southern part originated on a similarly inclined surface sloping to the south. The Arun, the Adur, the Ouse and Cuckmere are also mainly dip streams, with subsequent streams along the wide Vale of Sussex (notably the West Rother). It follows then that the rivers of the Wealden area originated on a surface which was folded to north and south, more or less as the rocks are folded at present. The relations of the rivers may more easily be understood if they are supposed to have begun when the Chalk extended over the area in the manner shown in Figure 23, though as a matter of fact some of the upper beds of the anticline had already been removed before the rivers began to erode the surface.

THE CLIFFS AND MARSHES OF THE COAST

The coast scenery of this area, like the surface relief, is intimately related to the geological structure. The Chalk cliffs of Dover have already been referred to; these continue northwards to Deal where the cliffs fall away as the

Tertiary rocks are reached. Sands and clays of this series form the wide bay at Sandwich where the Stour seeks so long for an exit to the sea, while to the north the Chalk reappears in the cliffs in the north-eastern angle of Kent at Ramsgate and Margate, brought up as a result of a small fold and separated from the Downs by the syncline in which Canterbury lies.

Following the coast around to the south, at Folkestone, the blue clay known as the Gault forms the foreshore to the east of the town, and the cliffs of dull white Chalk rest on this clay foundation. As a result, water passing down

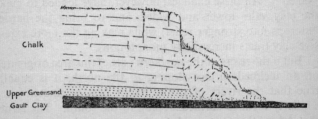

Figure 28.—Section of land-slipped cliff at Folkestone.

through the Chalk (and the Upper Greensand just beneath it) is held up at the top of the blue clays, and along the bottom of the cliff gives rise to a line of springs, the flow of water keeping the clay always wet and slippery. These form ideal conditions for the development of landslips, and the ' Warren ' of Folkestone shows the effects of numerous landslips in the jumbled and untidy face of the cliffs (Fig. 28). At Dover, on the other hand, the blue clay is far below sea-level and the cliffs remain strong and present clean regular surfaces to the sea.

The west cliffs of Folkestone differ no less strikingly from those of the east, for there is no Chalk, the beds below the Chalk being here exposed. The Lower Greensand gives rise to a series of low and variable cliffs, sometimes steep where hard sandstones break along vertical joints, through Folkestone to Hythe and Sandgate. The cliffs gently sink to the level of Romney Marsh, where the Vale of Kent meets the coast. This flat tract, now largely drained and used for sheep farming, is traversed by weedy streams which meander through the low ground as they seek a path to the sea, lacking energy to carry away the material they bring down, and ready to deposit it and to extend the flats. For the Marsh is made up of alluvial material, fronted along the coast by diverging ridges of shingle. Behind the Marsh the land rises sharply in what may well be an old line of cliffs: that continuing inland westwards from Hythe to near Appledore is very noticeable.

Probably at an early stage in its development the area of the present Marsh was occupied by a wide bay, now represented by the low ground from Winchelsea to Hythe; the sea at that time attacked the coast and cut the low cliffs which form the northern boundary. This bay is believed to have come into existence by the drowning of the lower part of the Rother valley, already eroded deeply along the soft belt of the Weald clays. The drift of shingle along the coast from the south-west led to the formation of storm beaches partly across the bay, and so to the impeding of the river and the silting up of the bay by the deposition of river-borne material. There have been many changes in the shingle beaches, and the history of Dungeness is very complicated, a large series of curved banks between Lydd and the shore marking former positions of the coast-line. At one time the Rother reached the sea at New Romney, on the north of Dungeness, but it now cuts through the shingle some eight miles further west. More recent changes in this piece of coast have left their mark on its history: the destruction of the old town of Winchelsea by the advance of the waves led to the designing of New Winchelsea as a channel port by Edward I, but the sea treated this in a different way, leaving it some way inland. Henry VIII, who sought to defend the estuary by a castle, was no more fortunate, for in a short time his Camber Castle was also left some way inland.

The Pevensey Levels have some points of resemblance, but the shingle bar of Pevensey is insignificant compared with those of Dungeness; inland the Levels are not bounded by cliffs comparable with those of Romney Marsh, possibly because this inlet was sheltered by Beachy Head more completely than the Romney estuary was protected by the cliffs of Hastings.

Beyond the Pevensey Levels the Chalk at Eastbourne almost immediately gives rise to high cliffs which extend through Brighton and with slight interruption almost to Bognor. At many places the cliffs are vertical, and are deeply cut along joint planes to form caves and projecting stacks of peculiar forms. Beachy Head, with its cliffs over 500 feet high, represents the eastward termination of the South Downs, which are there cut across at right angles; thence to near Worthing the coast follows the trend or strike of the beds and the cliffs retain a general uniformity of type for many miles. Here the cliffs truncate the dip valleys which formerly extended further to the south but which have been shortened by the attack of the waves on the cliffs, the coast-line moving steadily inland (Fig. 27). The cliffs thus vary in height according to the relief of the land they limit, as in the Seven Sisters, near Eastbourne.

The coast of south-eastern England thus presents two different aspects; from Margate to Beachy Head, where the alternating ridges and valleys made by hard and soft rocks are cut nearly at right angles by the coast-line, there is a corresponding alternation of cliff and wide beach or marsh, while south-west of this the coast more uniformly follows the trend of a single rock group, the Chalk, and its variety there depends on the relief and details of structure.

CHAPTER VIII

THE SOUTH COAST

THE region dealt with in this chapter is extensive, stretching along the south coast from near Worthing westwards to the borders of Devon: much of it constitutes the Hampshire basin, but a large part of it, the Isle of Wight, is detached, and another important part, the 'Isle' of Purbeck, is nearly detached, from the mainland. In many respects this region resembles the London basin, for much of it is a syncline holding Tertiary rocks, but its southern border has more variety of structure and its coast scenery is of extraordinary interest.

THE ISLE OF WIGHT

The Isle of Wight forms a convenient starting point for the description of this region. Cut off from Hampshire by the narrow waters of the Solent and Spithead, it has escaped some of the development which has affected many parts of the south-east coast, while its isolation has given greater attraction to its quiet beauty. The most important feature in the island is that ridge of Chalk which runs in almost a straight line from the Needles in the west to dazzling white Culver Cliff on the east, a narrow low ridge of downland which divides the island into two areas of entirely different character, and which constitutes the long diagonal of its lozenge-shape (Figs. 29 and 30).

This Chalk outcrop is for the most part narrow, for the beds here are dipping steeply and are often quite vertical. The ridge is thus closely comparable with the Hog's Back which in the Guildford area forms the boundary to the London basin: the hog's back pattern is more persistent in the south of the Hampshire basin. The chalkland across the middle of the island is not high, rarely exceeding 450 feet, but it stands out prominently above the clays and sands which flank it both to the north and south. Near the middle of the island, south and west of Carisbrook, the dip of the Chalk is lower and it spreads over a much wider area, about three miles across; here the downs are higher, Brixton Down reaching over 700 feet, and are deeply dissected by narrow dry valleys. To the north of the Chalk ridge the island is made up of Tertiary strata which compare closely

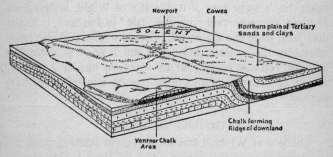

Figure 29.—The Isle of Wight.
Shading as in Figure 27.

with those of the London basin, and which stretch across the straits into Hampshire, while to the south clays and sands like those of the Weald form much of the island (Fig. 29).

The northern part of the island, from the Chalk ridge to the Solent and Spithead, is for the most part low-lying, and largely made up of clays. The soils are heavy and there are many copses and woods, of which Parkhurst Forest is the most extensive. Along the Spithead coast, these soft rocks generally give rise to a low shelving shore-line, the narrow sea looking like a great river in a wide shallow valley, and when low cliffs are present they are often overgrown. But along the Solent the coast is some-times bolder, especially where thin limestones occur among the clays. At the eastern extremity of the island, the Foreland is made up by the Bembridge Limestone, a harder bed occurring among the usually soft Tertiary strata. Where so few stones can be used for building, it is not surprising that this limestone has been used extensively, for instance in Yarmouth Castle, and it has also been exported into the Hampshire region. Elsewhere in this northern area bricks have been made from local clays, and they have been used in the majority of smaller buildings.

The wide spread of the Tertiary rocks as compared with the narrow strip of Chalk outcrop is noteworthy : the Chalk is more than 1500 feet in thickness and forms a belt only half a mile wide in places, whereas the Tertiary beds are about 2000 feet thick and occupy the whole of the northern tract, in the centre five miles wide. These differences in distribution are due to the structure ; while the Chalk is for the most part nearly vertical along this belt, so that the width of outcrop is not much greater than the total thickness, the Tertiary beds, except just along the edge of the chalk, are dipping very gently, and in many parts are nearly horizontal. The diagram (Fig. 29) shows how the Chalk and the rocks near it plunge steeply down in the middle of the island but almost at once curve away gently to rise to the north, the Chalk reaching the surface again near Winchester and in the Salisbury Plain. The basin thus produced is markedly unsymmetrical, and its deepest part lies much nearer the south than the north. It may be noticed that the London basin shows a similar asymmetry, its steepest dips (as in the Hog's Back) being likewise in the south (Fig. 23).

But the more interesting part of the island lies to the south of the Chalk ridge, where rocks belonging to the same series as those in the Weald form a broad belt : the Greensands, the Gault Clay, the Weald Clay and Sands are all represented and are seen in the low, yellow-green cliffs between Sandown and Shanklin. Accordingly this region shows greater variety of scenery than that of the north.

In the main these more readily denuded beds form a wide vale, extending from Brixton on the south-west to Sandown on the east, with fertile red-brown soils and rich green fields, a region of gentle relief bounded by wooded ridges made by the sandy beds, above which rise both to north and south the downlands made by the Chalk.

For this southern vale is essentially an anticline, more or less comparable with the Weald, but with generally steeper dips on the north and gentler on the south. Thus in the most southerly corner an outlier of Chalk introduces a delightful tract of downland, rising in St. Boniface Down to over 700 feet and forming the highest land in the isle; the wide outcrop of the Chalk, its greater elevation, and the steep scarp of its northern face, contrasting very sharply with the character of the central ridge. These southern downs are deeply indented by small valleys on this northern scarp, but they form near Ventnor a steep, well-wooded slope much disturbed by landslips, for here the conditions described at Folkestone are repeated on a grand scale, the porous Chalk and Upper Greensand overlying the 'blue slipper' formed by the wet Gault Clay: as the whole of the rocks have a gentle southerly dip, there is a strong tendency to slip seawards, and damage to the coast road beneath the cliff has been a frequent occurrence (compare Fig. 28).

Although the country between the southern downs and the central ridge is generally low and has been spoken of as a vale, it is not related to the main drainage of the island, which presents many features of extraordinary interest. For all the more important rivers—the river Medina and the Western and Eastern Yar—rise in the southern area, not far from the coast, and flow into the Solent and Spithead after cutting gaps through the Chalk ridge. Essentially these are dip streams, and the carving of the gaps through the central ridge and the development of the wide clay plain behind it are to be explained more or less in the same way as the similar features in the Weald (p. 104). The situations of Newport and Brading in these gaps need no comment.

But the positions of the sources of the rivers are very remarkable. The Western Yar rises very near the coast about three miles from the Needles, and the upper part of its valley cuts right into the cliffs, so that a very little depression of the land would make this western area into a separate island. Moreover, the gravels laid down in this valley are found right on the south coast and extend to the

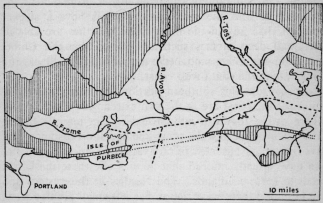

Figure 30.—The rivers of the south of England.
Chalk areas shaded. Broken lines show probable former courses of rivers.

Solent: obviously the river which cut the valley and deposited the gravels must at one time have been longer, and its headwaters must have risen some distance to the south of the present shore-line. From this vanished land it must have obtained the material which was deposited in the tract which then formed the lower part of its course. It is certain that wave action has led to the destruction of quite considerable areas of land which lay to the south of the present coast, and that this destruction has occurred since the rivers had carved their valleys to approximately the present forms (see Fig. 30).

The Eastern Yar has similarly lost much of its drainage area by the encroachment of the sea, the valley of a tributary near Sandown showing evidence of recent truncation. On the other hand the Medina, rising in the southern Chalk hills, has not so far suffered beheading by this marine advance.

Apart from this essentially northerly drainage, undoubtedly the original drainage of the area, there is little tendency to develop new streams except as tributaries subsequent to the main dip streams. But here and there small streams descend rapidly from the higher ground near the south coast into the sea. Such streams have a steeper gradient than any of the main rivers and they are able to cut small deep ravines such as that of Shanklin Chine, carved in the Greensand beds, and others like Blackgang Chine along the south-west coast.

Apart from this southern portion, the most interesting points of the coast are at the two extremities of the island, where owing to the locally steepened dip many different beds are brought into the coast-line in a short distance, and give rise to coast scenery of rare variety of colour and form. We have already noticed that here as elsewhere the Chalk tends to form headlands. The Needles at the western end are familiar; here wave action has left small pointed islets of Chalk by cutting through the ridge. Standing on the Chalk cliff above the Needles, they are seen to fall into line with the main ridge, and on a clear day, looking along this line, the cliffs of Chalk under Ballard Down across Bournemouth Bay may be seen continuing the ridge. The former connection of these areas is then not so difficult to appreciate, and just as the sea has detached the Needles from the island, so the wider breach may have been created, though over a longer period of time (Fig. 30).

South and east of the Needles the waves have worked away the rocks which underlie the Chalk, and for some miles the cliffs expose the southern face of the ridge, forming steep vertical faces of as much as 400 feet. But to the north

of the Needles the Chalk is overlain by the sands and clays
of the lower beds of the Tertiary, whose steeply dipping beds
prove more easily eroded than the Chalk, and have been
excavated to form Alum Bay, where the variegated sands
and clays make a pleasant contrast to the white cliffs of the
Chalk. Whitecliff Bay at the eastern end of the island
occupies a precisely similar position.

HAMPSHIRE AND EAST DORSET

In Hampshire the Tertiary beds cover a great area of
rather low relief. As in the London basin these rocks consist of sands and clays, but in this area there is a greater
thickness and a more varied succession, while on the whole
there is a bigger proportion of sand. So that whereas in
the London basin the clays (especially the London Clay)
make up vast stretches of heavy country, in this area there
are greater expanses of drier sandy country comparable, for
example, with that north of Aldershot. Over these sandy
areas extend great commons and woodlands, of which the
New Forest is a notable example.

The original forests included much oak, especially in
the wet clay regions, where ash and hazel were also common,
but on the more sandy parts beech and birch were common,
though pines are now spreading over many areas where
deciduous woodlands formerly flourished. The pine is not
strictly a native of Britain, though it grew here after the Ice
Age; it is probable that almost the whole of the British
flora disappeared during the time of the glaciation, for
although the ice did not come farther south than the Thames
basin, the country which was not ice-covered was almost
certainly too cold to maintain normal British plants, and it
is not unlikely that tundra conditions prevailed over all
except perhaps the extreme south-west of England. As the
ice receded and the climate improved forests spread northwards, the birch and pine (which still are the dominant trees
in Europe on the south of the tundra belt) being among the

first to enter England, to be followed in time by the oak and the beech, the former chiefly colonising the wet clay soil, the latter the drier uplands. In the face of this competition the pine shortly afterwards became extinct, and was not again found in Britain until its introduction in the eighteenth century, since which time it has spread rapidly, often at the expense of its former competitors. The pine-woods of the Bournemouth area exemplify the success with which this tree has colonised these sandy areas.

In the pine-woods (as also in beech-woods) there is little opportunity for undergrowth, for the thick carpet of pine needles and the deep shade prevent the growth of many plants. But in the more open parts of these forests bracken is abundant.

The forest-lands give to this area its most distinctive character, for in this part of England and in the Wealden region, woodlands cover a bigger proportion of the land than elsewhere, in spite of the great quantity of oak cut for ship-building, which continued in the estuaries of the Hampshire coast until about a century ago. In many parts of the county farms still appear as isolated clearings in the forest, and the villages scattered over the area are mostly small, at any rate those away from the coast, and are connected by roads which seem to straggle aimlessly across the countryside: probably many of them represent old forest tracks.

Where the Chalk hills dip down under the Tertiary sands and clays, there is as usual along such a boundary a more important line of towns, including Dorchester, Wimborne and Chichester.

At the eastern end of the area between Fareham and Havant the structure is complicated by smaller folds which result in an area of Chalk being brought up into the Tertiary lowlands. This isolated tract of downland, known as Ports Down, is some ten miles from west to east and rarely a mile across. Between this and the wider chalklands to the north lies a low belt of Tertiary beds, about three miles across, occupied by much woodland, including the Forest of Bere. London Clay forms the greater part of this belt, but small patches of Bagshot and other sands in the deeper parts of the little basin give rise to the irregular heaths of Purbrook and Walton.

Near its western end, the Hampshire basin narrows considerably and its direction is marked by the eastward-flowing river Frome, on which Dorchester is situated at the Roman crossing. Here tributary valleys coinciding with the dip of the Chalk trench deeply into the upland and cut it into narrow north-south ridges along which ancient ridge-ways have been converted into modern roads. In this region the Frome is running along the axis of the synclinal fold, the relations of this river and its tributaries to the basin being therefore very closely comparable with those noted in the London basin (p. 86). It appears that the Frome was developed along the bottom of a fold which was tilted to the east, and that into it dip streams flowed from both north and south. Its course to Wareham and into the sea below Poole accords with this interpretation (Fig. 30).

Still further east the Solent and Spithead continue along what is practically the same line, and it is considered that formerly the Frome extended eastwards along this line, receiving its tributaries the Stour, Avon and Test on its left bank and the Isle of Wight rivers, already noticed, on its right bank. Of course at this time there was much land to the south of the present shores, and Bournemouth Bay and the area to the south of it must have been land; possibly other tributaries from the south joined the Frome in this region and began the cutting of the wider breach in the Chalk there. The similarity of this extended Frome flowing along the bottom of a shallow trough to the Thames in the London syncline needs no emphasis, the tributaries in both cases following the dip of the beds. But in the case of the Hampshire basin the whole river system has been drowned under the sea, as a result of the lowering of the level of the land or rise of sea-level in relatively recent times (continuing to the New Stone Age) referred to already. In this way Southampton Water was formed by the flooding of the lower valley of the Test.

Wave action has also greatly modified the remnants of this extensive river system, for besides cutting into the south coast, where the Isle of Wight rivers have been beheaded, the waves have cut deeply into the mainland on the northern side of the original valley, on the coast of Bournemouth Bay; near Bournemouth they have cut low cliffs in the sands and clays. Along this coast some of the streams in the narrow steep-sided chines may constitute the last remnants of rivers formerly tributary to the Frome, whose lower courses have been removed by the advancing sea. In Branksome Chine a narrow gorge has been cut in the floor of a much wider valley, and it may be suggested that this latter represents the old tributary valley, the cutting of the gorge within it having been brought about by the steepened gradient given to the stream by the advance of the sea.

It may be worth pointing out the contrast between the effects of marine erosion on the rivers of the Isle of Wight and those of the Bournemouth area: in the former region the sea has cut away the narrow steep-sided valleys characteristic of the upper part of the river courses, leaving the stream with a very gentle gradient, while in the latter the sea, advancing towards the source, has left only the upper parts of the valleys, but with an increased gradient.

THE ISLE OF PURBECK

The Isle of Purbeck, which limits Bournemouth Bay on the west, affords some support to the views regarding the origin of the scenic features already discussed, but it also is an area of attractive coast scenery which merits very special consideration. Of course the Isle of Purbeck is no island, but it used to be more of an island than it is now, for Poole Harbour was formerly flanked by marshes which extended far along the Frome valley. This tract of country, some fifteen miles long and about seven or eight miles wide at its maximum, is bounded by cliffs at east and south but it tapers westwards, and in that direction it joins so un-

Figure 31.—Chalk stacks near Swanage.

obtrusively to the mainland that its boundary is not well defined (see Fig. 30).

We have already pointed out, from a viewpoint above the Needles, the continuation of the Chalk ridge westwards into Purbeck. On the east of Purbeck the typical Chalk uplands of Ballard Down end in vertical white cliffs, the lower part deeply fretted by wave action, which has detached numerous stacks (Fig. 31). These remains of the old cliff face show that here, as in the Isle of Wight, the coast is receding under the attack of the sea. The Chalk uplands form a very narrow tract, often not more than a quarter of a mile wide, once more the result of steeply dipping beds which in many places are quite vertical. As in the Isle of Wight the drainage flows from south to north, and the downland is cut by a narrow gap at Corfe where the grey stone village is overtopped by the large castle which guarded the converging routes.

North of the downs occur rocks like those of the Hampshire basin, sands and clays which have been worn back by the sea more rapidly than the Chalk of the headland, Studland Bay thus being closely comparable in structure and scenery with Alum Bay and Whitecliff Bay; here instead of Chalk cliffs dropping sheer into deep water we have a gently sloping sandy beach backed by pretty cliffs on which vegetation soon becomes established. To the south of the Chalk ridge the rocks are at first similar to those of the Isle of Wight, the most important group, the Wealden beds, being mainly clays which have been worn back to form the beautiful Swanage Bay. Nevertheless the country formed by the Weald clays is mostly lower than that to north and south, and it makes up a belt at first over a mile wide, but tapering gradually westwards to Worbarrow Bay owing to the diminishing thickness of the clays. The thinning of these beds, while the Chalk continues unchanged, will be understood when their origin in a lake of limited extent is borne in mind (p. 97); the shores of the lake were situated not far to the west of the Isle of Purbeck.

South of this clay belt the land surface is once more high, and where it meets the coast it forms the headlands of Peveril Point and Durlston Head. The east coast of Purbeck thus presents an alternation of projecting headlands backed by high ground and shallow bays fronting tracts of low ground. The bays are found along beds which are easily eroded, whether by the sea or by rivers and the atmospheric agencies of frost and rain; the headlands consist of harder and more resistant strata. These conditions of alternating bays and projections are often found along coasts where the sea is succeeding in its advance, or where a ridged land surface has been partly submerged.

The south-eastern part of Purbeck is made up chiefly of limestones which are more gently inclined than the rocks of the middle of the 'island': in many places along the coast they dip gently seawards, and the general structure closely parallels that of the south of the Isle of Wight. But as the fold rises westwards older beds are exposed along the coast, and the rocks seen on the south of Purbeck are not seen at the surface anywhere to the east. The limestones are of various kinds: immediately under the Wealden beds are limestones of freshwater origin, rich in the shells of freshwater snails, and they were formed in a forerunner of the Wealden lake. These beds are known as the Purbeck Limestones: they are tough and resistant, and have been widely used for building, some being especially important because they will take a good polish, for which reason they are commonly known as marbles. They have been very extensively employed in the interior decoration of churches.

Among these limestones are softer groups of clays which give rise to the shallow Durlston Bay, but, generally speaking, these beds and the Portland stone which underlies them, give rise to an impressive line of cliffs which reaches westwards to St. Albans Head, and terminates a plateau averaging about 400 feet above the sea. The limestones being nearly horizontal, the joints which cut the beds at right angles are almost vertical, and these have largely determined the form of the cliffs, which are steep and incised deeply along the weaker beds, caves being excavated by wave action as at the popular Tilly Whim.

Scattered on this limestone plateau are the many old quarries where the stone has been dug, and many small hamlets of grey stone. But the area is lightly peopled, for the soil is not very productive and there is little connection between the villages and the sea, for fishing has not prospered along this coast as it has farther west. Thus few houses are situated near the shores, and from many of the villages placed above this rocky coast there is no good road to the sea. Beyond St. Albans Head, however, the cliffs gradually fall away as the Kimmeridge Clay rises from beneath the sea-level. At first this clay creeps up to form the base of the cliffs, and here, along the west of St. Albans Head, landslips have given rise to an irregular coast-line, the thick limestones having slipped over the impermeable clays owing to the gentle seaward dip. Still further west the clays form the coast in Kimmeridge Bay.

LULWORTH AND THE COAST TO THE WEST

It is, however, along the coast some five miles west of this that the coast scenery is most fascinating, in the stretch of shore-line which includes Worbarrow Bay, Lulworth Cove

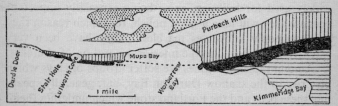

Figure 32.—The coast west of Purbeck.
Chalk, white ; Tertiaries, dotted ; Wealden and associated beds, vertical lines; Portland and Purbeck beds, black ; Kimmeridge Clay, horizontal lines.

and Man o' War Cove (Fig. 32). Throughout most of this tract the coast-line follows the strike or trend of the beds, in contrast to the condition in the eastern end of Purbeck, where the cliffs cut right across the various beds, and show a variety of coast form resulting from the alternating harder and softer rocks. Here in the west the position of the coast is determined mainly by the harder limestones of the Portland beds which form an almost unbroken line of rugged cliffs. These beds are steeply inclined to the north, and the underside of the rocks forms in many places an overhanging cliff, the softer Kimmeridge Clay having been stripped away for most of the distance. Along this part of the coast there is no tendency to landslips, for the beds are dipping steeply inland, and so there is thus little tendency for them to slip seawards.

Along almost the whole of this stretch of coast, therefore, the waves are hammering at the steep bedding plane of limestone, and in a few places they have succeeded in cutting a way through the limestone group, which forms

Figure 33.—Mupe rocks, the disconnected remnants of a hard bed.

only a narrow belt, and on reaching the softer group beyond have commenced the excavation of a larger bay. Worbarrow Bay and Lulworth Cove are excellent examples of these almost circular excavations widened out in the soft rocks behind the limestone barrier, through which only a narrow entrance has been carved. At the western side of the entrance to Worbarrow Bay the rock stacks known as Mupe (Mewp) Rocks continue the line of the barrier (just as the Needles continue the line of the Chalk further east) and show how it is only gradually being broken down, the waves meanwhile advancing more rapidly to the destruction of the softer rocks behind (Fig. 33). Lulworth Cove (Fig. 34) offers one of the few safe anchorages along this rocky coast, but its old village is a mile inland and like others in the neighbourhood has not been closely dependent on the sea for its existence, a state of affairs which is of course changing rapidly.

The way in which the excavation of these bays has been initiated is beautifully illustrated at Stair Hole, just to the west of Lulworth, where two small holes cut near the base of the limestone barrier have allowed the sea to scoop out deep holes in the softer beds behind (Fig. 34); in this neighbourhood, too, a complete breach in the barrier exemplifies a further stage in the advance of the waves. The

Figure 34.—Stair Hole and Lulworth Cove.

advance of the sea resulting from wave action has no doubt been checked in various places where hard rocks appear along the coast; but such a check is only temporary, and the Lulworth coast shows how a barrier may steadily be undermined and broken down.

Behind this simple coast-line Chalk downlands extend westwards to the north of Weymouth, but the wide Weymouth Bay is excavated in Oxford Clay. Purbeck and Portland beds reappear to the south in the Isle of Portland. Here the limestones are once more dipping gently southwards and are more closely comparable with those of southeast Purbeck. This region has been so scarred by quarrying and in the main is so treeless and drab, that except as a viewpoint it has little attraction.

From the heights of Portland, however, a magnificent view may be obtained of the pebble banks which link it with the mainland, the famous Chesil Beach, some sixteen miles long, connecting it with the coast at Abbotsbury. The beach is made up of rounded pebbles of flint (derived originally from the Chalk) and of quartzite (derived from the New Red Sandstone pebble beds still further to the west), and it has been built up by the transporting of these materials eastwards along the coast under the influence of wind and tidal currents, until they have been held up by the cliffs of Portland which, acting as a gigantic groyne, have checked further movement except into deeper waters. Hence these pebbles do not make their way around the point of Portland Bill and into Weymouth Bay, the beach from Weymouth to Portland along which the road runs being composed of shingle derived from the local limestones.

If we go farther west we leave behind the rocks which give character to the Hampshire basin and to the coast of the middle part of southern England. But the cliff scenery is interesting right on into Devonshire. For many miles, around Bridport and Charmouth and Lyme Regis the cliffs are cut in nearly horizontal rocks, limestones and shales of blue and yellow, similar in many respects to those of the north Yorkshire coast and likewise forming steep cliffs, vertical where the limestones are strong and well jointed, sloping where there are thicker shales, with small reefs across the foreshore marking the position of the hard bands. Overlying these Lias rocks Chalk and Greensand are found in the higher cliffs, occasionally slipped seawards, as in the famous Axmouth landslip, where in 1839 a great hollow 1000 yards long was produced in one great slip, giving a tumbled mass of irregular mounds on the foreshore. And still farther west, near Seaton, the blue and yellow cliffs give place to cliffs of deep red, as the gentle easterly dip of the rocks brings up still older beds, for here the Lias is in turn underlain by New Red Sandstones the colour of which gives a vivid richness to the cliff scenery in the coasts at Sidmouth and Budleigh Salterton.

At Dawlish and Teignmouth these red rocks also are often nearly horizontal. And when wave advance keeps the cliffs steep, the rocks are attacked along joint planes and give rise to the fantastic terracotta shapes which make the railway journey along this coast so attractive.

CHAPTER IX

EAST ANGLIA

No part of England has greater individuality than East Anglia. Its towns and villages are distinctive, and there are no other extensive areas in Britain with such generally low relief. Yet East Anglia is mainly founded on the Chalk, which might be expected to give rise to such features as would link the area closely to the Chilterns which adjoin it on the south-west. Over much of the area, however, the Chalk is buried beneath a cover of varying thickness consisting of boulder clays, sands and gravels; these superficial rocks to a great extent determine the nature of the soil, and their occurrence is responsible for many of the peculiarities of the area.

But the most notable feature is the low relief, and in this it differs greatly from the other chalklands already noticed. For even along the western border of the Chalk outcrop which extends through Suffolk and Norfolk, from near Newmarket to the coast at Hunstanton, its height rarely exceeds 400 feet, even though the scarp in places rises sharply from the fenlands on the west: from that scarp eastwards the Chalk surface falls gently, and in many parts of the area Chalk is only seen in some of the deeper valleys, while near the coast it is often well below sea-level. Thus at Norwich the Chalk surface is at about fifty feet above sea-level, while at Yarmouth it is 500 feet lower. It is therefore useful to regard the Chalk surface of East Anglia as a gently inclined plane. The deposits covering part of this tilted surface, especially those nearer the east coast, are of marine origin, and represent the youngest marine rocks in England; in fact East Anglia may well be spoken of as one of the youngest parts of England, not long and not greatly raised from beneath the sea in which some of its deposits were formed, and its elevation having been further reduced, in common with many parts of England, by still more recent subsidence. But East Anglia has also been modified by glacial action.

In fact, notwithstanding the apparent simplicity of its solid rocks, it is a region of some complexity and includes areas of very different character. Its superficial rocks are of great importance and their interpretation has given rise to no little controversy; in this account it is not necessary to discuss these problems at any length, but reference is made to those conclusions which throw light on the origin of the scenic features.

The region has long been isolated from the rest of England. In early Neolithic times the dense forests of Essex on the south and the wide fenlands on the west almost completely cut it off from neighbouring populated areas; more recently the major routes from London to the north have been carried farther west in order to avoid the fens and the Wash. True, the old land route into the area, along the narrow strip of Chalk downland from Newmarket towards Thetford, followed by the ancient tracks known as the Icknield Way, linked East Anglia with other populous chalklands to the south-west, but this connecting strip was so readily defended that the region long retained its independence and unity. At Doomsday it was the most populous region of England, its many villages and parish churches evidencing this early development.

Although this is an area of low relief, it is by no means a plain: parts of it are flat, especially the level alluvial stretches by the rivers and broads, but much of it is gently rolling country, often with rather surprisingly deep valleys. For the most part this undulating country is covered with arable fields, for two-thirds of the cultivated land in Norfolk is under the plough, and corn crops are very extensive owing to the dry climate and the light soils. So that over wide areas, pastoral lands are very restricted and the great stretches of cornfields give character to the scenery. This region has none of the dullness and lack of variety which sometimes characterise districts of low relief.

Although they are not very high, the Chalk areas along the western border of East Anglia are most similar to the other chalklands of England. Around Newmarket there are rolling downs with short grass and with dry valleys, while in western Norfolk the Chalk runs to the coast at Hunstanton and gives rise to low cliffs. In some of these western areas flint has been obtained from almost the beginning of human history, though the mining carried on so extensively at Grime's Graves, near Brandon, was chiefly done in the late Neolithic and Bronze Ages. In that area the Chalk surface is marked by hundreds of saucer-shaped hollows, varying in diameter up to seventy feet, the sites of ancient mine shafts made in the working of particularly suitable bands of flint. On these hills to the north-east of Brandon it is possible to descend one of these old mines, and at Brandon itself to see the surviving flint-knappers at work. The use of flint, so long characteristic of East Anglia, has continued with its employment as a building material, and nowhere else in Britain has it been so extensively worked for this purpose.

Apart from the flint, East Anglia may be regarded as a stoneless region, and its comparative isolation hindered the importing of stone. Flint thus acquired great importance as a building stone, although bricks are very extensively made from local clays. Various stages in the use of flint may be noticed : in some of the earliest buildings untrimmed flint nodules were used with much mortar, but very remarkable workmanship is seen in many later buildings, the flint being dressed and used with little mortar.

Around the coasts, especially in those places where many flint pebbles occur on the shore, a curious effect is made by the projecting rounded ' kidneys ' of flint, the use

E

of which is generally combined with brick, which forms the corners of the cottages. This type of cottage is characteristic of many villages near Cromer, as at Trimingham,

Figure 35.—Use of flint in building, with freestone, Yarmouth.

Weybourne and Kelling. But in many other parts away from the coast, even where brick is mostly used for the houses, the churches are still nearly always of flint. Among the oldest churches, round flint towers are characteristic, the round form having perhaps been developed because of the absence of any suitable large stones to form quoins or corner-stones. Many of these tall round towers, more particularly near the coasts, may have been used as watch-towers, and they date from the tenth or eleventh centuries; in Norfolk they are a most striking part of the landscape, more than a hundred round towers being found in that county as compared with less than fifty in Suffolk. But the larger square towers are no less impressive or varied; that at Winterton, north of Yarmouth, not only dominates the red-roofed village but affords a view out to sea over the sand-hills which hide the village.

In the building of many of the larger churches a certain amount of freestone, brought from the stone belt to the west, has been introduced, not always with happy results, for flint is a peculiar building material giving a curiously speckled effect which does not always fit in with so different a stone. The Church of St. Nicholas at Yarmouth is a good example in which limestone has been used for doors and windows and for places where it is desired to introduce ornament (Fig. 35). Cromer church also shows some remarkable flint work.

The rather cold and unusual effect of the flint buildings is the most notable architectural feature in the landscape; with this is associated the lack of decoration in the smaller churches and the quite beautiful effects produced in some of the patterned buildings with their curious chequer-board design, notably in the old Guildhall at Norwich and in the church at Southwold. And added to this, the frequency of thatched roofs, as at Acle in Norfolk and Theberton in Suffolk, gives to these village churches peculiar attractiveness.

Yet in many areas the cottages are for the most part of brick, usually of bright red colour and with red pantiles, and it is these which largely determine the colour of the villages, though in parts of Suffolk a dull yellowish-brown brick is frequent. Among these old brick buildings, more particularly in the coastal towns, are houses of distinctly foreign character, with curved gables and highly decorated circular chimneys, which are believed to owe something to the influence of the Flemings. The clays for brickmaking are dug from the superficial rocks of which such a variety is present. Here, too, are obtained the flint gravels which go to the making of the light-brown roadways of the area.

Much of the east of East Anglia, from Weybourne (west of Cromer) by Norwich to Ipswich, is made up of marine and estuarine gravels and shelly sands of very variable type, known collectively as the 'Crag' and referred to the Pliocene division of geological time. They are not of great antiquity as we have already noticed, but they were formed immediately prior to the Great Ice Age. They are loose deposits, rarely of any great thickness, and were formed as sandbanks or as estuarine deposits near the mouth of a great river; at that time Britain had attained the general structure familiar to us, but was still linked to the Continent, and the North Sea was a great gulf into which the Rhine flowed and was joined on its left bank by the Thames, the deposits of these rivers contributing to the formation of the Crag.

But much of this area of Crag deposits, as well as much of the Chalk itself, was further modified during the Ice Age, when ice sheets several times invaded the area. Between some of these advances of ice into East Anglia were intervals when the climate was mild and when prehistoric man lived in the area, but from the scenic point of view the most important effect was the deposition of great tracts of boulder clay, gravel, sand and loam. The details of the distribution of the successive deposits need not be discussed here. It is sufficient to notice only the most striking features.

THE CROMER RIDGE

The most notable is the Cromer Ridge, a belt of high land rising in parts to over 300 feet, which extends from near Cromer south-westwards to Holt. In detail this belt of high ground consists of a series of small ridges arranged more or less in the same direction. Along its northern border it rises sharply from the low ground near the coast, but its surface slopes more gently to the south; seen from near Sheringham its wooded northern slope forms a very impressive feature in this area of gentle relief. To the north of the ridge are small outlying masses of similar character, and from these the best views of the area may be obtained: the small hill about a mile west of Weybourne is an excellent example, its bracken and gorse-covered slopes contrasting sharply with the fields below. Great expanses of the main Cromer ridge are covered by heather and bracken, and indicate its sandy and gravelly nature.

Briefly, the Cromer Ridge is a great moraine or series of moraines left by glaciers advancing from the north. Its boulders include much Chalk, but there are also boulders from Scandinavia, from Scotland, and from the north of England. Generally the rocks from more distant sources are less common than those from beds over which the ice sheet had but lately passed, and therefore the rocks which occur immediately north and north-west of Cromer are plentifully represented, Chalk, sometimes in great masses, being very abundant. Near Holt and Weybourne the quantity of Chalk is so great that the material has been burnt for lime. The irregular hummocky surface reflects the original inequality of the deposits, but its structure is far from simple, as an examination of the coast between Happisburgh and Weybourne will show, for there the moraine is cut transversely and its nature is shown in the cliff sections. There the sea is rather rapidly attacking the cliffs in which can be seen a section of the boulder clays and sands comprising the moraine, the earlier series of glacial deposits contorted by a fresh ice advance. Though this ridge is so new a feature (not older than the Ice Age), it forms a watershed, and it is clear that the rivers of this area have nothing like the antiquity of those of the London basin, where, it may be remembered, the essential features of the drainage were determined a considerable time before the Ice Age. Few of the present valleys in East Anglia were cut until part of the Ice Age had passed and some boulder clay had been laid down over much of the area. Here again, therefore, the landscape of this region may be called ' new '.

Along this stretch of coast, familiar to visitors to Cromer and Sheringham, there is an almost unbroken line of cliffs whose height is controlled by the local height of the moraine, but in which no inlets have yet developed. The waves are rapidly attacking these cliffs, and few parts of the British coast are being destroyed more swiftly. Almost everywhere they show the same yellowish-brown colour, though the material composing them varies from sand to loam and from gravel to boulder clay, and though there are also considerable masses of Chalk, for example near Trimingham and Overstrand. With all their variety of constitution these cliffs rarely present the furrowed aspect of the cliffs formed by stiffer and more homogeneous boulder clays such as those already referred to at Filey and Scarborough. Where wave advance is most rapid the cliffs are nearly vertical, but elsewhere the frequent slipping of masses of loose material has given rise to an irregular, one might almost say an untidy, coast-line, the slumped masses being partly overgrown. The cliffs are often fronted by a stretch of sand, sometimes associated with pebbles and shingle (as at Cromer and Sheringham) produced by the disintegration of the cliffs. At most of these towns efforts are made to retain as much as possible of this beach material, which otherwise tends to drift east and south along the coast, leaving the base of the cliffs (or the sea-front of the towns) unprotected and exposed to the renewed and more powerful attack of the waves. At these places, therefore, groynes have been built out at right angles to the coast with a view to checking the movement of the material, and the success of the method can often be judged from a consideration of the heaped-up beach deposits on the northern or western side of a groyne as compared with the depleted deposits on its southern or eastern side. The movement of beach material in this way naturally has a great effect on the form of the shore-line, and in East Anglia the large quantity of shingle available from the destruction of the stretch of cliffs described above has led to considerable changes in the coast: these may more suitably be discussed a little later.

BRECKLAND

While the Cromer moraine ridge is the most impressive feature resulting from the glacial advance, other wide areas in East Anglia have been profoundly modified by the glacial deposits. The most interesting of these is Breckland, the great stretch of open heathland some 400 square miles in extent, which lies around and especially west of the old town of Thetford. Here are belts of gnarled Scots pines with extensive tracts of heather-covered country and of poor grassland, with thin gritty soil mostly unsuitable for cultivation. On it grow many plants which are scarcely known elsewhere in England. The superficial deposits which here rest on the Chalk consist mainly of gravels and sands carried by the streams resulting from the melting ice during one stage of glacial retreat. The deposits have been redistributed to some extent by wind action, for since the vegetation is so thin and the soil so porous, the surface rapidly becomes dry and powdery and the sand is swept up by the strong winds, forming great dust storms. This unusual tract of steppe-land was at times inhabited by early man, but is now very sparsely populated, the lack of water supplies being an important factor in this respect. For the occurrence of these porous surface deposits over the great sponge of absorbent Chalk makes for few streams and reduces the prospect of water in shallow wells. The villages are thus almost entirely confined to the valleys of the few rivers, and for miles at a time there are no dwellings even near the main roads. Thetford is the most important settlement in the area, at the junction of the Thet and Little Ouse, where these rivers were crossed by the Icknield Way.

This great area of open land, and of huge estates, has been little modified for many centuries, but latterly the planting of belts of pines has given some protection to the less infertile tracts. Large areas, moreover, are being planted by the Forestry Commissioners, nearly 30,000 acres having been already covered, chiefly with Scots pine and Corsican pine, although belts of oak, beech and chestnut by the sides of the straight roads are also greatly modifying the scenery.

There are other expanses of heath and common near the Suffolk coast, especially in the neighbourhood of Aldeburgh and Dunwich, where they are produced by similar patches of superficial sands and gravel. These uncultivated tracts are bounded sharply by the rich agricultural lands which occupy most of East Anglia and by undulating green patches with so many belts of trees as to give the appearance of lightly wooded country.

THE BROADS

Only in the neighbourhood of the Broads are there notable differences. Here the flat meadows, crossed by winding willow-bordered roads and traversed by meandering streams, merge so imperceptibly into the wide areas of shallow water, that the traveller often gets the odd impression of white sails gliding among fields. These reed-bordered stretches of water, found especially in the valleys of the Bure, the Yare and the Waveney, probably need no description. What may be regarded as the first step in the formation of the Broads occurred during the submergence, probably of Neolithic times, which converted the valleys of Broadland into a wide shallow bay. The drift of shore material southwards along the coast gave rise to spits or banks extending for some way across the bay, and this in turn promoted the deposition of material brought into the bay by the rivers. So the great spread of shallow water in the bay was more or less divided up by these irregular areas of newly formed land. Most of the existing Broads occur along the tributary valleys, for the main streams have deposited much of their material in such a way as to form banks on either side of their courses, the tributaries thus being dammed or ponded back. Everywhere within the Broads the rivers, of course, are still tending to silt up the shallow waters, and the great stretches of flat meadow-land bordering the Broads testify to the former wider extent of the waters, for they represent silted-up Broads.

THE COAST SCENERY

The coast of East Anglia has perhaps more features of interest than the inland areas. The cliffs of Cromer and Mundesley, and the coastal movement of the large amount of débris produced by their rapid destruction, have already been mentioned. The subsidence of the land in post-glacial times has also been referred to in explanation of the Broads. To these two factors more than to any others is due the form of the East Anglian coast-line. In the south of the region the long narrow inlets of the Stour and Orwell represent two valleys which were flooded by the subsidence, but farther north there are no such inlets and the coast-line as seen on a map is smooth and simple. This smoothness, however, results from the fact that inlets comparable with those of South Suffolk and Essex have been silted up, largely owing to the formation of shingle bars by the southward drifting of beach pebbles as in the case of the Broads.

The direction of movement of the beach material along much of the coast is strikingly illustrated by the southward pointing bars and spits. That stretching from Aldeburgh past Orford is perhaps the most impressive example in England. The Alde almost reaches within a few yards of

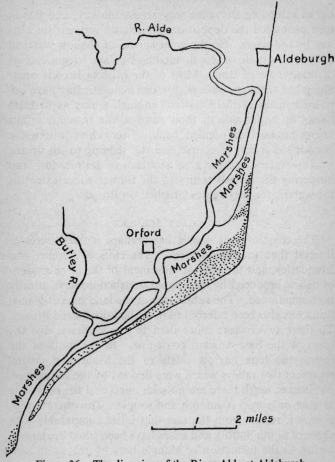

Figure 36.—The diversion of the River Alde at Aldeburgh,
Suffolk.
Shingle dotted. (Adapted from J. A. Steers.)

the sea at Aldeburgh, where its mouth must formerly have
been situated, but the drifting shingle has steadily deflected
the river southwards until its mouth is now about eleven

miles away (Fig. 36). Possibly Orford became a port when the river-mouth had been forced into its neighbourhood, the spit affording protection to ships in its shelter, but further growth of the spit has carried the mouth far beyond Orford. From the southern end of the bright little town of Aldeburgh the effect of the pebbly bank can be clearly seen; the seaward face is steep but inland it slopes gently to the marshy ground through which the wide shallow river flows in a direction parallel to the coast.

At Yarmouth and Lowestoft, too, the south-pointed spits are conspicuous. At the latter place the ponding back of the river has given rise to the Oulton Broad, while at Yarmouth the long sea-front extends along the face of the spit which has here pushed the mouth of the Yare to the south (Fig. 37). The location of Yarmouth on this narrow spit, between the river and the sea, has controlled the shape of the town, the long main streets broadening into the market-place following its length, while the narrow ' rows ' lead down towards the river-side. In the fourteenth century, however, the Yarmouth spit was much longer, extending then for about eight miles near to Gunton. Because of its interference with navigation it was cut through at various dates, the present mouth of the Yare dating from the sixteenth century. This allowed the material at the further end of the spit, freed from the control of the Yare, to move southwards again, exposing the cliffs south of Gorleston to further wave action and building new banks at Lowestoft Ness, where a wide series of shingle banks now form a low tract (shaded in Fig. 37) in front of the old cliff on which that town stands.

This movement of the beach material has been freely attributed to the effects of the tides, but Mr. J. A. Steers, in his studies of the East Anglian coast-line, has found evidence for the view that wave action under the influence of dominant winds has been a more important factor. The most effective winds appear to be from the north-east, and it is significant

that while in the neighbourhood of Cromer the movement of
material is to the south-east and thence gradually becomes
southward, near Blakeney on the west of Cromer the movement is westward. Blakeney Point is a shingle headland

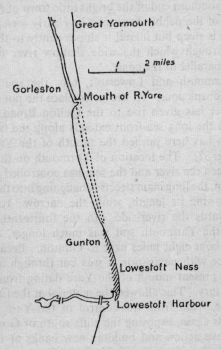

Figure 37.—The shingle spits at Yarmouth and Lowestoft.
(*Adapted from J. A. Steers.*)

which owes its origin to beach material drifted by wave
action; this spit runs for eight or nine miles, its western
end being marked by numerous curved shingle ridges. In
the shelter of this bar extensive marshy flats have been
formed, stretching seawards from the line of ancient cliffs
situated some way inland. Here, as in so many parts of the

Norfolk coast, new land has been formed by deposition in
the tranquil conditions in the shelter of the shingle banks.
Similar conditions are to be found in Scolt Head Island, a
detached spit a few miles further west, where movement of
shingle has caused a steady growth of the spit, the stages of
westward extension during recent years having been established in some detail by the work of Mr. Steers. Here there
are numerous long gravel ridges separated by tracts of salt
marsh where vegetation assists the accumulation of other
deposits.

On many of these gravel ridges at various places along
the coast there are sand-dunes, and dunes likewise occur
frequently on the coast, especially north of Yarmouth.
Sand-dunes have been formed by wind action, in these cases
by winds blowing in from the sea and bringing up sand
grains from the beach at low water when the surface is dry.
Thus the sand grains have been carried inland, building
great heaps or dunes with their long axes more or less parallel
to the coast. Such sand accumulations often continue to
move inland unless steps are taken to ' anchor ' them by
encouraging the growth on them of some hardy vegetation
such as marram grass, *Psamma arenaria*. Moving sand-
hills generally have a gentle slope towards the wind but a
much steeper slope on the leeward side, and the movement
can best be understood by noting the wind carrying grains
up one side and then more or less allowing them to fall
down the other. The steep slope is affected by wind eddies,
but generally it makes an angle with the horizontal which is
determined by the roughness of the grains ; they are just in
equilibrium, as those who have tried to walk up this slope of
a sand-hill will know. In many parts of England and Wales
sand-dunes have advanced inland for considerable distances,
destroying villages and spoiling good lands which lay in
their paths.

One of the best known instances of such destruction is
on the Norfolk coast where the church of Eccles north of

Yarmouth was gradually submerged by moving sand-dunes. Lyell called attention to this church in his *Principles of Geology*; the tower was of a familiar Norfolk pattern, round in the lower part, octagonal above, and although little information exists regarding the date when it was built, it is unlikely that the top was added before the sixteenth century. It is thus highly probable that there was no apparent danger from the sea at that time, but by the beginning of the next century the inhabitants were petitioning for a reduction of taxation on the ground that much land had been destroyed by the sea. Sand-dunes ultimately covered the area formerly occupied by part of the village, and by 1839 they had advanced so far as partly to bury the tower, while before 1862 they had been carried inland by the wind to the landward side of the tower, leaving it exposed to wave action, and more than forty years ago the derelict church tower was finally destroyed.

CHAPTER X

THE FENLANDS

As we have already noticed, the isolation of East Anglia was partly due to the Fenlands which extend southwards from the Wash and northwards up along the Lincolnshire coast. These wide areas of flat land, almost unique in British topography, rarely show elevations of more than fifty feet above sea-level, and for many miles form level expanses unbroken by any noticeable swelling. Formerly much of this region was swampy and almost impassable, and its few ' islands ' of more solid rock provided sanctuary and refuge against invaders until the Danes learned to penetrate the winding rivers. Many of these slight hillocks are made more conspicuous by the towns and villages placed on them, Ely Cathedral and the tall ' stump ' of Boston being especially prominent landmarks. Other important settlements grew up along the borders of the marsh, as at Cambridge and Peterborough, but they belong as much to the adjacent regions as to the Fens.

Little of the impenetrable swamp remains to-day, except in Wicken Fen about twelve miles from Cambridge, where the original conditions are preserved, rushes and sedges bordering the shallow waters, " slow rivers winding in the flat fens ". The draining of the Fens, begun by the building of embankments before the coming of the Romans, and extended by them particularly along the coastal parts, was more actively carried on from the seventeenth century, the installation of windmills after the manner of Holland giving character to the region ; Boston was once thought the most ' Continental ' town in England. The draining was not regarded as an unmixed blessing by the earlier inhabitants, who found their occupations as fowlers or fishermen or sedge-cutters becoming seriously hampered, and some did much damage to the works, but the richness of the new land which was made available guaranteed the continuation of the efforts. The high value of this land has led to intensive farming, and while wheat is a very important crop, special attention has been given to various crops of particular value : thus sugar-beet now occupies large areas, and fruit-growing and the bulb industry flourish in certain parts, and give striking character to the landscape. So the Fens now carry a larger population than most agricultural areas.

The Fenland includes wide areas in the basins of the Witham, Welland, Nen and Ouse. It represents a wide shallow bay, most of which has been silted up, but of which part still survives as the Wash. It obviously forms an old valley where these rivers had cut a wide gap through the Chalk. Much of the silt has been brought in by tides and is of marine origin, but some part represents material carried down by the rivers. There is also a great deal of peat, varying in thickness up to fifteen feet, and formerly cut for fuel in some places. In fact it is well to recognise in the Fens these two types of material, the silt mainly occupying the seaward portions and the peat spreading inland from some ten miles behind the coast. In the silt district there are often many trees, and farms are scattered rather irregularly over the landscape : for instance around Boston, trees, especially sycamore and chestnut, line many roads, but there is of course little woodland, for this reclaimed land is too valuable to allow it to become forested. On the peat country, on the other hand, there are fewer trees and not many villages ; buildings are placed more regularly along such elevations as exist.

The formation of land in this wide bay resulted mainly from the deposition of marine silts as a kind of barrier across its mouth. When these deposits rose to within about eight feet of the mean tide level, salt marsh plants such as the glasswort or samphire (*Salicornia herbacea*) established themselves. By hindering the flow of water these assisted in the further accumulation of silt, and the consequent growth of the barrier helped to keep out the sea, making the more inland part an area of freshwater in which peat was formed. Similar changes may be seen in progress along parts of the Lincolnshire coast, for land is still being added at many points and it may be expected that the Wash will become completely silted up.

The filling up of this great bay has been complicated and prolonged by the subsidence which has meanwhile taken place, and has led to a deepening of the original basin. This is shown by the presence of buried forests under the peat and silt, at depths below present tide-marks; since the trees must have grown above the reach of high tides it is clear that subsidence must have occurred. Trunks of oak are dug up under conditions which prove that a considerable forest growth formerly extended over much of the area. But these had almost certainly disappeared beneath the marsh long before the beginning of historic times, though on the Lincolnshire coast Professor H. H. Swinnerton sees reasons for the view that there has been some continuation of the subsidence since Roman times.

Probably in many places the peat surface has also sunk since the deposits were formed, exactly as has occurred in some of the Thames marshes. Partly as a result of the more rapid withdrawal of water resulting from the powerful pumps now in use, the level is falling by about an inch per year, though formerly the rate of shrinkage was much less. The surface of Whittlesea Mere has fallen eleven feet since 1848. One interesting result of this lowering of the peat surface has been the production of ' roddons ' or raised banks, formed by silt which once filled the channels cut by wandering streams in the peat; while the peaty deposits have shrunk the silt has remained practically unchanged in bulk, so that the river course, formerly below the level of the peat, now stands out above it. Major Gordon Fowler who has called attention to these sinuous silt banks believes that many have been ploughed down, but they have generally been selected for buildings, as at Rodham Farm, just over two miles north-east of March, where the roddon stands about eight feet above the level of the fen.

Low ground extends all along the coast of Lincolnshire and south Yorkshire. In Lincolnshire it forms a belt stretching to the coast from the old cliff bounding the Chalk Wolds. Within this belt two types of scenery may be recognised. Irregular hummocky land formed by the local boulder clay is found fringing the Wolds, while nearer the sea is almost flat marshland. The featureless surface of the marsh is almost treeless, as contrasted with the well-wooded boulder clay, but numerous islands of boulder clay stand up above the marsh, which thus repeats on a small scale the conditions of the fens.

HOLDERNESS

In Holderness, the south-eastern portion of Yorkshire, conditions are somewhat similar, a stretch of country of low relief lying under the shelter of the old Chalk cliffs which from Flamborough Head southwards to Hessle on the Humber stand twelve miles or more behind the present shore-line. Before the Ice Age this area was occupied by a wide bay, but the deposits of boulder clay left by the ice sheets formed new land. On this irregular surface of glacial material are tracts of marshland and mere comparable with those of Lincolnshire. A mere a mile and a half long, which still remains at Hornsea, repeats some of the characteristics of the Norfolk Broads, while the sites of others are recognisable at Bridlington, Skipsea and Withernsea or are indicated by such place-names as Marfleet and Rowmere.

Along much of the coast the low cliffs of red or purple boulder clay are rarely more than thirty feet high. As they are easily eroded by the sea, they are receding at an average rate of some two or three yards each year. Though this land was only added to England so recently as the Ice Age, no part of the British coast is being destroyed more rapidly.

But great as the losses have been along this part of the coast, there have also been important gains, for as in East Anglia the débris carried along the coast goes to form still newer land. Destruction and construction thus go on almost side by side. So far as the country as a whole is concerned, the area of land gained in this way exceeds the area lost, but of course the land destroyed is usually of greater value, for the newly-formed land is low-lying and of little use for many years. Such low land, almost covered at high tides, is being added to Spurn Point and is carrying its curved shingly tip further to the south-west, while along the Humber itself the village of Hedon, which formerly was a flourishing port, is now two miles from the coast, with its square church tower standing conspicuously above the flat lands, and its old docks and water-ways traceable among the green fields.

The Holderness lowland has only one river of its own, the Hull, at the mouth of which stands Kingston-on-Hull, the isolated city of the Humber. As in many parts of the more southern fenlands, bricks are much used in building, and most villages have thatched brick cottages, while bricks occasionally have found their way into church-building, as in Holy Trinity, Hull. Along the coast, however, many old churches and houses have been built from boulders derived from the boulder clay, particularly when they could be gathered from the beaches, and they then show much variety in colour.

CHAPTER XI

MOUNTAIN LIMESTONE

STANDING on the Devon coast at the top of Babbacombe Down on a clear day we may see the cliffs sweeping round the great bay which is bounded by Portland Bill. The red cliffs of Dawlish and Teignmouth, the blue grey of Lyme Regis, the yellow cliffs further east are all visible; beyond those come the white Chalk and the light brown sandy cliffs of Bournemouth. With the scenery of these cliffs and of the country made by the same rocks as they are followed across England to Yorkshire we have already dealt, and some reference has been made to most parts of England which lie to the east of that line. In those regions are many different types of landscape, red fields, limestone scarps, clay vales, Chalk downs, but apart from the cliff scenery of the coasts there is scarcely a crag or a hillside of bare rock in the whole area. With all their differences of hardness and of resistance to denudation, these rocks all break down fairly readily, their hills become grassed over and their steeper slopes are wooded.

To find inland crags and cliffs of bare rock we have to go further west than the Midland plain, and we have in general to seek rocks older than the New Red Sandstones. In England no type of rock gives rise to this exciting country more frequently than the Mountain Limestone or the Carboniferous Limestone (the latter name because it is found in close association with the Coal Measures, which it underlies). The Mountain Limestone is not found in continuous belts running right across England; its outcrops are practically limited to the west of a line from Lyme Regis to Whitby, but they are more complex than those already dealt with. Briefly, the reason for this is similar to that given for the comparatively complicated pattern of the Chalk outcrop, namely, folding of the beds followed by the wearing away of the tops of the anticlinal folds. But the Mountain Limestone in places has been folded much more severely than the Chalk or any of the newer rocks, for it was involved in mountain-building movements before the New Red Sandstone or any later rocks were formed, and in many places it shows none of that simplicity in broad structure which characterises the newer strata.

It is not surprising, therefore, that the Mountain Limestone forms discontinuous outcrops in many areas; in the Mendip Hills and many other hill masses around Bristol; along the Gower coast of Glamorgan, and round the edges of the South Wales coalfield; at Chepstow and along the borders of the Forest of Dean; in the Peak District, and around Settle and Skipton in Yorkshire and farther to the north; in the Great Orme at Llandudno and at Castletown in the Isle of Man. This limestone is a widespread formation, and over much of England it retains similar characters, which will be recognised by those who are acquainted with any of the areas just mentioned. In all of them there are rocky gorges with steep or even precipitous sides of bare grey limestone, magnificently seen in the Cheddar Gorge (Fig. 80) and in the gorge of the Avon at Bristol (Fig. 82) in the Wye Valley above Chepstow and so on through all the regions named.

As seen in any of these areas the Mountain Limestones occur in thick beds, individual beds often being ten feet or more thick so that the exposed rocks appear massive and compact, differing in these respects from many of the limestones of the Cotswold Stone belt and for this reason forming bolder country. The beds, moreover, are often tilted and bent into great folds (especially in the south-west), and have clearly been disturbed greatly since they were formed as horizontal layers beneath the waters of a clear sea, at which time all the areas referred to were at one level and were

continuous. The changes that have taken place since the
time of formation of the limestones will be more easily
comprehended when it is remembered that they are older
than any of the rocks so far mentioned in this book (except
those of the Charnwood Forest) ; not only has the sea in
which they were deposited no relation to any existing seas,
but much of England and Wales has been under an extensive
sea on at least two subsequent occasions. In short, when
the Mountain Limestone was formed scarcely any part of
England existed. Since that time the rocks laid down on
the floor of the Carboniferous sea have been heaved up to
form the tops of present-day mountains (and of much
higher mountains that have long been worn away) and de-
pressed in other places far below sea-level.

These limestones were obviously formed in a sea, for
in many beds fossil shells and corals are common, as well
as the remains of other less familiar creatures. The limestones in fact are almost entirely composed of carbonate of
lime, derived from the remains of skeletons of marine
invertebrates, very little material from any inorganic source
being present in some beds : it follows that little sand or
mud was then being carried into this part of the sea, and
the water must have remained clear. Yet for most of the
time it was quite shallow, for the animals whose remains
are found are mostly such as would live at no great depth.
The view widely held some years ago, that limestones must
have been formed in deep seas far from the land, very much
overstated the position, for most of our familiar limestones
have in fact been formed in shallow water, and often at no
great distance from shore-lines. Under these conditions vast
thicknesses of limestone were laid down on the subsiding
floor of the Carboniferous sea, the rocks being over 3000
feet in thickness in many places. Occurring among the
limestones are some layers of shale, which frequently become important near the top of the group and in places also
near the base, but for the most part the 3000 feet of strata

consist of limestones which from the scenic point of view are of similar character, almost universally grey in colour, tending to be black in some areas or white in others, though they are also occasionally stained red.

These Mountain Limestones are cut by well-developed joints, nearly always at right angles to the bedding. Along these joints the rocks tend to break cleanly into blocks giving clean faces, and in many places the joint faces determine the precipitous character of mountain-sides and gorges which is so striking a feature in all areas of Mountain Limestones. The great cliff of High Tor, seen in the familiar view along the Derwent at Matlock (Fig. 40), is a splendid example, but the cliffs of the Avon Gorge and of the Wye are equally impressive.

Like all limestones, the beds of this group are soluble in water containing a little carbon dioxide, so that rain-water (which normally takes up a little of this gas on its passage through the atmosphere) is capable of dissolving the limestone on which it falls. Owing to its purity, that is its freedom from non-calcareous and insoluble material, the solution of the surface of the Mountain Limestone by atmospheric water gives rise to very little soil, a condition already noticed in the case of the Chalk. Thus in some areas the limestone gives rise to great barren tracts devoid of any plants except such as have been able to secure a foothold in the crevices in the bare rocks. Such conditions are naturally best found on high ground, where there is no opportunity for soil to accumulate from higher levels, and where the rain-water gradually widens the joints into which is washed any soil that may be formed.

No areas better illustrate these conditions than the great ' karst ' plateaux around Ingleborough and above Malham Cove near Settle. Here are wide, level stretches of bare light-coloured limestone, with the joint planes enlarged by the solvent action of rain so that wide, irregular chasms (known as clints or grikes) trench the surface, the channels varying in width up to several feet and being of considerable depth. Here and there a bush of hawthorn contrives to exist on this upland, while in the shady crevices are the hart's-tongue fern, wood sorrel and other plants. In some of these areas there is heavy rainfall, but all the water rapidly passes underground. Likewise on the more extensive moorlands where grassy pastures are typical, as in the Craven Hills north of Skipton and in many parts of the Peak, the ground is generally dry, but a varied flora thrives, often with wild thyme and the yellow mountain pansy in abundance. On these uplands are stone walls and houses reminiscent of the Cotswolds, but the harder limestone has not favoured such ornament or elegance in building as is characteristic of freestone regions, and the houses are solid, grey and cold.

On the limestone uplands, especially of Yorkshire and Derbyshire, farms are chiefly occupied with sheep grazing; probably the grazing restricts the growth of trees. But where the Mountain Limestone is carved into valleys, trees are more frequent, especially on the valley slopes. The Derwent valley along the east of the Peak District is well wooded for many miles, and in numerous regions the steeper parts of the limestone outcrop are marked by woodlands. Rarely is there any arable land on these areas, for the soil is ordinarily too thin to allow of ploughing: different conditions may be introduced, however, by a cover of superficial gravel or clay.

The solubility of the limestone and the tendency for the joints to become enlarged have led to another important feature in its scenery, for here, as on other limestone regions such as the oolites and the Chalk, much of the drainage tends to flow underground, its passage in the case of the Mountain Limestone being generally through crevices dissolved out and enlarged to form caves. Thus on many mountains of this type the higher valleys are normally dry, or perhaps are occupied by streams during very wet seasons only: most of the water passes underground, sometimes unobtrusively by percolation, sometimes by large and definite passages or swallow-holes. The swallow-holes of the Yorkshire hills are well-known, the great chasm of Gaping Gill (or Ghyll) on the east of Ingleborough being one of the most impressive (Fig. 38, x); a vertical shaft over 350 feet deep opening out into an enormous cavern into which falls the highest known waterfall in England, the water arriving from another underground channel. The

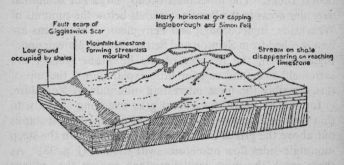

Figure 38.—The country near Ingleborough, viewed from the south-east, near Clapham. The Craven Fault scarp makes the feature along the south; the stepped surface above caused by thin horizontal limestones. Gaping Ghyll marked by a cross.

caves in the limestone worn by these underground streams scarcely enter, perhaps, into the category of scenery, but they are familiar attractions in all such limestone areas. Possibly they are best known to the ordinary traveller in the Mendip area where at Cheddar and Wookey Hole the rival caves are daily thronged throughout the summer with visitors from all over Britain. In these caves another aspect of the work of underground water is made evident, in the deposits of carbonate of lime both in the form of stalactites and stalagmites, and in the more irregular spreads of tufa, material which has been dissolved at one place being set free again in others when conditions decrease the solvent power of the water.

THE MOUNTAIN LIMESTONE OF WEST YORKSHIRE

The limestone uplands of Yorkshire are more extensive if less accessible than those of the Mendips, and while perhaps there are no gorges finer than that of Cheddar the great tracts of limestone of the north may most suitably be chosen as illustrations of the scenery formed by these particular rocks. The limestones occupy large but somewhat irregular areas in the Pennine uplands below the summits of Whernside, Ingleborough and Penyghent. These areas are best reached from Skipton and Settle. On the plateau under Ingleborough, the features of the limestone scenery are extremely clear and call for little explanation: the top of this, possibly the most interesting mountain in Yorkshire, is formed by nearly horizontal grits overlying shales with thin beds of limestone. An outlier of newer rocks, it stands out above the griked limestone surface, and down the steep mountain-sides flow numerous swift streams (Fig. 38). As these reach the more level limestone surface they plunge underground, Gaping Gill on the south of the mountain being one such swallet, Alum Pot on the north another. These streams flow underground for some distance, reaching the surface again either when they leave the limestone outcrop or when the valley is cut down below the level of saturation. The identification of each particular stream at its outflow by the introduction of chemical dyes into the water going underground has made possible the mapping of the direction of the underground courses.

The rivers flowing west from Ingleborough rise to the surface when they reach the base of the limestone, where in Chapel le Dale it rests on the impermeable and insoluble rocks which lie beneath it.

But all the country hereabouts shows features equally striking. Above the village of Malham, some five miles to the east of Settle, is found unrivalled limestone scenery. At Malham Cove is an outflow of water, a small stream which ultimately becomes the Aire; the spring occurs at the foot of a great limestone precipice, but it needs little imagination to realise that the gully above the cliff is the natural bed of a stream. Formerly it flowed across the high ground above the precipice from its source in Malham Tarn, making a great waterfall nearly 300 feet high, but gradually the water has found a new path underground beneath the plateau, and no water now dashes over the fall, although the change appears to have taken place fairly recently, for there are records of water coming that way during times of flood within the last century. Now no flood yields water enough to exceed the capacity of the underground channel.

Only a short distance away is Gordale, one of the finest limestone gorges in the country. It is probably a cavern of which the roof has collapsed. The walls are steep and mostly bare, the clean joint planes making great precipices where they cut through the massive beds; in several places the walls overhang slightly and at one point a remnant of the roof still remains. Near this is a small waterfall, for some water still flows along the surface, though the supply is much reduced owing to the fact that the greater part of the stream sinks below ground some way up the valley, to reach the surface again near the mouth of the gorge. Here then is an old cave which has lost its roof and has almost lost its water flow; the stream first passed underground to form the cave which is now represented by the gorge, and later found a still lower path. So the water is continually being "short-circuited". Waters in limestone regions continue to make lower courses, leaving one cavern dry when they have formed another, until they are at last held up by impermeable beds, temporarily if the beds are only thin and are underlain by more limestone, permanently if they have reached the real base of the limestones, as in the case of the Greta and its tributaries.

In the area near the Yorkshire and Lancashire borders, another type of feature is shown. Running in a straight line from north-west to south-east immediately above the road from Settle to Ingleton is a great wall of limestone. This scarp, known as Giggleswick Scar, is formed by bare grey limestone, and rises above a wide tract of more varied character made up of grits and shales (Fig. 38). Here is a feature quite unlike anything which has been discussed previously, for it differs from the scarps of southern England not only in its straightness but in the fact that the rocks occupying the low ground do not pass underneath the limestone ; in fact the limestone is present, at some considerable depth, underneath the rocks forming the lower ground. The beds forming the top of Ingleborough, many hundreds of feet above the limestone scarp, are represented at some depth in this low ground (Fig. 38). This scarp marks the course of a great fault or dislocation in the rocks, a complete break in the beds. Hitherto we have dealt with bent or folded beds, but no reference has been made to breaks in strata. Such breaks are not unknown in the areas already described, but they are not very frequent, and are generally inconspicuous in their scenic effects.

In Giggleswick Scar, however, the fault scarp is as impressive as any in England, a great break in which the ground on the south-west has fallen relatively to that on the northeast. It has generally been supposed that although the present cliff is along the line of the fracture, it does not represent the step produced when the break occurred, and that possibly great thicknesses of rock then covered both areas. It has been thought that the limestone edge stands out as a scarp because the fault brought the hard Mountain Limestone on a level with much softer shales and sandstones. More recently, however, Dr. R. G. S. Hudson has suggested that this fault scarp may actually represent a step produced by movements which occurred in Tertiary times, after the broad outlines of the present surfaces had already been developed, and that it owes little to the more rapid erosion of the softer beds to the south.

In the area around Settle are several faults of similar kind, running more or less parallel to one another and doubtless caused by similar earth stresses. These form the Craven faults, but the others do not give rise to any scarps so prominent as that of Giggleswick Scar, and in many places the scenic effect is very slight, the upland surface passing across the fracture line with little change of level (Fig. 38). For this reason it is believed that these faults existed long before the Tertiary movements but were not effected by them.

THE KNOLL COUNTRY

To the south of this region and north of the margin of the coalfield of Burnley and Accrington, is another great expanse of Mountain Limestone, occupying the Craven country between Settle and Burnsall and Clitheroe on the Lancashire border. These regions are not so high generally as the areas just described, and the limestones are inter-bedded with much shale. They are also peculiar in that there occur a large number of queer mound-like hills rising abruptly for as much as 200 feet above the surrounding country ; these hills are often conspicuously dome-shaped, but vary somewhat in form. Occasionally they are over half a mile across at the base, but small knolls only a hundred yards across also occur. They are seen in Burnsall and Thorpe in Wharfedale, and along the road by Cracoe to-wards Skipton ; near Clitheroe a line of knolls runs east towards Twiston, including Coplow and Salt Hill, just north of Pendle Hill. Such knolls are known in other parts of the north of England in Mountain Limestone tracts, but it is a type of scenery most familiar in this area. There has been much discussion regarding the origin of these extraordinary mounds, some believing that they have been produced by movements in the rocks after they were formed, others that the knolls are due to some original peculiarity of the deposit: in many knolls the limestone is exceedingly rich in fossil shells. While it is now considered that knoll topography has been produced in different ways, it is generally held that some special condition of deposition in that part of the Carboniferous sea is responsible, each dome corresponding to some 'reef-like' deposit of more resistant character: removal of the surrounding softer rocks has left it projecting.

THE PEAK DISTRICT

Another great area of Mountain Limestone forms the High Peak, the most southerly part of the Pennines, to which it is desirable to make some further reference since, quite apart from its special attractiveness, its characteristic features are more easily accessible than many of those of the Skipton and Clitheroe areas, for on its margin are such resorts as Matlock and Buxton (Fig. 39). In this region, as in that to the north, there are dry valleys and steep-sided gorges, underground streams and great caverns, but the larger limestone dales come down to lower levels and are more richly wooded, with sheer cliffs or fantastic crags of white and grey rock rising abruptly above the trees.

In shape this limestone tract is half an ellipse, and this form reflects its broader structure, for the region is essentially a denuded anticline, partly buried under the New Red Sandstone of the Midland plain near Ashbourne, a small market town on the borders of these two regions. On the western margin at Buxton the limestones dip to the west under the Millstone Grit moors of Axe Edge, while on the east at Bakewell the dip is easterly under the similar moors of south Derbyshire. From some of the higher hills it is possible to see the steep scarps of these grit moors bounding the limestone tract both on the east and west. Between the limestone and the grit edges occurs the outcrop of the shales already referred to as occurring above the limestones (which it will be convenient to refer to as the Yoredale Beds) and as might be expected this belt has fixed the positions of the

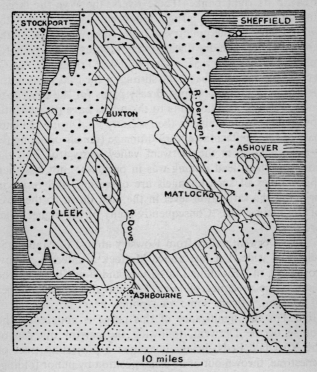

Figure 39.—Map of the Peak District.

Mountain Limestone, unshaded; Yoredale Beds, oblique lines; Millstone Grit, heavy dots; Coal Measures, horizontal lines; New Red Sandstone, fine dots

more important rivers, the deepening of the shale outcrop leading to the etching out of the harder bands.

Along the eastern outcrop the shales are followed for a great distance by the Derwent, its wooded valley overhung by the continuous wall of the unbroken grit scarp. From

that eastern side it scarcely receives a tributary of importance, though it is joined by several rivers from the limestone
area on its right bank. These rivers, the Wye the largest
among them, flow through limestone dales; and " the
whole glory of the country is in its dales ". Most of the
upland valleys are dry during many months of the year, for
much of the water is underground. Professor W. G.
Fearnsides believes that " the slitting of the lead veins in the
limestone country has opened easy paths for the descent of
surface water, and the adits to the mines have permanently
lowered the water-table in their vicinity ". During the later
part of the eighteenth century drainage tunnels or ' soughs '
were driven from the Derwent valley westwards into the
country where lead mining was in progress: not less than
thirty miles of such channels are operating, and result in
bringing the saturation level in the area down to the level
of the main river. Consequently many of the higher dales
are dry.

The Derwent valley from Rowsley almost to Matlock is
relatively wide, but just above Matlock it enters a narrow
gorge cut in Mountain Limestone, and flows between the
picturesque precipice of High Tor and the wooded slopes
of Masson. From some view-points near the summit of
High Tor the significance of this gorge is apparent; the
course of the Derwent, following the narrow outcrop of
the Yoredale Beds, brings it against a projecting tract of
limestone, thrown out of its usual position by minor folding.
A slight detour to the east would enable the river to continue
along the shale belt, which gives rise to a noticeable depression behind High Tor, but the river keeps to the limestone
until it reaches Cromford, where it returns to the shales.
Beyond Cromford it turns on to the Millstone Grit country
to Ambergate and Belper.

On the other side of the great anticlinal fold which
forms the Peak District the River Dove for some time
occupies a corresponding position on the western shale

outcrop, but like the Derwent it also turns on to the limestone tract above Ashbourne, cutting there the wonderful
wooded gorge of Dove Dale. Unlike the limestone area
near Settle, these rivers have nowhere cut down to the
bottom of the limestone, and no older rocks are seen in
Derbyshire.

Between these deeply cut valleys the grassy limestone
uplands reach a height of well over 1000 feet. But it is
scarcely the bleak moorland which might be expected at
this altitude, and there is much pasture-land. Seen from

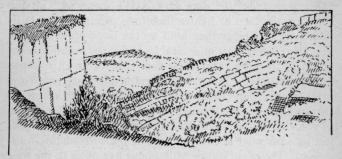

Figure 40.—High Tor above Matlock :
a Mountain Limestone crag.

above, the valleys often seem mere scratches in this plateau
surface. Since the valleys are so narrow the chief routes
have crossed the uplands themselves, and the Roman road
follows the crest from Wirksworth to Buxton. Many of the
stone-built villages are found up on the high land.

In the country west of Matlock and again between
Tideswell and Buxton, the uniformity of this great expanse
of Mountain Limestone is broken by the presence of dark
rocks of quite different character. The most important of
these is an almost black basalt, two beds of which lie between the limestones near Matlock. Basalt is a volcanic
rock, different in all its characters from sedimentary rocks
which make up most of the country already described : it

F

consists of a fine mass of crystals of minerals (olivine, felspar and augite), formed by the rapid cooling of molten material. The basalt represents a lava poured out on the floor of the sea, which spread over a wide area before it became solid, when deposits of limestone were laid down above it. Evidence of volcanic activity is not of frequent occurrence among rocks of this age in England and these areas afford the best examples. Locally the dark rocks are known as toad stones, possibly owing to their speckled aspect.

As these beds are not of great thickness their scenic effects are slight, the dark lavas being traceable here and there on the face of lighter limestone precipices, while by their impermeability they hold up the underground waters in a few places. But at several localities the volcanic rocks give rise to more remarkable features, for small rounded hills at Castleton, Grange Mill, Hopton and Kniveton Wood mark the position of the vents or pipes of ancient volcanoes from which the lava was ejected. These hills are composed of volcanic débris, the hardness of which leads to them projecting somewhat above the level of the surrounding limestones. Those at Grange Mill, about five miles to the west of Matlock, are quite conspicuous and are typical of some others : two grassy dome-shaped hills, the smaller only 300 yards across and rising a little over 100 feet, differ in contour and in colour from the craggy limestones around. Another vent occurs about a quarter of a mile west of the entrance to the Peak Cavern at Castleton.

Away to the east of the Peak, limestone again reaches the surface in small areas at Ashover, and at Crich. Both these areas are surrounded by extensive tracts of grit, and represent small subsidiary dome-shaped anticlines where the erosion of the higher beds has exposed patches of the limestone.

No special reference is made here to the Mountain Limestone areas of South Wales and the Bristol District, since these are more appropriately described in later chapters.

They show underground streams, steep-sided gorges, bare rocky uplands and other features comparable with those already described. In these areas, however, the rocks are often more sharply folded or more steeply dipping, so that they rarely occupy such wide areas as in the north, although they present no less variety of scenery.

CHAPTER XII

THE PENNINE MOORLANDS

THE mountainous country which forms the axis of northern England includes many limestone regions of the types referred to in the last chapter, but there are even greater tracts of barren moorland, covered by heather and by peat bogs and crossed by walls of dark stone. These rather sombre areas differ greatly from the limestone uplands, where the bare white crags and light-coloured walls give a distinctive brightness to the landscape.

These moorlands are based on the Millstone (sometimes called Moorstone) Grit, a series of rocks which in west Yorkshire are several thousands of feet in thickness, although this includes some bands of shale which have worn down to form lower ground between the outcrops of the grit bands. These form precipitous scarps, often of dark-brown rock, such as are well seen in the Roaches in north Staffordshire, in Standedge and Millstone Edge in south-west Yorkshire, and in Almscliff Crags near Harrogate.

In these cliffs the characters of the rock are readily seen; it occurs in thick beds of coarse material, often with that oblique arrangement of the layers that is known as current bedding. There is no doubt that the deposits were laid down in shallow water under the action of powerful currents, for in some places conglomerates or pebble beds occur among the more normal grits, and it is obvious that pebbles measuring in some cases several inches across could not have been transported by any gentle stream. The grit bands themselves are often of very coarse texture, and have more than once been mistaken for granite, notably by Charlotte Brontë in her description of the moorland scenery in *Jane Eyre*. But this mistake is perhaps to be understood when

it is realised that the most abundant minerals making up the
grit are quartz and felspar, both dominant constituents of

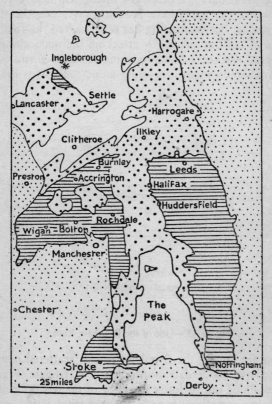

Figure 41.—The Millstone Grit Moors.
*Millstone Grit, heavy dots; Mountain Limestone and Yoredale, blank;
Coal Measures, horizontal lines; New Red Sandstone, fine dots.*

granite. It is likely that they were derived from some granite
mass which was undergoing denudation during the time
while the grit was being laid down, and that the river or

rivers which brought the material was supplied with débris
largely from this source.

The great bare scarps of grit often form nearly vertical
cliffs where the rocks have broken away along the strong
joint planes, but weathering has often carved the rock into
blocks of curious shapes by attacking the mass along any
planes of weakness and producing fantastic forms which
are familiar on many Yorkshire moors. Perhaps the best

Figure 42.—One of the Brimham Rocks.

known are among the Brimham Rocks, scattered over the
moor above Nidderdale, north-west of Harrogate (Fig. 42).
The scooping out of softer layers or of the weaker bedding
planes has sometimes been assisted by wind action, and in
many places large masses have been quite detached from
their bases to form 'rocking stones'.

The steep grit scarps, however, only consist of grit near
their summits, for the grit bed is mostly resting on clays or
shales (Fig. 43). The escarpment has thus the normal
characters already described in the case of the Cotswolds.

Along the base of the grit there is frequently a line of springs, and slips of rock down the scarp face are frequent. In fact this scarp is notably weak, owing to the well-developed joint planes in the grit along which the beds tend to fall away. It is believed that many of the landslips may be of some antiquity, resulting in part from the excessive steepening of the shale slopes during the closing stages of the Ice Age, when the higher parts of the shale surface were rapidly lowered each summer by 'mud flows' produced during the melting of the frozen surface.

Around Mam Tor in Derbyshire are many landslips, some of them not very ancient, and Mam Tor has been called the Shivering Mountain. Occasionally landslips have blocked valleys and formed deep lakes; Mickleden Pond, about two miles from Langsett, has been formed in this way.

Above the scarps, the grit outcrops form broad plateaux and long gentle dip slopes, for in most areas within the Pennines the rocks are inclined at low angles. These tracts of simple relief, mostly over 1000 feet high and in many places over 1500 feet, are generally wide open expanses of bleak uncultivated heaths and moorlands, crossed by rough walls of dark grit. The grit plateaux are in part sandy and dry, in part wet and peaty where rainfall is heavy and drainage is poor, or where a covering of boulder clay conceals the pervious grit. The drier areas are occupied by heather moors, with much gorse, bracken, bilberry and quite a variety of plants, but the peaty tracts, often known as 'mosses', are mostly covered with cotton-grass (*Eriophorum*), the soft white tufts of which have led to the frequent use of the name 'feather-bed' moss in several parts of the southern Pennines. Dr. T. W. Woodhead analysed the distribution of the names 'moor' and 'moss' and found that in areas above 1200 feet, where the rainfall is from fifty-six to sixty-two inches, there are many mosses and few moors, but that at altitudes from 700 to 1200 feet with a rainfall of up to forty-two inches, moors are many times more frequent than mosses. Heather moors are thus most frequently found on well-drained uplands of moderate elevation, as in the north-eastern districts above Pateley Bridge in Nidderdale and on Ilkley Moor, and also near Huddersfield on Crosland Moor, while cotton-grass moors are very extensive in south-west Yorkshire.

On these barren plateaux there is but a scanty population, for only small areas are cultivated. Some sheep are kept, and scattered grey farms are almost the only habitations; on the higher parts many derelict farmsteads tell of the failure against these harsh conditions. There are no trees on the exposed parts, and the uplands present " a grey and austere aspect ", which is unhappily accentuated in many districts by the smoky atmosphere, since the moors lie in the track of prevailing winds from the industrial regions of south Lancashire. Even the heather is dying out in the smokiest regions, leaving the more vigorous crowberry to expand into irregular masses which form islands in the dreary stretches of dark-brown peat. Peat deposits are very widespread, and are often eight feet in thickness, but they are being cut through by streams or eroded by wind in many places, and little peat is being formed at present in most areas. It has been suggested that the obstructed drainage resulting from the irregular deposits left by ice was perhaps responsible for the initiation of some peat formation, and certainly the deepest parts of many Pennine peats were formed as long ago as Neolithic times, when birch trees contributed to their growth, but the upper parts are largely made of cotton-grass, *Sphagnum* or bog-moss, heather and other moorland plants.

Some four main grit belts are present, but there are many other less persistent beds, and all show changes in thickness as they are traced along their outcrops. Accordingly there is some variation in the land forms to which they give rise. The hard bands stand out prominently along the scarp faces which are known as ' edges ' in many

Yorkshire place-names. In the tract of moorland some ten miles wide which separates the border of the Yorkshire coalfield near Huddersfield and Halifax from the Lancashire coalfield at Rochdale and Oldham, a succession of edges running more or less north and south may be traced, the scarps of the Lancashire side facing eastwards, those of the Yorkshire side facing west (Fig. 43). Here the Pennines are at their narrowest; in contrast to the Peak District to the south, it may be pointed out that the Mountain Limestone is not brought to the surface in this tract, and the narrow upland area is made up only of Millstone Grit (see

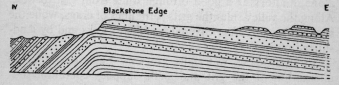

Figure 43.—Section across the Pennines at Blackstone Edge.
Faults omitted.

Fig. 41). The structure is that of a fairly simple anticline, the scarp faces being of course determined by the outward dips: the fold is asymmetrical, however, and the dips to the west are steeper than those to the east. Accordingly the scarps on the west are more crowded and less elevated, the wide stretches of grit to the east having retarded denudation on that side. These features are shown in Figure 43, which is simplified by the omission of the faults which cut the area; the essential characters of the land forms, however, are indicated sufficiently. The long gentle dip slopes on the east are occupied by open moorland. One of the most prominent of these escarpments is Blackstone Edge, about ten miles west of Huddersfield, which is formed by the rock known as Kinderscout Grit; Defoe amusingly speaks of this ridge as the English Andes. Between this and the Western edge of the coalfield at Huddersfield there is a succession of similar crag-capped edges, running parallel to Blackstone Edge, and dissected by deep dales.

Most of the familiar dales of West Yorkshire are valleys cut by east-flowing streams in these uplands: Wharfedale, Airedale and Calderdale all represent narrow strips of low-land extending far up into the high moors. These streams and their tributaries, which occupy still narrower valleys or cloughs, have dissected the plateau surface, but between the valleys there are generally great areas of the plateau surface which are little affected by them. Most of these valleys are bottle-necks ending in the uplands, and the Aire is almost alone in affording a good through route from east to west. Along the valley sides the grits form lines of crags, while the shale slopes are often covered by fallen blocks and by land-slipped masses.

In these dales waterfalls are very numerous, for the alternation of the grit and shale supplies conditions admirably suited for their development. Examples are so numerous that it is perhaps unnecessary to name them; the Lumb Falls near Hebden Bridge are caused by the Kinderscout Grit, which also gives rise to the fall in Marsden Clough, at Holmbridge near Huddersfield. These falls, like many others in England, are due to the presence of hard bands among softer rocks, in this case the grit bands among shales. Examination of most British waterfalls will reveal a shelf of limestone or sandstone (or occasionally igneous rock) resting on softer clays or shales; the hard band ends sharply at the fall, while underneath it the softer rocks are frequently so excavated that it is possible to walk behind the fall (Fig. 44). Further erosion in such a case must eventually lead to the collapse of the undercut shelf, and to the recession upstream of the fall, while a gorge marks its former position. In the case of the Niagara Falls a gorge some miles in length has been left as the fall has been cut back to positions further upstream. So in the dales almost every waterfall occurs at the head of a more or less distinct gorge, while above it the valley is actually shallower.

A rather different type of waterfall is sometimes produced where a fault line running across the valley brings grit against shale. If the shale is on the downstream side of the fault it becomes rapidly worn down to a lower level than the grit, so that the fault plane is excavated and forms a wall over which the water falls: if, as is frequently the case, the fault plane is nearly vertical, the grit bed may not be undercut for some time, and there is thus less tendency for the fall to recede and to produce a gorge. An admirable example of such a fall is that known locally as the Dolly

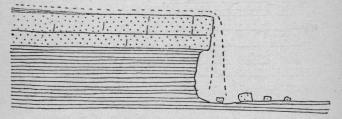

Figure 44.—Section of a typical Pennine waterfall.
Grit bed, dotted; shales, lined.

Folly Waterfall, near Meltham, where a little stream falls over a fault face showing over thirty feet of massive grit (the Huddersfield White Rock) which is brought against soft black shales, which are being rapidly eroded and which are seen in front of the fall dipping steeply downstream (Fig. 45).

Each hard band thus acts in the river-bed more or less as it does on the higher surface, giving rise to a step because the shales beneath it and downstream from it are worn away more rapidly, while above the waterfall the hard ledge tends to act as a temporary check to down-cutting, since the stream is unable to cut down at any point more deeply than its own level further downstream. In these dales, therefore, the streams frequently have 'stepped' gradients, as the water rushes rapidly down to lower levels, now plunging over waterfalls, then for some way flowing more slowly until it reaches the fall formed by another hard band. The contrast between the steep and irregular gradients of such streams, and the gently inclined beds of mature rivers like those of the Midland plain needs no emphasis; here in the higher regions most streams are actively cutting down their beds, producing deep valleys which are only slowly widened (as by land-slips) and thus making little effect on the upland surfaces, while in the lowlands the sluggish rivers cannot cut vertically since they are little above sea-level for most of

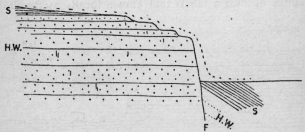

Figure 45.—Section through the Dolly Folly Waterfall, near Meltham.

F, the fault plane; H.W., the Huddersfield White Rock; S, the overlying shales.

their courses, but are able to widen their valleys by their shifting meanders and so reduce further the level of considerable areas.

These immature valleys of the upland tracts show many signs of this activity. In many torrents great masses of rock testify to the power of the waters to move heavy loads, especially at times of flood. On the surfaces of many sandstone beds are cylindrical pots or pot-holes cut by boulders when swirled by the torrents. The growth of a series of such pot-holes rapidly leads to the destruction of a hard band and represents one way in which the lowering of the stream-bed is brought about.

In the valleys trees are more frequent than on the uplands, birch and oak at times being abundant. The wider dales are more populated than the uplands, and there is some cultivation. Where they are crossed by old routes there are grey stone towns: the ancient narrow bridges have determined the location of many of these. The local grits have been used in the buildings and flags sometimes for roofing, their dull colours fitting into the austerity of the view. The grits have been used in building the churches as well as the cottages and walls; their use appears to have begun at a very early date, while it is surprising to find that they were also carried into east Yorkshire and Lincolnshire for church-building in pre-Norman times.

With the development of the woollen industry, at first merely a supplement to sheep raising, the population of the dales steadily increased, and the expansion of home weaving led to the building of stone cottages with large windows. The introduction of water power caused the industry to prosper still further in these valleys beside the rapid streams, which later supplied the lime-free water needed for other stages in textile manufacture. But the greatest expansion of the industry took the bulk of the population on to the lower ground further to the east, where the dales open out on to the Coal Measures. Here a series of old towns has grown to industrial eminence, though among their newer and less attractive scenic developments they have occasionally retained some traces of their earlier character.

The coalfield is much lower than the moorlands, but running across it are several prominent edges due to hard sandstone bands occurring among the more usual grey shales of the Coal Measures. Much of the lower ground in the coalfield was formerly wooded, and trees are common even now, especially in the hedgerows which take the place of stone walls in this country. Stone was much less freely used in building than was the case in the moorland dales, and old half-timbered buildings of the sixteenth century still occur in some towns.

THE FOREST OF ROSSENDALE

The Pennine area referred to above extends from the Peak northwards and then eastwards to Harrogate. Separated from it and a little distance to the west lies a somewhat similar upland tract in the Forest of Rossendale (Fig. 41). This region is situated between the South Lancashire coalfield, around Rochdale and Bolton, and the Burnley coalfield. It is thus of anticlinal structure, the coal-bearing rocks dipping away from it very much as they do from the

N   S

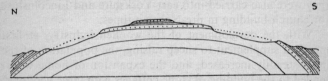

Figure 46.—Generalised diagram of the Rossendale uplands to show the form of scarps: much simplified and faults omitted.

grit areas of the Pennines. The plateau is made up of Millstone Grit which is closely comparable with that already described, the rocks in this case being gently folded. In the middle of the area, in the region including Haslingden and Ramsbottom, the beds are practically horizontal, and form a terraced landscape, each step corresponding to the outcrop of a grit bed, while above it a sloping shelf marks the presence of softer beds (Fig. 46). Near the borders of the upland area both towards Rochdale and Accrington the dip increases and the rocks give rise to a succession of scarps and dip slopes. The whole region, however, is cut by numerous faults and its structure is much more complicated than would appear from this brief account. It is deeply trenched by narrow valleys in which hard grits give rise to waterfalls.

THE INGLEBOROUGH DISTRICT

Capping Ingleborough is a small area of grit, the lowest part of the Millstone Grit (Fig. 38). Ingleborough may thus be regarded as an outlier, the cap being a small remnant of a bed of grit, locally horizontal, which formerly covered the whole of the middle Pennines. Other larger remnants of this same bed occur at the tops of Whernside and Peny-ghent; these three mountains rise to well over 2000 feet, their summits differing in aspect from the more extensive grit uplands to the east and south, for moorland grasses and mosses comprise their principal vegetation. Seen from Ingleborough the isolation of these peaks emphasises the effect of denudation on the great sheet of grit and under-lying rocks which formerly connected them, while away to the east the wide expanse of Masham Moor where the grit still extends in a continuous bed illustrates the earlier con-dition of this area.

It will also be recognised that these isolated peaks stand out conspicuously above a plateau; the dales have been cut in the latter but many hilltops are flat and are generally at comparable levels, so that it is natural to suppose that before the dales were commenced this region consisted of a fairly uniform plateau, out of which Whernside, Penyghent and other mountains stood up sharply. Such a nearly level surface may have been produced by marine action, that is by wave advance and the cutting of an almost level platform just below sea-level, or it may have resulted from river erosion, meandering mature rivers and their tributaries reducing the area practically to base-level. Whichever agency was responsible for the formation of a platform, it involved a very long period of denudation at a time when the present plateau surface, now about 2000 feet high, was not far above or below sea-level. Such a denuded surface is generally called a peneplain (" almost a plain "). Many plateaux owe their characters to the uplifting of old pene-plains, reflecting distant periods of denudation whose actual date is often fixed with difficulty. Reference is later made to the uplifted peneplains in Wales (p. 226), but it may be noticed that in each case the raising of the peneplain has given rivers the opportunity to cut deep valleys and so has led to its dissection. In most peneplains, moreover, it is possible to recognise 'islands' which escaped erosion and which now stand out more or less conspicuously above the ancient plain, as do Ingleborough and Whernside. Such islands are frequently spoken of as 'monadnocks'. It is possible that this Pennine peneplain was carved in early Tertiary times, though some geologists believe that it is much older.

THE EFFECTS OF ICE ACTION IN THE PENNINE DALES

The dales cut in these uplands were mostly begun during later Tertiary times, but in any case the essential characters of the drainage were determined before the Ice Age. The modifications resulting from ice action have been worked out in great detail by the late Professor P. F. Kendall in his classic work in Yorkshire, and by Dr. A. Jowett in Lancashire. It is not proposed to discuss these changes fully, for while they are complex many of them are comparable with the changes already described. The ice sheets which invaded the Pennine areas came mostly from the north and west. In the western areas they gave rise to lakes which produced important overflow channels, forming Rudyard Gorge in the Leek area in the south-western Pennines, and Cliviger Gorge south-west of Burnley. This western ice was held up by the high land of the moors, some of which may have escaped glaciation. In the more northern parts the ice movement was partly guided by those valleys which cut through the uplands, particularly by Teesdale ; these received ice from the areas north and west of the Pennines. Other valleys which have closed heads received little ice from this direction, but ice formed on the high ground at their heads and gave rise to valley glaciers. During the periods of maximum glaciation some of these glaciers came into contact, and besides forming the boulder clay deposits, scattered large boulders on many uplands, giving evidence of the former extent of the ice. Particularly well known are the great perched blocks of dark grit which stand on the limestone platform at Norber near Settle (Fig. 47).

It was during the retreat of the ice, however, that the most striking of the existing features were produced. The shrinkage of the ice uncovered many parts of the uplands and of the smaller valleys. While extensive valley glaciers filled the main valleys, their tributary dales were free of ice, and lakes were formed by their dammed-up drainage which produced great numbers of overflow channels. Those at

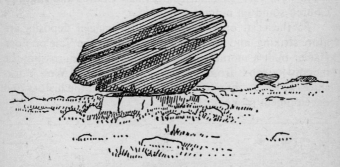

Figure 47.—Perched block of grit on limestone upland, Norber, Yorks. An ice-transported boulder.

Chellow Dean and Wibsey Bank Foot, near Bradford, may be mentioned; they were formed as spillways from lakes held up by Airedale ice in dales tributary to the Aire.

In most of the valleys the retreating ice left behind deposits the form of which has remained little modified to the present time. The shrinking valley glaciers, comparable in form with those of Switzerland, built end-moraines whenever their retreat was checked by climatic fluctuations, for much of the transported material was deposited where the glacier ended, and if the end of the glacier remained in one position for some time a considerable heap was accumulated, whereas when retreat was more rapid the material was spread less conspicuously over the whole distance of the retreat. In many dales a series of five or six such moraines extend at intervals almost completely across the valley. Many of these morainic heaps formed dams across the valleys after the ice had retreated above them, and for a time held up the drainage, deposits accumulating in a narrow lake until the dam was breached and the lake drained. In the Aire valley there are well-marked moraines between Shipley and Keighley, one extending across the valley at Bingley, where the river has cut a gorge to avoid it on the south-west side. In Wharfedale, Ilkley Church and Leathley Church stand on morainic mounds.

To the east, on the lowlands, the glacial deposits are more striking, and the terminal moraine of the Vale of York glacier built a moraine which provides a ridge crossing the marshy lowlands from the Wolds to the hills of West Yorkshire, which has been of great importance in the history and development of York.

Figure 48.—A grit edge above Ilkley.

CHAPTER XIII

SOME FEATURES OF NORTH-EASTERN ENGLAND

THE counties of Northumberland and Durham embrace a wide range of country, in which there are several features of outstanding interest. The description of a few of these occupies most of the space in the present chapter, and little reference is made to the attractiveness of parts of the coasts, to the beauty of many of the rivers or to the setting of the industrial towns. It is rather to the moorlands that attention may first be directed, to Cross Fell and the moors around Alston and to the Cheviots. These areas are less familiar than the Lake District or many of the upland tracts described in the last two chapters, but they are rich in interest.

THE ALSTON MOORS

The portion of the ' Pennine Chain ' which extends into this area in some respects resembles the part which forms the moorlands of Yorkshire. Stretching from the borders of that county to the Tyne valley, the higher parts of this desolate upland are chiefly occupied by peaty moorlands and by bleak pastures. Reaching more than 2000 feet above sea-level along its western edge, it falls gradually eastwards to sink almost imperceptibly into the rolling grass-lands which border the Durham coalfield. The general slope of the surface is in approximately the same direction as the dip of the rocks, which are tilted towards the east; the western border, along the line through Cross Fell, forms a great scarp along a fault which brings the New Red Sandstone of the Vale of Eden in contact with the older rocks of the moors (Fig. 50).

This part of the Pennines is not made up to any great

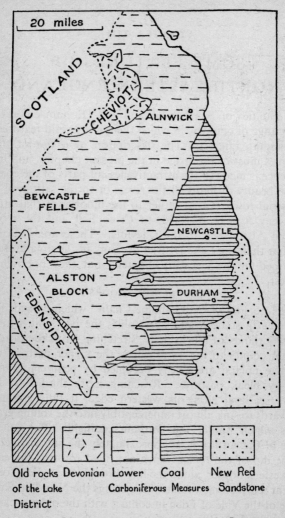

Figure 49.—Diagram map of North-East England.

extent by the Millstone Grit, for the thickness of that formation is very much reduced as compared with York-shire; these northern moorlands are built up in part by rocks comparable in age with the Mountain Limestone of areas further south. But when a sequence of almost pure limestone was being deposited in those areas, Durham received a varied series of deposits, consisting of sandstones and clays with only occasional beds of limestone. This lateral change in the character of the rocks comprising the Lower Carboniferous is important in interpreting a geo-logical map of these regions, for the Pennine moors of Durham are coloured in the same way as the Mountain Limestone regions of Yorkshire and Derbyshire, though there is little similarity in their scenic characters.

In these Durham uplands the only town of any size is Alston, situated on the South Tyne in the north-west part of the moors. A dark, stone-built town, it is one of the highest market towns in England.

This tract of country is of great structural simplicity, and it has escaped any serious geological disturbance. On the north, west and south it is cut off from the adjoining areas by faults of some magnitude, so that it may be thought of as a structural unit consisting of an almost rectangular block of gently tilted rocks showing little sign of any earth move-ments; it has lately been spoken of as the " Alston Block ". It seems to have had a long history as a region more stable than those around it.

Its upper surface shows wide tracts of nearly level moorland. Deeply trenched as it is by many valleys, there are yet great expanses of plateau surface between them. Seen from any high viewpoint, it is difficult to escape from the conclusion that these smooth-featured uplands were once continuous, for the remnants of the surface rise to a uniformly level sky-line. This upland represents an old erosion-surface comparable with and perhaps of similar age to that already referred to beneath Ingleborough and Whernside, a surface planed down practically to sea-level, probably by weathering agents and by rivers, and subsequently uplifted to its present height.

Standing out from this smooth plateau are detached mountain masses, Cross Fell, Great Dun Fell, Mickle Fell and Cold Fell, which are probably remnants of isolated hills which stood out above the general level of the planed-down surface. Like Ingleborough and its neighbours they form monadnocks, conspicuous because their outlines are less subdued than those of the main part of the plateau. The heights of these monadnocks vary according to the height of the plateau in the different parts of the block. Whereas under Cross Fell the plateau is over 2000 feet high, near the north-west corner it is only 1700 feet and Cold Fell is a prominent hill although it reaches little over 2000 feet. Dr. F. M. Trotter believes that the level surface of the plateau was carved in Tertiary times and that its uplifting took place at no very remote date (geologically); such variations as occur in its height are attributed mainly to a warping of the early peneplain.

The heights of this plateau are thus to a large extent unrelated to the nature of the rocks composing it, and softer and harder rocks alike build parts of its surface. Many of the streams flowing across it occupy narrow immature valleys, indicating that they have scarcely begun the dissection of the area. Most of these valleys may be looked on as having been formed by consequent streams, flowing with the inclination of the plateau towards the east. Tributaries of the Wear and Upper Tees are the most important of these. Along these dales, settlements and cultivation penetrate into the moorlands, with many small fields and meadows separated by grey stone walls. Grey farm buildings, roofed by heavy slabs, are scattered in these dales, but the upper limits of cultivation are marked by walls which bound the open moorland.

Perhaps the greatest interest of the Alston Block lies in

its borders. Of these the western edge is far the most impressive, falling away sharply along a straight line coinciding with the Pennine fault, which determines the great scarp beneath Cross Fell, to the low ground of Edenside (Fig. 50). In this low country the New Red Sandstone forms a deep inlet extending southwards from the Carlisle basin between the Lake District and the North Pennines, a long tract of pretty undulating land almost hemmed in by mountains. The steep western slope of the Cross Fell range is drained by swift streams flowing into the Vale of Eden.

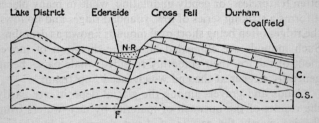

Figure 50.—The structure of Cross Fell and Edenside.

Many of these have deep picturesque valleys, wooded in their lower parts; the Valley of Geltsdale, north-east of Castle Carrock, is among the best known of these. But they only furrow the scarp face, and the Pennine edge is not crossed by any conspicuous valley between the Tyne Gap on the north and the Stainmore Pass, connecting the southern end of the Vale of Eden with the valleys of the Greta and the Tees.

Both these breaks in the Pennine watershed have determined the routes of roads and railways from west to east. During the Ice Age they played a similar part in controlling the directions of ice movement; ice pressed on the Pennines from north and west and escaped along these two channels, by which débris from Scotland and the Lake District was carried to south and east. As the ice sheets retreated they left behind great deposits of material in the passes, and these less elevated areas have gained much in diversity of land form from the irregular mounds of clay and gravel dropped by the melting ice.

Among these glacial deposits the boulder clays are most important. Normally they consist of unstratified masses of clay containing boulders of every size dumped without any arrangement when the ice melted. The colour varies and with it the colour of the soils, for where a glacier moved across an area of New Red Sandstone its deposits acquired a predominantly red colour. The surface of boulder clay is often featureless, or gently undulating, while in many places it forms a striking series of low, rounded ridges and hollows, the ridges often being short oval mounds known as drumlins. Such mounds are elongated along the direction of movement of the ice, their smoothly rounded whale-backs being generally steeper at the end which faced ' upstream '.

Sands and gravels among the glacial deposits are partly the results of the outwash of material by melt-waters from the ice, partly the results of direct deposition by the ice during its waning or retreat. Since they thus date from a late stage in the Ice Age their original character and form are sometimes clearly retained. The country covered by such gravel deposits may be more diversified and sharper in feature than that covered by boulder clay. The country near Brampton shows the characters of these sharp gravel ridges very clearly. The ridges rise for 100 feet or more above the general level and form a belt some eight miles long and several miles wide, probably marking temporary halting places during the retreat of the ice. Such ' kames ' frequently enclose small lakes or kettle-holes, representing places where masses of ice were stranded in the deposit, to leave a more or less circular hollow when the buried ice at length melted : in many cases such lakes have subsequently become peat bogs.

North of the Tyne Gap are the Bewcastle Fells and beyond them the Carboniferous rocks sweep around the great dome of the Cheviot Hills. In Northumberland the Carboniferous rocks are generally thicker than in the Alston Block, and in the lower part are still more unlike their equivalents in Yorkshire, for they contain only thin limestones and consist mainly of shales and sandstones with some coal seams. These rocks dip southwards and eastwards from the Cheviots and give rise to a succession of alternating scarps and dip slopes. But this region is much more disturbed and complex than the Alston Block, and the ridges formed by the sandstones are often interrupted where they are cut by faults.

The most important sandstone in this country is the Fell Sandstone, which sweeps westwards away from the coast at Berwick, and forms a line of flat-topped hills almost completely shutting off the Northumberland coast from the Cheviot region. This imposing scarp is cut through by only two rivers, the Aln and the Coquet, both of which have succeeded in breaking across it owing to its weakness where it is affected by faults, which enable them to avoid the necessity of cutting down through the full thickness of the sandstone barrier. The Fell sandstones give rise to moorlands which rise in the Simonside Hills to over 1400 feet.

THE WHIN SILL

Most of the high moorlands and scarps of Northumberland and Durham are thus formed by sedimentary rocks of the Carboniferous. Of quite different origin is the ridge along which Hadrian's Wall extends north of the Tyne at Haltwhistle. Here a bold craggy scarp faces the north, and from its summit the rolling country may be seen stretching away to the Scottish borders. This scarp, however, is not formed by a sandstone or by any sedimentary rock; it results from a body of igneous rock known as the Whin Sill. The rock forming this mass varies somewhat, but it is mostly dark blue-grey in colour (as seen on a fresh and un-weathered specimen). It is very similar to the basalt of the

Derbyshire lavas in composition and in many other respects, save that it is normally of coarser texture : the rock is known as a dolerite. It was formerly regarded as a lava flow of Carboniferous age like the basalt, since it always occurs between Carboniferous rocks. More detailed study, however, and especially the mapping of its distribution, have revealed that the Whin does not always occur between the same two Carboniferous beds. Thus if it were interpreted as a lava it must be of different age at different places, since it sometimes comes among higher beds in the series, sometimes among lower beds. Under Bamburgh Castle it is seen to cut across successive beds of sandstone (Fig. 51). Moreover, in places the sill splits into two or more separate sheets. From the field relations it is therefore clear that this rock cannot have been poured out as a lava flow making a definite bed amongst the other rocks of the Carboniferous series, and it is now known that the material composing the mass was injected into the rocks at some date after they had been formed. In parts it has a bedded appearance, but more frequently it is cut by numerous joints which give rise to a weak columnar structure comparable with that which is familiar in the Giant's Causeway (Fig. 51).

This injected or intruded material was molten and in many ways similar to a lava at the time when it found its way from some deeper source along the weaker places between the beds, sometimes leaving one level to find a higher or lower path where it met less resistance. In the Whin rock we have an example of an igneous rock, formed from the consolidation or crystallisation of molten material, but which unlike a volcanic rock solidified underground and not at the surface. The slower cooling allowed the growth of larger crystals than are to be found in such rocks as basalt, which, having been cooled on the earth's surface, has crystallised more quickly and has a finer texture. It is interesting to note that along the margins of the Whin Sill the rock is sometimes indistinguishable from a basalt, for the reason that the molten material was there rapidly chilled by its contact with the bounding rocks.

The thickness of this intruded sheet or sill naturally shows great variation. In places it exceeds 200 feet, but the average thickness is more nearly 100 feet. This sill occurs over a very extensive area, coming to the surface at places determined by the structure, for although its relations are not exactly those of a bedded rock, its form is comparable with that of the Carboniferous strata among which it occurs.

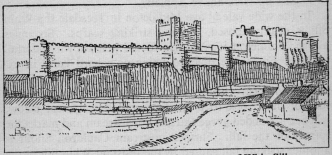

Figure 51.—Bamburgh Castle, on crags of Whin Sill.

With them it has been arched into wide folds or broken by faults. To some extent, therefore, the Whin Sill behaves as a particularly tough bed among the shales and sandstones where it occurs, and its scenic effects are mainly due to its resistance to erosion. The great scarp already referred to, crowned by the Roman wall on the west of the North Tyne valley, is similar in general characters to any escarpment formed by sandstones or limestones, though the dark rock in places forms more rugged crags; frequently, too, the soft shales beneath the dolerite have been scooped out by ice action, and small tarns and mosses are common.

The most northerly occurrence of the Whin Sill is in the Kyloe Hills, whence the outcrop trends south-eastwards to the dark cliffs under Bamburgh Castle (Fig. 51); still farther east its course can be traced in the low and rocky

Farne Islands, the existence of which is due to the resistance of the tough dolerite when the softer sedimentary rocks have been worn away from around them by the waves. To the south again, in the columned cliffs of Cullernose Point, near Alnwick, the sill again forms dark vertical cliffs, but at that point it ceases to be a factor in the coast scenery, its outcrop turning inland to form the ridge mentioned above, and extending southwards along the high fault scarp which bounds the Alston Block. It forms the well-known crags in High Cup Nick above Appleby.

In the wide vale above Middleton in Teesdale the Whin Sill is again exposed, forming striking scarps. Six miles above Middleton it gives rise to the well-known waterfall of High Force, the dolerite acting as a hard band in exactly the same way as the sandstones in the Yorkshire dales ; the brown peaty waters of the Tees fall over a vertical face of dark rock to a swirling pool seventy feet below, whence a wooded gorge extends downstream and marks the retreat of the fall. Further upstream Cauldron Snout is another striking fall caused by the resistant Whin Sill in the river's bed, the water cascading down great stairs of black rock.

THE CHEVIOTS

Passing beyond the Carboniferous rocks towards the Scottish border, the great dome of Cheviot forms the highest and wildest tract in Northumberland, nearly twenty miles across, round which the scarps just described form irregularly concentric belts. The Cheviots reach a height of over 2600 feet but they include no impressive mountains : rounded peat-covered slopes are typical of much of the area, such rocky crags as occur being inconspicuous. The Cheviot itself, the highest part of the area, is one of the least remarkable of mountains, for the smooth summit is covered with thick peat, but it affords splendid views of the north of England. In places peat is still growing, but as in the Pennines many of the deposits are undergoing denudation, and they are deeply furrowed. In this lonely brown upland rivers have carved some picturesque deep gorges, but speaking generally it shows few of those more impressive features which might be expected on mountain-land built up of igneous rocks. For the Cheviot region is best described as a deeply dissected volcano.

Since Carboniferous rocks rest on the Cheviot lavas and dip away from them, it follows that the volcano is of pre-Carboniferous date. It has been established that the lavas date from the earliest part of the Devonian period, at which time they were poured out to form a great mountain on an ancient land surface. Into this tract other igneous rocks were also intruded, giving rise to the large mass of pink granite which occurs in the middle of the upland. The resulting land-forms have suffered greatly from the denudation which began during Devonian times and has been renewed at different periods ; finally the whole was overridden by ice in glacial times, leading to still more smoothing of the surface and to the burial of much of it under a cover of ice-borne deposits. In short, the Cheviot Hills, whatever the attraction of their peaty summits or heather-covered slopes, are disappointing as examples of topography due to the presence of igneous rocks. Although some of the rocks have been used for rough walling, surprisingly few local rocks have been used in building, the isolated shepherds' dwellings being built from freestones carried into the area.

The glacial features of the Cheviots and the country around them are of particular interest. Dry valleys, frequently cutting across spurs between neighbouring stream courses, are very numerous, and represent overflow channels cut during glacial retreat. On the lower ground are deposits of boulder clay and gravel comparable with those described in the Tyne gap. Kettle-holed moraines supporting small lakes, such as that south of Cornhill, are typically developed.

THE COALFIELD AND THE COAST

The coalfield region of the north-east of England is not treated in detail. It consists mostly of country of lower altitude than that farther west, but since there are thick sandstone beds among the shales and softer rocks of the Coal Measures, there is great diversity within the coalfield. In particular, a group of sandstones which occur just above the most important series of coal seams is responsible for some of the highest ground in the coalfield. It gives rise to the steep hills in Newcastle itself, while its outcrop extends southwards to Low Fell. In Durham the dips in the Coal Measures (as in the higher ground to the west) are very low, and the sandstones frequently form almost horizontal cappings to even-topped hills. Along the coast these same sandstones are responsible for much variety in the cliff scenery north of Tynemouth.

To the east of the Coal Measure outcrop lies a wide tract of red and brown rocks belonging to the New Red Sandstone, the most important member of this series being the Magnesian Limestone. This rock group forms an almost straight outcrop from Nottingham, where it is weak and inconspicuous, through Knaresborough to the coast, where it extends from Hartlepool almost to South Shields. The Magnesian Limestone is a yellowish brown dolomite, a limestone with a considerable proportion of magnesium carbonate, but like other limestones it is frequently cavernous owing to the action of the underground waters, while large areas on its surface are streamless.

The Magnesian Limestone forms the coast-line of Durham for many miles, giving rise to steep yellow cliffs which are in marked contrast to those formed by boulder clays and by Coal Measures further north. In places, as at Marsden, tall stacks have been left standing by wave erosion along vertical joints. The cliffs are also varied by attractive ' denes ' cut by the east-flowing streams.

Inland, the Magnesian Limestone forms a sharp scarp facing to the west and crossed by few rivers. It is possible that many of the consequent streams from the Alston Moors formerly continued eastwards across this tract, but if so they have been captured by the middle portion of the Wear, which from Bishop Auckland to Chester-le-Street is evidently a subsequent stream flowing beneath the limestone ridge.

There is little doubt that the Wear formerly continued still further northwards to join the Tyne at Newcastle, for a deep buried channel known as the Team Wash marks its earlier course; this channel is now almost completely filled in with glacial deposits, and as the deepest part is over 140 feet beneath sea-level it must have been cut when the land stood a good deal higher than at present. The Wear left this course owing to the changes brought about during the Ice Age, and it now turns sharply eastwards over the Magnesian Limestone escarpment to Sunderland. This course of the lower Wear is determined by an overflow valley cut when the Wear drainage was dammed up by ice to the north. As in the case of the Pickering lake the deepening of this newly established course led to its persistence after the ice had disappeared and left masses of glacial débris blocking its former course. The deep channel at Ferryhill probably represents a still earlier outflow from the Wear lake, before the ice had retreated so far north.

For much of its lower course the present Wear thus occupies a valley which has been entirely cut since glacial times. The valley, however, is deeply incised and at Durham a sharp meander forms a hair-pin gorge from Elvet Bridge to Framwellgate Bridge; the almost completely detached portion of the plateau enclosed within the bend of the river forms the splendid site of the cathedral and castle. It has been suggested that after the retreat of the ice and the disappearance of the lake the river meandered over a fairly even landscape, but presently these meanders were cut deeply down into both the glacial deposits and the solid rocks, possibly owing to a rise of the land which gave added power to the rivers, but the story of the changes of sea-level in this region is not yet fully known.

CHAPTER XIV

THE LAKE DISTRICT

THE scenery of the Lake District is so well known and has been so eloquently described that there is no need to praise it here. Since Englishmen have overcome their dread of desolate heights and have learned to appreciate mountains, the Lake District has attracted so many writers that many of its place-names have become part of English literature. Wordsworth and the other lakeland poets, Ruskin and more recent writers have made its richness known so that its popularity has become almost a danger. Much of this region of " lovely rock-scenery, chased with silver waterfalls " is still almost unspoiled, however, except along a few main roads and beside some lakes ; it is still impossible to see the greater part of its mountains except on foot, and while these conditions remain at least the worst results of popularity are not likely to be too prominent.

The Lake District is a small and compact area. Within this tract, only about thirty miles across, the craggy mountains, bare fells, deep ravines, impressive falls and lakes of differing pattern afford examples of scenic features nowhere else to be seen in England. Although the increasing numbers who travel to the Alps and further afield in search of mountain scenery have the advantage of larger lakes and higher peaks, those who best appreciate the greater mountain masses find their enjoyment of the Lake District enhanced ; its mountains are small but it is easier for the ordinary traveller to know them better, while the lakes and cascades show all the essential characters of Swiss scenery, with an added daintiness if with less vivid colouring. Only the glaciers are wanting, and they have not long disappeared.

This area is of high relief, and only small tracts within

its valleys are cultivated; where the valleys open out on to the surrounding lowlands there are wider agricultural areas, and here are situated the old market towns, such as Cockermouth, Penrith and Kendal. Within the uplands, apart from the larger tourist centres, there are only small villages and isolated hamlets built of the grey local stones and often tucked away in lonely valleys.

The systematic description of the Lake District, area by area, is beyond the scope of the present chapter. It is proposed rather to describe those features peculiar to its scenery, with references to some examples, and to indicate their origin; to discuss, in the words of Ruskin, " first what material there was to carve, and then what sort of chisels, and in what workman's hand, were used to produce this large piece of precious chasing and embossed work ". The materials of the Lake District are old, older than those which occupy any considerable tract in the areas already described; they are comparable, however, with the old rocks which underlie the Carboniferous in Cross Fell (Fig. 50). But although the rocks are old, the features incised on their surface are new; the valleys have no greater antiquity than those of the Pennines or of the London basin, while the lakes are even younger.

THE INFLUENCE OF ROCK TYPES ON SCENERY

The old rocks of the Lake District are often hard, but the height of these uplands is not primarily due to this fact. While it is generally true that older rocks are mostly harder than newer ones, there are many exceptions; on the other hand, there are many areas of low ground which are occupied by quite resistant rocks. For example, the rocks of Anglesey are in part older and harder than those of the Lake District, yet that island is almost a monotonous plateau only a few hundred feet above sea-level. The altitude of any area is naturally determined in the first place by the extent to which it is raised by earth movements: the Lake District is be-

lieved to have been so raised during mid-Tertiary times
(when the peneplains of the Alston Block and middle
Pennines were also elevated). If exposed to the action of
denuding agents for a sufficiently long time the softer rocks
will be greatly lowered while the harder beds will stand out ;
to a certain extent this has already occurred, but on the
whole the uplift is so recent that soft as well as hard materials
are still contributing to the upland surface.

The scenic differences due to the varying materials which
build up the Lake District may be understood without
going far from such popular centres as Keswick or Ambleside. From the Friar's Crag by Derwentwater, possibly the
best-known viewpoint in the area, there may be seen the
smooth slopes of Skiddaw to the right, beyond Keswick,
while to the left at the head of the lake the crags of Lodore
and the mountains of Borrowdale show an irregular
' crinkly ' skyline and steep rocky precipices of quite
different appearance. A line drawn from near the southern
end of Ullswater along the east and south of Derwentwater
towards Ennerdale separates off an area of slaty rocks to
the north from an area of predominantly volcanic rocks to
the south.

The rocks of the northern belt are known as the Skiddaw Slates ; they include grits and sandstones and are all
of sedimentary origin, representing muddy and sandy sediments laid down in a shallow sea. They have since been
upraised and severely crumpled, the squeezing to which they
were subjected having converted some of the muddy beds
into slates, which split into layers along planes produced by
the pressure. Many of the Skiddaw Slates are by no means
soft rocks, but they are very much less resistant than the
volcanic rocks which lie to the south of them. Yet Skiddaw
reaches an altitude very little below that of Scawfell and
Helvellyn, in the volcanic tract, and higher than that of
many imposing summits there. Undoubtedly the Skiddaw
rocks are being much more rapidly lowered by weathering

and other eroding agents, and the fact that Skiddaw is so high makes it probable that the uplift of the region took place at no very distant date. In this slate region many small streams have cut deep gorges, leaving narrow ridges and sharp peaks, but no wide expanses of level uplands, such as may be found in the volcanic areas.

Skiddaw is a mountain with few crags, but its steep slopes, covered with bracken and heather, are none the less attractive. It is interesting, too, as one of the first English mountains known to have been climbed for the sake of the scenery and the thrill. For the travellers of just over two centuries ago seem to have been stirred by this " stupendous mountain " with its " chasms and enormous depths in the bowels of the mountains ". Further east Saddleback (or Blencathara) is a more exciting mountain, for it has some sharp crags. Generally, however, the mountains formed of Skiddaw Slates both east and west of Bassenthwaite are of smooth aspect and have few bare rocky cliffs, giving a type of scenery which is quieter and more restful than that beyond the head of Derwentwater.

The rocks which lie to the south are known as the Borrowdale Volcanic Series. They include thick beds of lava together with other rocks formed from the dust or ' ash ' thrown out by the volcanoes, and agglomerates made up of a concrete-like mass of broken fragments produced during the volcanic explosions. Among these volcanic materials some beds of mud are included, subsequently converted into slates by pressure. There is practically no evidence as to the position of the actual volcanoes from which the lavas were ejected. It cannot be too strongly emphasised, however, that the form of the present mountains is quite unrelated to the original volcanoes; the higher peaks stand out from the rest of the area because of their particular resistance to the agencies which have worn down neighbouring tracts, but not because they mark the sites of the vents. Generally the more compact lavas and the harder ashes tend to stand out as crags and cliffs while the softer beds are worn down, and the extraordinary diversity of the area and the irregularity of the hill-forms are largely due to the variability of the great pile of volcanic material. The strong joint-planes cutting through thick tough beds give rise to many steep precipices.

The mountains in this belt include Helvellyn, Scawfell, Great Gable and the Langdale Pikes. The volcanic belt, however, is not so much to be regarded as an assemblage of great mountains but as an irregular upland traversed by deep valleys which are sometimes so narrow as to make little impression on the upland surface : the mountains are the more conspicuous heights left between the valleys and combes. Thus the most familiar traverse through the volcanic country, by the main road from Ambleside by Thirlmere to Keswick, does not help in an appreciation of the real form of the uplands ; from the valley the hills seem of very uneven height and the valley appears an enormous channel, while from the mountain summits the wideness of the upland is more easily recognised.

It is from the summits that the form of the country is best appreciated, and Helvellyn and Scawfell afford almost equally fine sights of the mountains, separated by the deeply trenched valleys (Fig. 52). The Lake District, indeed, is so small that from one viewpoint almost the whole of it can be taken in, though every new viewpoint shows a fresh aspect. From Scawfell the valleys are seen to radiate in almost every direction. The twin towers of Scawfell and Scawfell Pike, joined by the ridge of Mickledore, illustrate the weathering of the massive volcanic rocks. Looking over the precipitous northern face the view embraces the bare slopes of Great Gable and a great expanse of bleak, rocky country with the upland lake of Styhead Tarn, while beyond Derwentwater are the gentler contours of Skiddaw and its neighbours. Great Gable with its cliffs and pinnacles of thickly-bedded rock is another fine viewpoint, since it rises sharply at the

head of the fiord-like valley of Wastdale. Here the lower
ground, occupied by alluvium and by the more uneven
glacial deposits, is sufficiently fertile for cultivation, and an
irregular patchwork of fields follows the valley floor, but as
the slopes steepen upwards, bare crags and screes bring to
an end all attempt at cultivation. The view from Honister
Crags along the straight and steep-sided valley occupied by
Buttermere and Crummock is similar in many respects,

Figure 52.—Great Gable (left) and Skiddaw (distant sky-line) from
Scawfell, showing general level of upland surface.

although here patches of woodland by the lakes tend to
soften the landscape (Fig. 56).

The bleak and rather desolate tract of the Borrowdale
Volcanic rocks extends southwards as far as Ambleside,
where it merges into the lower and pleasant park-like
country that extends by the shores of Windermere. The
highest hills in this tract do not reach 2000 feet, and their
smoother outlines recall the hills of the Skiddaw belt. The
long lake of Windermere with its small bays and bordering
stretches of woodland lies between hills of great charm, but
only in the distant mountains beyond its northern end is
there a hint of wildness and grandeur. The rocks forming
this southern part of the Lake District are somewhat like
those of the Skiddaw belt, but whereas the latter are older
than the volcanic rocks, those of Windermere are newer:

these rocks, known as the upper slates, also include a varied series of grits and limestones, and form a great series over 13,000 feet in thickness. Resting on the volcanic group, these newer slates are dipping to the south, and form hills which generally present steeper faces to the north. Practically the whole of them belong to the Silurian System, while the underlying Borrowdale Volcanic rocks and the Skiddaw Slates represent the older Ordovician.

The materials out of which the core of the Lake District have been carved thus consist of ancient rocks belonging to the Ordovician and Silurian, which fall into three groups giving rise to three well-defined areas. These old rocks have been involved in intense earth pressure, which converted the muddy sediments into slates, and impressed on the rocks a complicated structure. Into them, moreover, were intruded igneous rocks, including the granites of Shap, Skiddaw and Eskdale, and some of these form conspicuous hills ; the famous gabbro intrusion of Carrock Fell stands out clearly above the Skiddaw Slates which adjoin it on east and south. Most of these changes occurred before Carboniferous times ; the rocks of the area had been raised to form part of a great range of mountains which were worn down and then submerged beneath the Carboniferous sea. Carboniferous rocks were laid down on the worn surface, almost horizontal beds thus coming to rest on the highly disturbed strata of Ordovician and Silurian Age. These Carboniferous rocks now form an almost continuous ring around the older rocks of the Lake District. South-eastward they pass from Kendal into those limestone areas already described around Settle, while south-westwards they give rise to the beautiful scenery bordering the estuaries near Dalton-in-Furness and Grange-over-Sands. Here the limestone country is marked by long white scars and gentle grass-covered dip-slopes, like those of the Warton Crag above Carnforth. On the north of the Lake District around Whitehaven the Mountain Limestone is succeeded by Coal Measures, which have brought a small industrial area into very close proximity to lakeland scenery.

All round this ring, the Carboniferous rocks dip outwards, and their scarps face the higher uplands of the Lake District. It is obvious that these beds formerly extended further over the uplands, and since an extension inwards of the present dips would carry them well over the tops of the highest mountains (Fig. 55 B) it is highly probable that the limestones were laid down over the whole region, the central portion having been removed after the strata were domed upwards (Fig. 55 A).

THE STRUCTURE OF THE LAKE DISTRICT

The relation of the Carboniferous rocks to those on which they rest is different from anything described in the previous chapters, where we have mostly dealt with beds laid down in regular series, each layer resting on that immediately older and the whole forming a continuous and conformable series; the Carboniferous rocks in the Lake District are, however, unconformable to the older rocks, resting in different places on different beds. The complication is made still greater owing to the fact that the New Red Sandstone and probably other newer rocks were laid down over the whole after the Carboniferous rocks had been bent upwards and the higher part had been removed, so that the New Red Sandstone in its turn came to rest unconformably, in some places on the Carboniferous, in others on still older beds (Fig. 55 C). Later the whole was forced up into a dome and the newer rocks have been worn away in the centre.

These somewhat complex arrangements of the rocks have been described briefly in order to facilitate discussion of the origin of the most striking feature of the relief of the Lake District, namely, the radial arrangement of the drainage lines. This peculiar feature was recognised and described by Wordsworth in his *Topographical Description of the Country of the Lakes in the North of England.* Standing on

Scawfell it is at once apparent that several valleys radiate
from the centre; within two or three miles of this mountain
seven important valleys extend outwards towards the north,
south and west of the Lake District. These include the great
Windermere valley (running to the south), the Duddon
valley, Eskdale (towards the south-west), Wastdale, Ennerdale (to the west), the Buttermere-Crummock valley and the
Derwent valley (to the north).

The explanation of these radial drainage lines depends

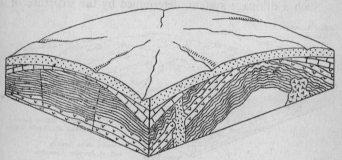

Figure 53.—The Lake District, showing the initiation of the radial
drainage on a domed surface of newer rocks.
(*Shading as in Figure 55.*)

on the essentially domed structure of the area. Bearing in
mind that the newest rocks known to have covered the area
were at one stage arched up into a low dome, it may be
regarded as quite probable that the river system was initiated
on this surface, rivers flowing outwards in nearly every
direction from the centre of the dome more or less as the
rain streams outwards from the top of an umbrella. We
may suppose that Scawfell is not far from the original top
of the dome. Of course the simple domed structure, illustrated diagrammatically in Figure 53, has now almost
completely disappeared, the newer rocks having been removed from the greater part of the region as the rivers have
cut down: the rivers therefore flow on older rocks of com-

plex structure whose arrangement generally bears no close relationship to the courses followed by the rivers, but on the fringes of the area the rivers pass on to the newer rocks. These changes are shown in Figure 54, where rivers occupying positions closely comparable with those in Figure 53 are shown occupying deep valleys in the uplands formed by the old rocks. The drainage remains radial although the conditions which controlled the initiation have been destroyed as the rivers cut down more deeply.

Such a drainage system, determined by the structure of

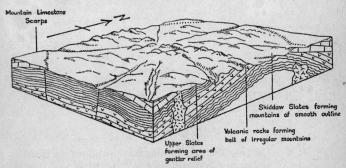

Figure 54.—The Lake District, showing very diagrammatically the influence of the various rock types on the scenery.
(*Compare the earlier stage shown in Figure 54 : shading as in Figure 55.*)

one group of rocks but later impressed on an underlying group, often of greater complexity of structure, is known as a superimposed system. Not all such superimposed systems are radial, and it is in the combination of these two features that the Lakeland drainage is most interesting. East of Scawfell the valleys are not strictly radial in their arrangement, and it may perhaps be worth noting that the uplift was not quite a simple dome, the form being sometimes described as that of an old caddy-spoon : thus there are the Thirlmere valley, Ullswater and Haweswater running northwards from a parting which runs roughly eastwards from Scawfell to Shap. This deviation from a truly radial arrangement is, however, only of minor importance, and the accompanying diagrams illustrate a simply radial

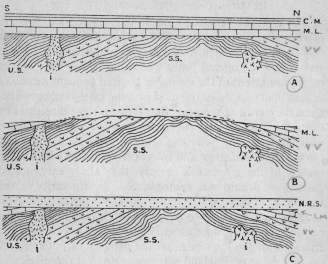

Figure 55.—Diagrams showing the building of the Lake District.

A. Ordovician—Silurian rocks, folded and planed down, overlain unconformably by horizontal Carboniferous rocks.

B. The Carboniferous rocks arched up by further folding, and the central part worn away.

C. New Red Sandstone and newer rocks covering the old rocks unconformably (this stage immediately precedes that shown in Figure 53).

S.S., Skiddaw Slates; V.V., Borrowdale Volcanic rocks; U.S., Upper Slates; i, granite and other intruded igneous rocks; M.L., Mountain Limestone; C.M., Coal Measures; N.R.S., New Red Sandstone (and other newer rocks).

system. The rivers were established long before the Ice Age, for the final uplifting of the dome is supposed to have occurred in mid-Tertiary times, when the peneplains of the Pennine region were raised and when the final folding of the

Wealden anticline and the London basin led to the initiation of the drainage systems of south-eastern England.

THE SCENIC EFFECTS OF THE ICE AGE

The changes in scenery resulting from the Ice Age are of enormous importance. The Lakeland mountain group was an area on which ice formed early during the Ice Age and where it lingered long, while during the time of the maximum extent of the ice it was covered beneath ice sheets of vast thickness. For the most part the ice moved outwards from the centre of the area, thus following the directions of the main valleys, and the most impressive changes have resulted from the scooping out of material along these tracts. In this district and in North Wales, just before the middle of the nineteenth century, the former existence of glaciers in Britain was demonstrated, the similarity of the valleys and their construction to those associated with modern glaciers being so striking as to leave no doubt concerning their interpretation. For long afterwards the character of the ice which left the deposits of boulder clay on the plains of England was uncertain, but the glaciation of these mountain valleys has never been seriously questioned since that time. All the main valleys have many features in common, and description of a few examples will serve to illustrate the essential characters of all.

The valley of Buttermere and Crummock, running north-westwards from Great Gable, is sufficiently well known to form a suitable introduction. Viewed from Honister Crags or from any high point near its head, this valley is seen to extend almost in a straight line; the hills which flank it rise with surprising abruptness from the borders of its lakes, or from its floor in the rather small areas where lakes are absent (Fig. 56). From the Crags at its head the valley falls steeply to a low green tract which is traversed by the streams entering the head of Buttermere. Beyond this lake stretches the longer water of Crummock, and just visible in the distance, almost in the same line, is Loweswater. Though the hills rise so steeply from the valley, they are for the most part less craggy than those of Honnister, for the valley is cut in Skiddaw Slates, and the uplands have not the rugged bleakness typical of the volcanic tract. The valley is thus a great trench, open from end to end, the south-western side being especially straight. In many river valleys in high country every turn reveals a new view, every projecting spur hides the next stretch of the valley, but in

Figure 56.—Buttermere and Crummock from Honister.
A glaciated (U-Shaped) valley with lakes invaded by deltas.

Buttermere the whole length of the valley may be taken in at one view, and there are no projecting spurs running out from the valley sides ; this valley gives all its secrets away at once. These features are essentially the result of glacia-tion, for while the greater part of the excavating of the trough was done by the river before the Ice Age, the move-ment of the glacier smoothed out its pattern, and gave it that wide U-shaped cross-section, and that simplicity of line which are its most striking characteristics.

The tributary valleys are very different in character, for they are less conspicuous, the streams tumbling rapidly from the uplands and giving rise to numerous picturesque falls in their sharp descent. Some streams, like that which descends from Bleaberry Tarn on the south-west of Buttermere, have cut only an insignificant notch in the steep valley side, and the tributary valleys may be said to ' hang ' above the main valley ; this is a further result of the work of the ice, which greatly deepened the trench, leaving the tributary valleys high above its floor. On the upland the tributaries are more or less normal streams in shallow valleys, but when they reach the valley they cascade down its side to the new level of the main river, as in Sourmilk Gill, as the foaming stream from Bleaberry Tarn is so expressively named. The streams are cutting new beds more in accord with the over-deepened valleys which they enter, but so little time, comparatively, has elapsed since the ice disappeared that little progress has been made in most cases.

On the other hand, the high waterfall of Scale Force, made by a stream which descends rapidly to Crummock Water, is situated in a dark gorge, showing that this stream has done more in adjusting itself to the changed conditions. The waterfall occurs where the stream crosses a hard igneous rock overlying softer Skiddaw Slates, and therefore is rather similar to the more usual English waterfalls, but it may be noticed that most of the cascades made by the streams which dash from their hanging valleys into deep-cut glacial trenches do not depend mainly, if at all, on the existence of hard beds, the falls here being due to steps produced independently of stream erosion.

It is at once apparent that the form of both Buttermere and Crummock is due primarily to their occurrence in a valley ; in this respect they resemble the other large lakes of the region, Windermere, Thirlmere, Wastwater and Derwentwater, which coincide with the lines of main drainage already described. Primarily they are flooded valleys, partly owing to the overdeepening of the valleys by ice excavation, partly to the blocking of their exits by glacial deposits. The close relation of Buttermere and Crummock is obvious; they are at practically the same level and it scarcely needs be pointed out that the flat green area which separates them is but the delta formed by deposits carried into the once continuous lake by the stream which comes down the east side of the valley from above Buttermere. Gradually this delta must have grown outwards from the lake margin until, almost reaching the other side, it finally cut the lake into two, forcing the outflow from the upper lake to the extreme border of the valley where it flows between the deltaic flat and the steep slopes of solid rock. Such alluvial tracts, both those at the head of the lakes (for example beneath Honister) and those formed by streams entering further down the valley, are naturally of great importance in lakeland, introducing small level fertile areas into an otherwise bleak and uncultivated tract: in the central part of the Lake District only about two per cent of the land is cultivated, and this is mainly represented by the alluvial flats.

The lakes of the Derwent valley are similar in many respects. Situated in a trough where the ice rapidly deepened the valley on leaving the volcanic rocks of Borrowdale, the hills bounding it take generally the smoother forms characteristic of the Skiddaw Slates. The tributary streams hang above the main valley and the famous falls of Lodore (disappointing though many find them in dry weather) mark the rapid descent of one such tributary. At the northern end of Bassenthwaite are great stretches of glacial deposits, especially along the valley from Bassenthwaite Lake Station to Cockermouth. At Keswick the growth of the great delta formed by the Greta on one side of the valley and Newlands Beck on the other has led to the separation of Derwentwater from Bassenthwaite; it is interesting to see how in this instance the presence of the opposite streams has forced the outflow from Derwentwater to find its way to the lower lake between the two deltaic flats, and not along the margin, as in Buttermere, while the abundant material brought down by these streams has extended the delta downstream for a mile beyond their mouths. It is obvious that the continuation of this process must eventually lead to the complete silting up of Bassenthwaite.

Lakes are indeed only temporary features in a landscape and their abundance in parts of Britain, mostly a result of the Ice Age, emphasises the short time that has since elapsed. Ultimately most of these lakes must disappear, either by becoming filled up with alluvium or by the cutting of an outlet which allows of the drainage of the waters. We have already noticed how many lakes of the closing stages of the Ice Age were drained by the latter method in other parts of England; the silting up of the lakes has also been completed in some cases, notably in Kentmere valley, northwest of Kendal, where two lakes, each rather over a mile in length, have been silted up; the upper lake, dammed by a moraine, caught most of the sediment brought down the valley, and is filled by alluvium, but the lower lake, into which the clear water then passed, is partly filled by diatomite, formed from the siliceous remains of lowly vegetable organisms which lived in the lake. Many of the wide flat stretches in the Eden valley may also be silted-up lakes, while Rosthwaite in Borrowdale and the Naddle valley and St. John's Vale (north of Thirlmere) are other examples.

The long ribbon of Windermere shows many features similar to those of Bassenthwaite, but the lower elevation and the gentler slopes of the surrounding hills give rise to a softer landscape. Near the southern end of the lake are great banks of drift, and these glacial materials by choking up the lower part of the valley have been responsible for the formation of the lake, the waters of which now escape seawards, not along the old valley to the south but by a gap cut through the ridge near Newby Bridge into the valley adjoining it on the west; this gap thus represents another overflow channel which has become a permanent outlet.

But interesting details of scenic development may be

found in all the greater lakes, and possibly sufficient has been said regarding their major features. The lakes dealt with are all situated on one or other of the slate groups, and most of the larger lakes occupy basins excavated in these less resistant groups. A few, however, notably Wastwater, Thirlmere and Haweswater, are placed on the volcanic series, their steep rugged sides giving a wilder grandeur to their surroundings. Possibly Wastwater has the finest situation of all the lakes, the straightness of its south-eastern side and the hanging valleys opposite being most impressive. Wastwater is one of the best examples of a glacially over-deepened valley, its surface being about 200 feet above sea-level while its deepest part is over fifty feet below sea-level. At the head of Wastdale is a considerable expanse of alluvial country, but its sides are bare, and apart from small deltas along its length, the rest of the upper valley is bleak. The south-eastern side is famous for its screes, composed of angular blocks broken by frost and other weathering agents from the cliffs above; the loose material extends in fan-shaped masses high into the notches of the precipice, in places almost to the top. The surface of the scree slopes steeply, its slope being determined by the angle of rest of the blocks; as in the case of the leeward side of sand-dunes material so lightly placed affords very poor foothold. The scree slopes are mostly bare right down to the lake-side, where the material extends below water-level. Although Wastwater is glacially overdeepened, and would therefore be a lake if all superficial deposits were removed, the water-level is raised by a dam of glacial material at its lower end.

But the evidence of ice action in the characters of the scenery is by no means confined to the neighbourhood of the larger lakes. Some wonderful glaciated valleys are not occupied by lakes; the neighbouring valleys of Long Sled-dale, Kentmere and Troutbeck (the southerly Troutbeck, between Windermere and Ambleside, is meant here) are long steep-sided troughs; the ice appears to have excavated these valleys some 200 or 300 feet deeper than they were in pre-glacial times. Kentmere was then a winding valley and in converting it into its canal-like form the ice cut across its projecting spurs, whose truncated ends now stand out in the great crags of Froswick, Ill Bell, Rainsborrow and Raven Crag.

In many parts of the Lake District there are great semi-circular basins high on the hillsides, marking the sites of small glaciers which occurred during the final stages of glaciation. They are known as corries, cirques or cwms. These cwm-glaciers lingered longest on the shady northern slopes, and cwms are extremely numerous on the areas formed by Skiddaw Slates and the volcanic series. Above Buttermere, Burtness Combe and the basin holding Blea-berry Tarn afford good examples of cwms, while under the Langdale Pikes, and in Mardale (Blea Water and Small Water) are many others. The famous Striding Edge of Helvellyn is bounded on the north-east by the great precipice of the cwm which holds Red Tarn.

Many of these cwms enclose small lakes, the water fre-quently held up by a dam made by the terminal moraine of the little glacier. Bowscale Tarn on the southern side of the Caldew valley near Carrock Fell, and Red Tarn, on the east of Helvellyn, are typical and fairly accessible examples of such cwm lakes. Great numbers of small tarns are also found in parts of the upland tracts, where they occupy hollows formed in some cases by the excavating action of the ice, in others by the damming of shallow valleys by the moraines. The outflow for some tarns is over such a moraine dam, but for others, even when such a moraine is present, the outflow channel has been cut through solid rock; this must have presumably afforded a lower exit from the lake than the newly heaped-up moraine, just as in the case of the outflow of such larger lakes as Windermere. Levers Water, reached by an easy route in about a mile and a half from Coniston, illustrates such a tarn.

CHAPTER XV

NORTH WALES

IN many respects the scenery of North Wales resembles
that of the Lake District, save that its greater area holds
wider tracts of desolate upland, and its long coast-line has
many beautiful bays and rugged cliffs. Moreover, the solid
grey castles of Carnarvon, Conway and Harlech, guarding
the entrances into Snowdonia, show something of the influence of history on the scenery.

SNOWDONIA

A beginning may best be made in Snowdonia itself,
among the highest mountains of Wales. Here the mountains have many features in common with those of the Lake
District, for they include many which are chiefly built up
of volcanic rocks, products of volcanoes which were active
at approximately the same time as those of that area. Lavas
were poured out, frequently on the sea-floor, to form thick
beds of hard rock, while ashes from the volcanoes also gave
rise to considerable deposits. The actual summit of Snowdon itself is made by such ashes, laid down on the floor of
the Ordovician sea, and fossils of marine shells may be
collected in this material on the mountain-top. But much
of Snowdon is formed by lavas, and by intruded igneous
rocks. The structure is complicated, but in general the
various beds form a syncline or downfold so that it is clear
that Snowdon stands out from its surroundings only because
the material which formerly extended around it (and, especially to the north and south, far above it) has been worn
away (Fig. 60). As in the case of the Lakeland rocks
the actual volcanoes are unknown, but it is probable
that the Snowdon volcanic rocks were poured out from a

number of vents at no great distance.

From the Snowdon summit the craggy country formed by the volcanic rocks may be seen stretching north-east-wards through the Glyders and the Carnedds, and south-westwards into the Lleyn peninsula of western Carnarvon-shire. This country has been profoundly modified by glaciation, and the deep valleys cut it up into blocks and greatly influence the accessibility of the different parts. Snowdon lies between three such main valleys, the Llanberis Pass, the Glaslyn Pass and the Cwellyn valley, and may thus be approached easily from several different directions. The least exciting ascent, from Llanberis (or by the railway which takes the same direction) shows something of the steep precipices. There are many tarns on Snowdon, most of them held up by morainic dams. From the Llanberis track the deep indigo pool of Llyn Du'r arddu is seen cradled in a dark cwm.

The Llanberis Pass has so many points of similarity to those of the Lake District that the effects of glaciation need not be again described. In its lower part are the twin lakes of Llyn Peris and Llyn Padarn, separated by the delta of the Afon Arddu which rushes heavily laden down the slopes of Snowdon; higher up, the valley is narrower and more rocky as the road climbs sharply to the top of the pass (Fig. 61).

Beyond the Glyders the valley of Nant Ffrancon runs nearly parallel to that of Llanberis, and exhibits still more clearly the features of a glaciated valley; Nant Ffrancon played an important part in the early study of the effects of land ice. Extending inland from Bangor and through Bethesda to Capel Curig, this pass makes a sharp bend near the lower end of Llyn Ogwen. The northern part of the valley, seen from that viewpoint, stretches wide and open in almost a straight line to Bethesda, the floor an irregular patchwork of fields, with a few scattered farmsteads above the humpy glacial deposits and peaty tracts; the sides rise to sharp bare crags so that the valley section is typically U-shaped, and the spurs are truncated. Several tributary streams rush down the left side, but these occupy valleys or flow from cwms which hang considerably above the over-deepened floor of Nant Ffrancon. On the other side of the valley the slope is even and unbroken, and there are no impressive cwms, for as is usually the case, small glaciers lingered longest on the hillside facing north-east.

This straight and simple section of the Nant Ffrancon

Figure 57.—Ice-worn rocks at the head of Nant Ffrancon.

valley ends at Rhaiadr Ogwen in a sharp step, the valley floor having that exaggeratedly stepped profile which is produced by ice action. Travelling up the pass the valley here seems to end suddenly against a high rocky cliff; down this the river falls in a most beautiful cascade, escaping from Llyn Ogwen, situated almost immediately above the fall, by a shallow gorge, where great masses of ice-smoothed rock form bare mounds. Rising from the lower wide valley over this rocky step it is surprising to find the valley once more opening out into the smoother tract which encloses Llyn Ogwen and which extends on to Capel Curig. It is believed that the drainage from the Llyn Ogwen valley formerly flowed eastwards in that direction, but a gorge initiated by a sub-glacial stream led to the cutting of the original watershed.

Llyn Ogwen is obviously a valley-lake, taking its form from the shape of the valley it occupies. It is joined by streams coming down the steep slopes to the south, their courses showing another step. The stream which joins the Ogwen at Rhaiadr Ogwen, rushes down this step in a series of torrents which in some places have already succeeded in cutting shallow gorges. Following this stream up from the main road, it may be traced over a huge moraine of large grey blocks behind which lies a gloomy cwm holding Llyn Idwal, backed by the dark precipices which rise to Glyder Fawr and Y Garn. In this desolate upland tract the effects of glaciation are most impressive; the grey erratic blocks of enormous size left by the ice, and the irregular morainic dam, as Ramsay noted in 1860, showing four concentric lines which mark stages in the retreat of the glacier.

A similar lake lies less than a mile to the east, between spurs of Glyder Fach and Glyder Fawr, in Cwm Bochlwyd. This is also a hanging valley, and the torrent which emerges rushes down the slope into Llyn Ogwen, carrying with it an abundance of débris which is building a wide delta some way along that lake, and which may ultimately cut it into two.

Northwards from Snowdon, along a belt which runs through Llanberis to near Bethesda, is the most important slate-quarrying region in Britain, where the best slates in the world have long been obtained. The more accessible parts are thus scarred by great purple-grey quarries, and disfigured by heaps of refuse from the workings. Slate is used in this belt for many purposes for which stone (or even wood) is employed elsewhere. The area is otherwise attractive, lacking the rugged aspect of the volcanic tract, and more often wooded in the lower parts. These slates are older than the rocks of the volcanic series, belonging to the Cambrian, and derive their characters from the intense pressures to which they have been subjected.

The great expanse of mountain country which lies to the
east of Nant Ffrancon, and extends thence to the Conway
valley is much less accessible, for this area of some eight
miles by ten miles is cut by no important valley and for
that reason is crossed by no road. Owing to their remote-
ness its mountains (including the little-known Carnedd
Llewelyn, less than eighty feet lower than Snowdon) and its
lakes may perhaps be left with no more than this passing
mention. But this mountain tract is better known near the

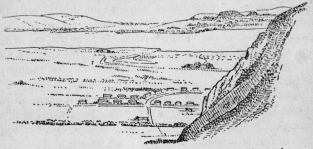

Figure 58.—The Conway Estuary from Conway Mountain.
In the distance irregular hills of volcanic rocks above Deganwy are
seen on right, the limestone of the Great Orme on left.

coast, where, although it is little over 1000 feet high, it rises
sharply above the sea at Llanfairfechan, Penmaenmawr and
Conway. Here the volcanic rocks produce craggy hills of
considerable beauty; owing to their small elevation they
have a richer vegetation than the rocky heights of Snowdonia, and the brilliant colours of Conway Mountain in late
summer, the deep purple heather mingled with golden yellow
gorse, are not to be surpassed in any upland area.

From the precipitous northern slope of this ridge across
the sands and marshes of the estuary of the Conway river
there is a delightful view of Deganwy and Great Ormes
Head (Fig. 58). The steep and irregularly broken hills
above Deganwy coincide with outcrops of volcanic rocks

similar to those of Conway Mountain, but the Great Orme is made up of Mountain Limestone which in its light grey cliffs and crags makes a striking contrast with the scenery of the older rocks.

To the east of the Conway valley rise the Denbigh Moors, another great expanse of little-known mountain country built up by rocks newer than the volcanic group, roughly corresponding to the Upper Slates of the Lake District : most important among these rocks is the Denbigh Grit which determines much of the character of the moors. Seen from a distance, they appear smooth-topped and monotonous, differing greatly from the more irregular craggy country of the volcanic tract. But the plateau of the Denbigh Moors is deeply dissected by many streams and in detail much of the area is extremely attractive, though it is much less known than most parts of North Wales.

Away to the east the Clwydian Hills really form an extension of the Denbigh Moors, for they have many similar features. But separating these two areas is another long tract of fertile lowland, much of it underlain by New Red Sandstone which imparts its own characteristics to this strip of country. Along it flows the river Clwyd, and several old towns, Ruthin, Denbigh, St. Asaph and Rhuddlan are spaced throughout its length, with Rhyl almost an anticlimax at the coastal end. This green valley is a piece of the Midland plain which literally has been dropped amidst the Welsh uplands : it is bounded by faults, and is a miniature rift valley. The eastern boundary is especially sharp, a true fault scarp.

ANGLESEY

But this brings us into the borders of Wales, and it is necessary to turn back into the west, to make some reference to Anglesey, the lowest county in North Wales. For Anglesey is a low plateau, and most of its surface reaches to less than 400 feet above sea-level. Broad flat-topped ridges rise to this height, and separating them are shallow valleys

cut by streams which flow in directions parallel to the line
of the Menai Strait. Here and there small areas rise above
the general level of between 200 and 400 feet: these
isolated hills are bare and rugged, the highest, Holyhead
Mountain, reaching over 700 feet, but the remainder are
nearer 550 feet. They stand out as monadnocks above the
lower plateau, not because of any special hardness, for
these projecting hills vary as much in structure as does the
rest of Anglesey. They are relics of higher levels left standing by denudation.

The almost uniformly low level of the Anglesey surface
is the more remarkable when it is remembered that the
island is made up very largely of extremely hard old rocks
(some of the oldest yet encountered in this survey of England and Wales); great areas of Anglesey are made of Pre-
Cambrian rocks, often much contorted by pressure and
altered by heat; these metamorphic rocks include gneisses
and schists which may be paralleled in the Scottish High-
lands. Besides these, granites, slates and limestones are
also present, the whole showing great complexity of structure. It is apparent that the relief has little relation to the
distribution of the rocks or to the structure, save that the
rivers have tended to etch out the weaker belts, which trend,
as do all the more important features in North Wales, from
north-east to south-west, the direction of the folds in these
highly disturbed rocks. The wide level tract of Anglesey is
thought to result from a time when the land stood some 400
feet or more lower than at present, and it is generally believed that the surface represents a platform cut by the
waves during a period when the sea advanced over this
whole area by cliff attack and the destruction of the land
above sea-level. The waves have thus reduced all the area
to one level, cutting across hard and soft rocks alike and
truncating their structures. Possibly the rather higher levels
present in Anglesey mark somewhat earlier stages when the
land stood still lower, the higher platforms having in this

case been almost obliterated by the fresh wave advance. Looking across the Menai Strait from the island it is at once apparent that the plateau levels of a few hundred feet above the sea persist into the coastal parts of Carnarvonshire, for in a strip several miles wide the mainland is more closely comparable with the island than with the rest of the county. Above this level coastal area, behind Bangor and Carnarvon, the mountains of Snowdonia rise suddenly in a line of ancient cliffs which formed the shore-line when Anglesey was planed down.

Over the Anglesey surface the great variety of rock type (from Pre-Cambrian to Carboniferous) is partly obscured by glacial deposits, and its smoothing clearly preceded the Ice Age. Across much of the island, ice moved from north-east to south-west in its passage down the Irish Sea, though the Menai Strait was crossed by ice pushing outwards from the North Wales mountains. But although ice of great thickness crossed this land, its regular relief precluded much active erosion, and the broader surface features were not greatly altered, though the valleys were no doubt deepened and straightened. The main direction of ice movement shows itself, however, in the arrangement of the low whale-back hills of boulder clay, of which great numbers are present in the valleys. Most of the area is under cultivation, but there is much moorland, and in some parts the bare rugged hills, stone walls and houses, and dwarfed wind-bent trees recall the features of bleak uplands rather than of a low-lying coastal region. There are many small lakes, some true rock basins, like the Bodafon tarns, others held up by glacial dams, and one, Parciau, formed by the solution of an area of Mountain Limestone. Holyhead, now the largest town, on the bleak Holy Island, is on the old rocks of the extreme west, but Beaumaris, the old county town, has a more sheltered though less impressive situation by the strait.

The Menai Strait calls for some attention. A channel some fifteen miles long, it is bordered by low cliffs and by

woods for much of its length, and looks much like an enlarged river valley. It is probable that it represents a somewhat larger valley than those which run parallel to it on the
island, drowned in the Neolithic submergence, as were so
many English valleys. It is not a straight channel, and Dr.
E. Greenly has suggested that the two ends represent separate
valleys deepened by ice and connected by a middle section
which is an overflow channel from a glacier-dammed lake.
But the details of this explanation need not be pursued here;
the essential factors to emphasise are the uplifting of the
wave-cut platform which constitutes Anglesey, not long
before the Ice Age, and after that the drowning of the valleys
which became the strait.

With this incomplete description we must leave Anglesey,
and only a hint can be given of its attractive coast-line, the
sandy bays and warrens, some backed by wide marshes, and
the varied colours of the cliffs. The scenery of the mainland
must be traced further south, and with only a passing reference to the extension southwards from Snowdon of the outcrop of the volcanic rocks through the rugged mountains of
the Arenigs and the Arans, it is proposed next to turn to the
consideration of the district near Dolgelly and Barmouth.

THE COUNTRY AROUND CADER IDRIS

The dominant mountain here is Cader Idris, which rises
splendidly from the Barmouth Estuary in a great line of
foothills surmounted by almost unclimbable precipices
which face northwards towards Snowdon (Fig. 59). Looking
from the crest of this cliff, the irregular country which
stretches down to the estuary at Barmouth, wooded in its
lower part, presents quite different features from that which
stretches away to the north, rising into the Rhinog Mountains some eight miles away. To the right, Rhobell Fawr
introduces yet another area of volcanic scenery.

Cader Idris itself is a mountain of volcanic rocks, comparable with those of Snowdon, the massive beds of lava

being here augmented by great thicknesses of other igneous rocks which were similarly forced up in molten state but solidified beneath the surface. Cader stands out because of the strength of these igneous rocks, which dip steeply to the south; it is really a great escarpment, trending with the run of the beds more or less east and west, and with its scarp facing to the north.

Once the volcanic group extended continuously north-wards over the Rhinog Mountains to Snowdon, joining the great circle of craggy scarps which may be traced thence to

Figure 59.—The scarp face of Cader Idris.

Blaenau Ffestiniog and Dolgelly (Fig. 60). Arched up into a dome, the central area has been worn away, exposing in the centre between Harlech and Barmouth a thick series of grits and slates of Cambrian age. In this domed area the grits occupy the high ground, the massive beds giving rise to great steps on the desolate and almost uninhabited up-lands; the slates produce softer scenery in a greener and more fertile belt which forms an almost complete ring around the Rhinog Mountains. Here denudation of the arched-up rocks has produced surface features in some ways comparable with those of the Weald, for although the rocks are much older and often harder, the hills much higher and the whole area more barren, the general structural relations are quite similar.

But closer at hand, the view from the crest of Cader Idris embraces the great ice-worn cwms beneath the summit. The steepness of the precipices which form the northern face of the mountain is due to the cliffs which back the cwms, whose basins, aided by moraine dams across their mouths, hold such lakes as Llyn y Gader and Llyn Cau. These great basin-like hollows on Cader Idris have often been likened to craters, especially by those who, knowing that the mountain is largely formed of volcanic material, have expected to find in it some shape resembling a volcano. Perhaps it is unnecessary to repeat here that Cader Idris is

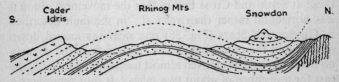

Figure 60.—Section showing the arrangement of the rocks from Cader Idris to near Llanberis.

V.V., Volcanic rocks of the Ordovician ; vertical shading Pre-Cambrian.

now a mountain simply on account of the hardness of its materials, and that its present form has no relation to any volcano from which its materials were originally derived. It is in fact an escarpment, with a scarp face to the north, differing only from the scarps of the Cotswolds and Pennines in having igneous rocks as its stronger beds. The main features of its relief were carved out long after the formation of its lavas and intrusions, and the basins on its scarp, the result of the Ice Age, are almost a thing of yesterday.

The southern side of the mountain lacks these craggy cliffs, both because the conditions were more favourable to cwm-formation on the shady side, and also because the volcanic rocks are succeeded by softer slates, mudstones and sandstones which form the steep dip slope down into the Talyllyn valley. Southwards almost as far as can be seen from Cader extends the great plateau made of these rocks, belonging to the upper part of the Ordovician and to the Silurian, a rather monotonous expanse of even-topped hills when contrasted with the irregular and ragged summits of the volcanic tracts.

The main features of the Talyllyn valley will readily be recognised as due to glaciation, for it is a U-shaped valley holding a lake with alluvial flats at the head. The course of this valley has been largely determined, however, by the existence of a belt of shattered rocks coinciding with the line of a great fault, whose movements had led to the crushing of the rocks on either side. It differs from such faults as those at Settle and Cross Fell in that the movement along it was horizontal rather than vertical; in the fault described in Giggleswick Scars (Fig. 38) one side was moved down relatively to the other, but in the Talyllyn fault the country on the south side has moved almost horizontally towards the east for a distance of about two miles. It thus represents a great wrench or tearing of the rocks, and the faulting is accompanied by considerable shattering along its course. Along this belt, therefore, stream erosion proceeded with unusual rapidity and the rivers which developed in it cut down their beds so rapidly that they captured the earlier drainage. To the east the same shatter belt is responsible for the trough in which Bala Lake is situated.

Accordingly the tributary streams in these areas are energetic and immature, for the main valleys have been deepened rapidly owing to the elevation of the land when the Anglesey peneplain was raised, and owing to their weak situations and to the erosive work done by the ice; many tributaries thus hang above the larger valleys, and just before they join the main streams they often occupy narrow and deep gorges of great beauty cut into their older and wider high-level valleys. The Clwydog, as seen from the Torrent Walk near Dolgelly, is an admirable example of these rejuvenated streams, with a wooded gorge incised in the flat floor of the old valley which provides a strip of cultivated land above the tumbling stream and beneath the barren crags. Higher upstream, the gorge diminishes and the wide valley is of simpler type, for the rejuvenation has not yet affected areas far from the overdeepened main valleys. Such features, however, have already been discussed in relation to the comparable examples in the Lake District, where many of the waterfalls and the most fascinating gorges owe their origin to similar causes. North Wales thus presents similar contrasts of bare rocky uplands, often dull in colour, and picturesque wooded gorges, with rare expanses of flatter and more fertile lowland.

Figure 61.—Llanberis Pass.

CHAPTER XVI

CENTRAL WALES

SEEN from the crest of Cader Idris, Central Wales appears as a monotonous plateau rising to nearly 2000 feet above sea-level, stretching through Cardiganshire to north Pembrokeshire and to Radnorshire. Lacking craggy mountains like those of the volcanic tracts, its hills are generally smooth in aspect, reaching so nearly to one level that from any high viewpoint the upland surface presents a surprisingly even aspect. There are few crags and in many wide areas on the plateau there are few places showing bare rock; over vast stretches the uniformity of relief and colouring is remarkable. Few habitations are found on these higher regions, and in many parts walls are only found occasionally, apart from the wall which usually limits the upland pastures.

Plynlimon is the highest mountain in this tract, and from its summit most of the essential features of the landscape can be seen. In fact, it is probably the best viewpoint in Wales. The ascent, for it can hardly be called a climb, is most easily made from the Aberystwyth-Rhayader road, where it crosses the watershed between the tributaries of the Rheidol and the Wye. Here a grey upland farm is situated in a wide open valley which is almost devoid of trees, its sides covered by vegetation of that dull olive green which characterises so much of this country. Where the little torrents have cut shallow rocky gorges, bright clumps of gorse and heather add richness to the colouring, but for much of the way to the summit the path leads over poor pasture with patches of bog. As the track rises and the view expands, there comes a point when, a few hundred feet from the summit, the whole expanse of the plateau becomes visible for miles to the south and east; the flat-topped hills, reaching a common level at which we are standing, seem to form a vast plain out of which Plynlimon slightly raises its head.

But while Plynlimon may thus be one of the easiest mountains in Wales to ascend, its northern face has none of the gentleness of the other slopes, for beneath the summit a little lake lies in the shelter of a deep cwm, from which rise steep grey cliffs. Here, as is so frequently the case, ice erosion has led to the production of precipices in otherwise subdued country, and these effects are most pronounced on the north-facing slopes.

On a clear day the view from the summit of Plynlimon embraces parts of nearly every county in Wales, and of the Welsh borders. The level plateau stretches northwards to the shoulders of Cader Idris and Aran Mawddwy; these mountains and the higher peaks of Snowdonia rise from it like ragged hills upon a plain. Turning to the south, the plateau gradually declines in height, but the Prescelly Hills rise abruptly from it just as do the North Wales mountains, while further east the crest of the Brecon Beacons is likewise raised above the platform sufficiently to prevent any glimpse of Glamorgan. Near at hand, the level falls quite rapidly to the west, and along the shores of Cardigan Bay, visible from end to end, extends a plateau at a lower level, traversed by the narrow valleys of rivers which flow into the bay, and much of it covered with a multi-coloured patchwork of fields.

There are in fact two main plateau levels in this region, which Professor O. T. Jones has named respectively the high plateau and the coastal plateau. The main features of the high plateau have already been described; the coastal plateau is several miles in width, and from the Dyfi (Dovey) estuary southwards it forms a characteristic feature, reaching about 400 or 600 feet near the coast, and rising inland to about 900 feet. Where it meets the high plateau it often rises in a rather sharp curve, and the surfaces are readily

H

distinguished. It is at once apparent that these two areas have had different histories, and it may be useful to indicate what is known about the origin of each before going further with the description of the region. In the first place, however, it must be emphasised that the rocks which build the high plateau are identical in all respects with those of the coastal region; they consist of slates, mudstones and sandstones of many types but frequently of a grey colour. All of these rocks have been subjected to folding and faulting, and the whole area is of great complexity. It is clear, therefore, that the plateau surfaces do not reflect the geological structure, but have been cut across harder and softer beds alike. They are therefore surfaces produced by denudation, and it is in the history of their erosion that their origins must be sought.

The high plateau was regarded by Ramsay, who long since described its chief characters, as the result of wave action at a time when the area stood some 2000 feet lower in relation to the sea. Although most writers have accepted the view that this land was planed down when it stood near sea-level, attributing its uplift to a later date, there has lately been a tendency to regard the levelling rather as the work of meandering rivers and their tributaries. Generally speaking, the older geologists were more ready to attribute features to marine erosion, but recent work, particularly that associated with the late W. M. Davies, has led to the recognition of the adequacy of rivers and weathering agents to produce peneplains if sea-level remains nearly constant for sufficiently long periods. There is thus room for some difference of opinion regarding the origin of the high plateau; at many times, while the Jurassic and Cretaceous rocks were being laid down in England, this area may well have been situated at no great distance above sea-level, and rivers almost certainly played some part in its planation, while any temporary extension of the sea may have carried it over at least some of the district. Both agencies may thus have been concerned in smoothing out the outlines of this tract, but there is as yet little evidence on which their relative importance can be gauged.

Some geologists have held that the Chalk sea extended over the greater part of Wales, and have seen in its advance the principal cause of the levelling of the high plateau; they couple with this belief the view that Chalk was also deposited (unconformably) over the whole area, and that the south-easterly direction of many of the rivers resulted from their initiation as consequent streams on a surface of Chalk raised from beneath the sea and gently inclined in that direction: the rivers having removed the Chalk cover have become superimposed on the complex structures beneath, in a manner similar to that discussed in regard to the Lake District rivers (although there was no striking radial arrangement in Wales). The superimposed character of the drainage is widely accepted but the former occurrence of the Chalk is disputed, and it may be that the peneplain of the high plateau is older, or, on the other hand, much more recent, than the Chalk.

The coastal plateau was probably cut at a later date. Professor Jones believes that it was planed down by a west-flowing system of streams which reduced it to a height not far above the sea-level then existing. Subsequent uplift has led to the rejuvenation of the rivers and they have thus incised deeper valleys in the surface of the low plateau. In this tract also there are thus large expanses of fairly level upland, but whereas many valleys of the high plateau are wide and mature, the coastal plateau is crossed by narrow valleys which are often picturesquely wooded; where the valleys have wider floors, as in the case of the Rheidol above Aberystwyth, they are occupied by cultivated land, but cultivation is generally confined to the plateau surface. Here the farms have both arable and pasture land, and there is a surprising amount of corn grown, especially oats in many places; above 600 feet, on the other hand, the proportion of pasture is greater, for the growing season is much shorter. It is only in some of the highest farms of the high plateau, however, that the pasturing of sheep is the sole occupation. Formerly these farms were used mainly for summer pasturage of stock from the lower levels, and there is still a considerable transference of sheep for summer grazing.

Within the area of the high plateau there are few villages and such as occur are placed in the valleys : above these there are only scattered farms, and great tracts are almost uninhabited. Between the valley of the Teifi, with its little market towns, Tregaron, Lampeter and Llandyssul, and that of the Towy, with Llandovery and Llandilo, is one of the biggest tracts of bleak upland in southern Britain. About twelve miles across and twenty in length, it is almost everywhere above 1000 feet high, merging northwards into the Plynlimon plateau. Much of its drainage goes southwards into the Towy or to the Wye system. Professor T. Neville George has shown that the Towy drainage has gained recently at the expense of the Wye and other south-east flowing streams. In the higher parts the valleys are wide and of mature aspect, with gentle slopes passing gradually into the plateau surface, but as the streams approach the borders of the upland, their valleys steepen into gorges. In the case of the Towy itself this change occurs near Rhandirmwyn. The uplift which caused the rejuvenation of these streams has only enabled them yet to deepen their valleys in the lower reaches ; it may be expected that in time the gorges will be cut back into the higher upland, but the uplift is too recent in date for this to have occurred so far above the sea.

Within the uplands, apart from the few rough tracks climbing sharply up from the valleys, there are no roads, and scarcely any habitations. There are in fact few more desolate areas in Wales. To many, these higher uplands may seem monotonous, and they are not likely to attract any except those who appreciate clean air and open moorland.

The towns of this region, so closely related to the main valleys, are not usually so attractive as the small market towns of England; when seen from a distance, however, they often fit very appropriately into their background, for the use of local stone ensures a suitable if dark colouring. The stone is usually in large blocks, with little ornament, but the mortar is sometimes picked out in white with rather a startling effect. Many cottages, however, are regularly washed over with white or a very attractive pink, and grouped picturesquely on the hillsides they are then bright and conspicuous. Some cottages are thatched, while others have heavy slates, but it is regrettable to find that even so near the home of slates the use of galvanised roofing is spreading into many villages.

Only rarely do churches add to the beauty of villages, for the parishes are large and the churches few. More frequent are the bare rectangular chapels, so characteristic of most of Wales, and often less beautiful than many a Cotswold barn.

Stone walls are found in some areas, but in many places, especially on the coastal plateau, the lanes are lined by rough walls of vertically piled slates, above which rise high grassy banks, often bright with flowers: in late summer great masses of yellow ragwort dominate the colour of the landscape. Generally, however, the high plateau lacks these striking colourings.

Where the high plateau meets the coastal plateau the rivers are often incised in deep gorges of great charm. None is more famous, or more deserving of fame, than the glorious valley at Devil's Bridge. Near here the Rheidol, leaving the wide and mature valley which it follows from its source in the cwm-lake under Plynlimon, plunges into a narrow rocky gorge and takes a sharp turn to the west. Here in fact are two valleys, belonging to two different rivers, for the upper

part of the Rheidol was formerly a south-flowing stream of
the high plateau which has been captured by the rapid head-
ward erosion of a powerful stream with a steep gradient
occupying a deep valley on the coastal plateau.   The fine
chasm, with " woods climbing above woods ", seen from
the front of the hotel at Devil's Bridge, has been cut down
several hundred feet lower than the wide old valley on the
floor of which runs the road to Pont Erwyd.   Into this deep

Figure 62.—River Teifi, Cenarth, Cardigan.

gorge the little river Mynach also crashes in the magnificent
series of falls at Devil's Bridge, the narrow cleft through
which this river flows and the pot-holed bed being typical of
the work of an energetic stream.

The Teifi valley also has many attractive features.   Near
the great bog of Tregaron it has the width and gentle slopes
of a mature valley, but it narrows before reaching Llandyssul,
and thence to the sea its course is through a deep and
picturesque valley, often with steep wooded slopes by
Henllan and Newcastle Emlyn.   At Cenarth, above the
narrow grey bridge, is a small but attractive fall (Fig. 62),

and the river is actively deepening its valley with an energy which is surprising when it is remembered that this place is little more than ten miles from the sea. Still lower, where Cilgerran Castle stands on its rocky cliff, the wooded gorge is even more striking, while at Cardigan, where the river is tidal, and where the castle stands above another old bridge, the valley is deeply incised in the coastal plateau, and the village of St. Dogmell's scrambles up the steep slopes.

The smaller valleys crossing the coastal plateau are just as picturesque. Many of them are so narrow that they hold

Figure 63.—Stack on the coast at Llangranog, Cardiganshire.

no road save where old villages are situated on the coast at their mouths or a mile or more inland : the bright colour-washed houses of Moylgrove, hanging on a steep valley-side west of Cardigan, and Aberporth and Llangranog on their little bays, are typical of the gems of this coast. The main road between Cardigan and Aberayron keeps some way from the coast along the more level plateau top, avoiding the sharp gradients of the narrow valleys in which the roads are often unpleasantly steep. Most of the coast can only be seen on foot ; it has few great cliffs, and it appears as if a smoothly moulded green country has been chipped by the waves along its edge, revealing the rocks which build this region in all their variety of colour and form (Fig. 64).

At Aberporth are cliffs of silver-grey slate, while at Llan-granog dark and highly disturbed shales stand out in stacks of grotesque form (Fig. 63).

Leaving the coast for the eastern part of Central Wales, we may turn to the green and fertile vale of the Towy, with its flat alluvial meadows through which the river meanders from Llandilo to Carmarthen. Here is a tract quite unlike that of any other part of the region described, a wide plain extending far inland, whose accessibility and richness are marked by a line of finely placed castles.

This same structural line extends still farther to the north-east, through Llanwrtyd and Builth to Llandrindod, where anticlinal folding has brought to the surface volcanic rocks belonging to the same Ordovician group as those which build Cader Idris and Snowdon. The reappearance of these rocks, deeply buried under the Central Wales plateau, introduces into this tract something of the variety and raggedness of hill outline found in North Wales, features which add not a little to the attractiveness of the ' Wells ' country.

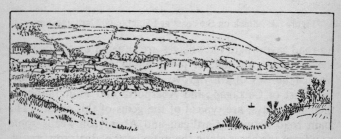

Figure 64.—Aberporth, Cardiganshire, showing the smooth surface of the coastal plateau.

CHAPTER XVII

SOUTH WALES

SOUTH Wales is usually entered along the low coastal tract near the Bristol Channel from Newport to Cardiff, but we need not linger in this region. Cardiff is in many ways a bright and even beautiful city, but its immediate surroundings link it rather with England than with Wales. Its commercial foundations are of course laid in Wales, but we are not directly concerned with these; the city itself is only a short way over the border. It stands where three rivers from the hills enter the Channel, the Ely, the Taff and the Rhymney, two of which meander amazingly through the low estuarine flats of soft grey mud. The earliest settlement, on a river terrace above these flood plains, marked the crossing of the Taff by the most important route into South Wales, on a site used successively by Romans and Normans. But the city now extends in several directions on to higher ground. Eastwards it spreads up the slopes of Penylan, where a small patch of Silurian limestones and mudstones stands out above the surrounding plain.

From this viewpoint the scenic features of the region can be picked out. Away to the north rises a series of hills marking the borders of the coalfield, backed by bare uplands of over 1000 feet in height; in that direction the mountain scenery is typically Welsh. Nearer to Cardiff, however, and extending westwards almost to the shores of Swansea Bay, is an area which more nearly resembles the English Midlands, an undulating tract of great fertility recognised long ago as one of the richest agricultural regions in Wales.

THE VALE OF GLAMORGAN

This fertile coastal tract is called the Vale of Glamorgan, but it is not a valley in any sense, for several small rivers drain its different parts. Varying in height up to just over 400 feet, it has wide areas at 200 feet or thereabouts and may be regarded as a low plateau, its surface having been cut, possibly by the sea, at the same time as the plateau of Anglesey, when the whole of Wales must have stood at a lower level. Whatever its origin, this coastal tract ends abruptly at the shore-line in cliffs which are nearly always vertical. The land is obviously being attacked continuously and with success, for the weather scarcely manages to reduce the sharpness of the cliff-top before another fall produces a new steep face.

The cliffs along this portion of the coast, from Penarth to Porthcawl, are never much above 100 feet high, but they can rarely be climbed, and for miles at a time they present a continuous front to the sea, broken only where little valleys have cut V-shaped notches in the cliff face (Fig. 65). In front of the cliffs is an extensive platform cut in the rocks by the waves, in places heaped up with débris of boulders from the destruction of the cliffs, elsewhere swept bare by every tide. It is from this tract beneath the cliffs that the beauty and interest of this coast can best be appreciated.

Penarth Head shows at once the rocks which determine the character of the area ; beds nearly horizontal succeed one another regularly up the face of the cliff in striking bands of colour, red marls with tinges of green, pale green marls, black shales and blue and yellow limestones. The sequence is exactly that which underlies the Vale of Gloucester, red marls of the New Red Sandstone followed by the limestones and clays of the Blue Lias. Southwards from Penarth to Lavernock the red and green marls form much of the cliffs and foreshore, but gentle undulations of the beds form a wide syncline and bring blue limestones down to sea-level, the harder beds making small but distinct headlands at either end. Although red rocks once more form the cliffs beyond St. Mary's Well Bay, the greater part of the coast of the Vale is occupied by Lias limestones, the regular thin beds being cut by vertical joints and often gently inclined so that stronger and weaker groups alternately form cliffs of differing resistance (Fig. 65).

In its cliff features this attractive coast-line is strongly reminiscent of Whitby, where similar rocks occur, but it differs greatly in the villages. There are few villages actually near the sea, and most are quite invisible from the shore. The grouping of cottages along the sides of every bay, so typical of the Yorkshire coast, is lacking in Glamorgan, for although this area is quite heavily populated when compared

Figure 65.—Cliffs in horizontal Lias limestones at Monknash, Vale of Glamorgan.

with much of rural Wales, the inhabitants of the villages depend on agriculture more than on the sea. The villages are often in the valleys a short way inland, and are spaced at intervals of only a mile or so, indicating that the area was well peopled from an early date. The remarkable early history of Llantwit Major, the ' University ' of ancient Wales, illustrates the degree of settlement before Norman times : castles too are numerous, for the richness of the land was appreciated by the Normans, and its conquest was completed before the end of the eleventh century. Many of the villages are pretty in a simple fashion, the cottages often built of the grey-blue Lias limestone, sometimes washed with colour, and dominated by small grey churches with tall square towers.

This unspoiled green ' Vale ' is the more remarkable since it is in such close contact with the densely populated industrial regions along its northern borders. For apart from the growth of Bridgend, where the coalfield valley of the Ogmore comes out to the coastal plateau, and of Porthcawl, a modern resort by the sea, the greater part of the Vale has remained essentially unaffected by the changes of the Industrial Revolution. Cowbridge, for long its principal town, avoided the influence of the main railway line, which was deflected some miles to the north, and remained a quiet country town until the return of road transport led to rapid and unpleasant changes in its main street. But away from the great road to the west, most of the Vale is still quiet and undisturbed. The country around Barry is the most important exception, for here a hamlet became a large town almost in a year, following the construction of docks when the coal export trade was developing most rapidly. Probably no town in Britain grew up more quickly, from a population of about 100 at the census of 1881 to 13,000 in 1891.

The coast at Barry shows some striking differences when compared with that of most of the Vale, for pointing to the south are three rocky headlands quite different in aspect from the red marl cliffs of Penarth or the regular Lias cliffs of Rhoose and the area to the west. Built of thick and steeply dipping beds of massive grey limestone, belonging to the group of the Mountain Limestone, these rough low cliffs are capped in several places by the basal members of the New Red Sandstone, nearly horizontal red rocks thus resting unconformably on the terraced surface cut in the steeply inclined limestones. In short, at Barry the base of the rock series which floors most of the Vale of Glamorgan (that is the New Red Sandstone and Lias) is seen above sealevel, exposing the older and more disturbed rocks beneath. Similar conditions recur near Southerndown ; from Nash

Point to Dunraven the cliffs consist of regular Lias beds except that Witches Point is a ragged headland formed mainly of Mountain Limestone, which reappears along the foreshore beneath Sutton and in the low cliffs at Porthcawl. Inland the irregular surface of the older rocks is still higher in places and the newer beds have been removed so as to expose tracts of Mountain Limestone which determines the character of small but characteristic limestone regions in the Vale, such as that between St. Bride's Major and Ogmore. Formerly the newer rocks had a still wider extent, and some of them may have stretched far to the west and north, but from most areas they have been removed by denudation. Almost the whole of the rest of South Wales is thus built up of older rocks.

THE COALFIELD BORDERS

These areas may best be approached by going northwards from Cardiff, traversing first the wide tract of undulating country around Llanishen and Lisvane, which is made up by a group of red marls similar in aspect to those of the New Red Sandstone but belonging to a much older series, underlying the Carboniferous rocks and known as the Old Red Sandstone. Above Rhiwbina the ground rises to an escarpment which in turn is succeeded by a dip slope, and then by two other escarpments. These features are narrow, with steep dip slopes, a result of the high dip, and they trend approximately east and west. They give rise to a pleasantly varied tract of country, wooded on some of the higher ground and on many steeper slopes, with narrow strips of more fertile country excavated along the softer beds. The nature of the ridges and their formation by an alternation of hard and soft rocks are indicated on the accompanying diagram (Fig. 66).

The first ridge, which extends to the heights on which Ruperra Castle stands, is made up of tough conglomerates, with white quartz pebbles set in a red matrix, the uppermost part of the Old Red Sandstone. The second ridge, familiar in Cefn On and extending to the hill above Castell Coch and the beautiful Garth Wood or Little Garth, results from the Mountain Limestone, which gives rise to characteristic grey crags ; the depression beyond corresponds to the outcrop of shales, the lower part equivalent to the Millstone Grit of other areas, the upper part being the lower portion of the Coal Measures. North of this again is a scarp which rises above Taffs Well into Garth Hill and Mynydd Rudry,

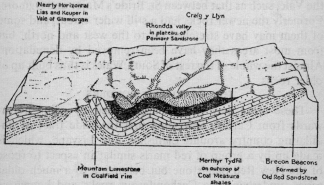

Figure 66.—Diagram of eastern part of South Wales coalfield, looking west.

*Old Red Sandstone, broken lines ; Carboniferous Limestone, blocks ;
Millstone Grit, large dots ; lower part of Coal Measures (mainly shales),
black ; Pennant Sandstone and upper part of Coal Measures, dotted ;
Keuper Marl, blank ; Lias, horizontal lines.*

the dark barren summits of which, covered by coarse grass and bracken, form an impressive contrast to the wooded ridges further south : these higher hills, situated just within the coalfield border, are very reminiscent of the grit moorlands of the southern Pennines. They are built by a group of dull grey-green sandstones, the Pennant Sandstones, which outcrop over a great part of the surface of the South Wales coalfield and are responsible for most of its more distinctive characters (Fig. 66).

These successive ridges of the coalfield border are

breached by the rivers which flow across them. The Taff, for example, has cut fine gorges at Taffs Well and Tongwynlais where it crosses the harder beds, but the valley changes in width as it passes from harder to softer beds. In cutting for itself this exit from the coalfield the river has lowered its bed, but has been unable to widen its valley where the rocks are hard, although where the rocks are less resistant the valley has been greatly enlarged, often with the aid of short tributary streams. So in parts of the valley there is scarcely room for the railways, canal and road, while elsewhere the alluvial plain spreads considerably and villages find more extensive sites.

To the west, these border ridges are generally less distinct, but eastwards around the coalfield rim to Pontypool they are very conspicuous, and where they are cut through by the rivers, the Rhymney at Machen and the Ebbw at Risca, the conditions already described in the case of the Taff gorge are reproduced.

THE COALFIELD

The main part of the coalfield, however, is quite different from these sharp border ridges. Wherever the Pennant Sandstone forms the surface the tract is high and barren, the smaller areas occupied by the shales which occur below (and in a few places above) the sandstone leading to rather more fertile and generally lower areas. Thus Caerphilly is situated in a wide basin of coal-bearing shales, where the Rhymney escapes from the confinement of the hills and almost loses its way to the sea, while all around the smooth bare dip slopes, marked here and there by great black tips, rise to the Pennant uplands. This fertile tract, though within the coalfield, is rather of the lowlands than of the uplands, and hence it was selected as a site for a great castle comparable with those near the lowland borders, for Norman influence penetrated but slowly into the upland plateau regions. This splendid ruin, built of the green-grey stone from the Pennant rocks, is almost in the straggling main street, with its old and rather picturesque stone-built houses. Caerphilly was one of the earliest towns to grow up within the coalfield, and it developed rapidly in the early days of the coal trade when the shallow seams were mined extensively. These were of limited extent and were rapidly exhausted, and as the more important seams of the coalfield here occur at great depths, industrial development has been almost arrested in this area.

Most of the coalfield area of Monmouthshire and east Glamorgan is occupied by high plateau, rising from about 1000 feet on the southern border to just under 2000 feet in Craig y Llyn near the head of the Rhondda valleys (Fig. 66). This tract is one of the most populous areas in Britain owing to the great development of coal mining, more particularly in the last hundred years, but the high uplands show little evidence of such a change, for the new towns are confined to the valleys and the open moorlands remain bleak and almost uninhabited. The scattered hamlets and shepherds' huts, connected by ancient trackways across the hills, date back to times before the Industrial Revolution, when the valleys were densely wooded and often marshy and impassable. Here and there on this almost level upland are old village churches, few in number because the old parishes in this sparsely peopled area were of great size ; nowadays many of these churches stand on the lonely uplands right above the crowded industrial valleys. These hill-tops are often remarkably flat, for the valleys are deep narrow trenches cut into the plateau surface, and from many points the sky-line appears to be level and scarcely broken, the towns of the valleys being quite invisible. The plateau surface is probably continuous with that of Central Wales, and represents a peneplain formed at the same time, but as in the case of that region, the exact mode and date of origin are open to some doubt.

The valleys which are cut deeply across this plateau are

more familiar than the upland itself, for the excessive ugliness of these industrial towns made them notorious in a generation which learned something of town planning, while their still more pitiable condition during the depression of later years has attracted even more sympathetic attention. These valleys which drain into the sea at Cardiff and Newport extend far into the hill region, sometimes commencing beyond the northern boundary of the coalfield; the Rhonddas, the Cynon, the Taff, the Rhymney, the Sirhowy and the Ebbw all follow nearly parallel courses from the north-north-east, flowing swiftly along their steep beds to the sea. The simplicity of this arrangement of the rivers is at once suggestive of a series of consequent streams. But the rivers are not following the dip of simple beds, and if their courses were determined by such conditions, it is clear that the gently dipping beds have all been removed and the rivers superimposed on older rocks of more complex structure. Thus the rivers now cross various structures on their way to the sea, sometimes flowing with the dip, sometimes against it. The presence of newer beds covering these older structures in the Vale of Glamorgan is notable in this connection, and many suppose that other newer rocks formerly stretched over the coalfield and formed the surface on which the simple river system was first developed.

These coalfield valleys often have steep sides, rising sharply from a narrow strip of more level ground, where river and railway (and in some cases, canal) can barely find space; the main road winding along the valley is flanked by almost continuous works or shops, one town or village joining with the next, each having no centre, no beginning and no end. And on the lower slopes of the hills are dismal terraces of dull grey houses, built of the Pennant Sandstone which forms so much of the landscape, and rises in the barren bracken-covered hillsides to bare brown crags. But from the towns these open moorlands seem forbidding, adding to the sense of gloom and isolation.

The Rhondda valleys are bottle-necks starting among the highest hills of the coalfield, and for long there was no route out to the north, but lately magnificent roads have been made from one valley to another, and those linking the Rhondda with Hirwaun and Cymmer afford wonderful views of the plateau. The more easterly valleys, however, open out before they reach the plateau, for the shales of the lower part of the Coal Measures have there been worn more quickly than the Pennant Sandstone which hems in

Figure 67.—Cwmavon. A coalfield valley.

the valleys just below. Here the readily accessible coal and ironstones led to early developments, and the bigger and rather older towns which form a chain along this belt, Brynmawr, Merthyr Tydfil and Aberdare, have grown on more spacious sites than those of the narrower valleys (Fig. 66), but the more quickly exhausted mineral wealth has left some of them even more desolate.

South of this subdued belt the Pennant Sandstone rises in a steep scarp, most prominent in the west, where Craig y Llyn towers in dark and nearly vertical cliffs above two cwm lakes. From the crest of this ridge the view to the north embraces a series of ridges corresponding with those which form the coalfield borders on the south; here, however, the dip of the rocks is to the south and is more gentle, the rocks forming wider outcrops and higher scarps. That of the conglomerates at the top of the Old Red Sandstone is the most impressive. From Craig y Llyn we see the gentle dip slopes of dull green pastureland, peat bogs and cotton-grass moors rising to the crest of Fforest Fawr and the Brecon Beacons; these, like Craig y Llyn, have mighty scarp slopes facing north, almost as high as Cader Idris and many of the more famous mountains of the north, exposing great cliffs of the red rocks. This line of hills stands out above the peneplain of the coalfield and Central Wales, much as do some of the mountains of North Wales. It affords a splendid view of the country around Brecon, an undulating region of rich greens and deep red fields comparable with that just north of Cardiff.

The arrangement of the various rocks of the coalfield borders is thus similar in both north and south, for the coalfield is a basin with the rocks older than Coal Measures outcropping in regular sequence around the margins (Fig. 66). Westwards these northern ridges continue beyond the heads of the Neath and Tawe valleys, the conglomerates of the Old Red Sandstone capping the precipitous scarps of Fan Gihirych and Fan Hir; the last-named rises in a sheer cliff above the cwm which holds the moraine-dammed lake of Llyn y Fan fawr. But west of this area the conglomerates become thinner and this ridge diminishes rapidly in strength, so that between Ammanford and Llandilo it is relatively inconspicuous. As the conglomerate scarp diminishes, however, another ridge rises just to the south of its line to form the great moorland of the Black Mountain, its bare and stony dip slope emerging from beneath the coal-bearing shales of the Amman valley to the crest of a scarp. This mountain is built up mostly by tough white quartzites which here make the Millstone Grit more like its equivalent formation in Yorkshire than is usual in South Wales.

The coalfield west of Neath is less elevated than further east, partly because the Pennant Sandstones here contain greater proportions of shale. Thus while there are many bare and dreary upland tracts, the valleys on the whole are wider and are cut down more nearly to sea-level. Consequently their tributaries have been able more actively to erode courses on the softer shale outcrops, and the drainage shows a greater harmony with the geological structure than it does near Cardiff. For example, the Loughor for much of the way from Ammanford to the sea meanders in a wide and often marshy valley of quite mature aspect, enabling its tributary the Amman to cut a great valley along the strike of the shales of the Coal Measures. Around the Loughor estuary, too, wide valleys are excavated in the softer shales. So the harder sandstone bands stand out in prominent ridges, like that which fronts Swansea Bay. This is breached at several points, but notably by the Tawe, which occupies quite a narrow gorge between Town Hill and Kilvey Hill just before it enters the sea at Swansea.

This steep scarp, rising to about 600 feet within a short distance of the coast, has greatly affected the growth of Swansea, and although terraces now extend over most of Town Hill, the sister hill on the east is still almost bare, the town creeping round its flanks. On the north of the town metal works have produced a dreary desert, and the view of Landore from the railway is one of the most depressing in Wales, except perhaps at sunset when the glowing river winds among the dark masses of derelict works. Almost in contact with these relics of industry are little hill farms and whitewashed cottages which have somehow contrived to exist through the period when fumes obliterated nearly all vegetation from the hillsides; with the decline of copper-smelting some grass has lately been encouraged to grow. But in its southern and western parts Swansea shows far less the presence of industry, and spreads, a pleasant and friendly town, around the sandy shores of a wide bay.

THE VALE OF NEATH

The most important rivers entering this bay, the Tawe and the Neath (or Nedd), flow in valleys quite unlike those of east Glamorgan, for they are almost straight trenches, open for many miles inland, running from north-east to south-west. Both of these valleys have been determined by belts of crushed and weakened rocks, and are thus in some ways comparable with the Talyllyn–Bala valley of North Wales. Along these easily eroded belts the rivers have cut down rapidly to near sea-level ; their tributaries, however, have had to contend with normal rocks, and they occupy mature high-level valleys from which they tumble into narrow gorges before joining the main valley. These effects have been increased as a result of glaciation, for much ice from the Brecon Beacons reached the sea along these valleys ; during their retreat, the valley-glaciers built up terminal moraines across the valleys, that at Glais, north of Swansea, being the most impressive.

These features are most familiar in the Vale of Neath, where industrial development is so localised that great stretches of really attractive country remain. At many points the River Neath flows in a narrow alluvial plain, but the valley sides are steep, especially where they are cut in the Pennant Sandstone. About half-way up the valley, near Resolven, several torrents fall swiftly into the main stream, making picturesque waterfalls in their rapid descent ; that at Melin Court is the largest, the stream falling over a ledge of massive sandstone into a short wooded gorge left by the receding fall. In North Wales such falls would be visited by thousands, but in the south they are little cared for, and it is not uncommon for refuse to be deposited in the most beautiful of the gorges.

Still further upstream, near the head of the Vale of Neath, the river scenery is even finer, for at Pont Nedd Fechan (or Pont Neath Vaughan) several streams occupy gorges of extraordinary beauty, and give rise to a series of waterfalls which have become deservedly famous. And further upstream other attractive scenic features are shown where some streams cross the outcrop of the Mountain Limestone, as in the case of the Mellte south of Ystradfellte, which plunges into a cave (Porth yr Ogof) beneath a limestone cliff, leaving the old bed dry, until it reappears some distance below.

GOWER

Away to the west of Swansea stretches the peninsula of Gower, a low coastal plateau for the most part outside the coalfield and thus, like the Vale of Glamorgan, bringing a pleasant rural area into the closest proximity to the industrial regions. But Gower is more isolated than the Vale, through which passed the old routes to the west; Gower is so deeply cut by the Loughor estuary on the north-west that it forms a cul-de-sac, and it has escaped many of those influences which modified the Vale. It has no railway and no towns, and is almost shut off from the Welsh-speaking areas in the adjacent coalfield by the scarp of the Pennant Sandstone which has long formed a barrier between the two regions.

The Gower peninsula consists of sharply folded Old Red Sandstone and Carboniferous rocks, forming anticlines and synclines running nearly east and west (Fig. 68). Small patches of New Red Sandstone here and there, and a red staining of the rocks in many places, indicate that the newer rocks found in the Vale once spread over much of this region, but if this were so, they have almost completely disappeared. Structurally the Gower peninsula may thus be compared with the basement of the Vale of Glamorgan.

The relief of the peninsula shows some relation to its structure, for the anticlinal areas where Old Red Sandstone is brought to the surface all stand up as hills about 600 feet above sea-level, but apart from this the peninsula is a low plateau. Their resistance to denudation is mainly due to the presence of quartz conglomerates identical with those which form the summit of the Brecon Beacons. Running almost through the middle of Gower, the narrow ridge of Cefn Bryn marks the position of a sharp anticline whose steep slopes to north and south are littered by irregular blocks of the tough conglomerate. From the old track which follows the crest of this bracken-covered hill the best views of Gower may be obtained. Cefn Bryn and its westerly extensions in Llanmadoc Hill and Rhossili Down are then seen to stand

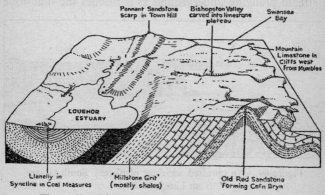

Figure 68.—Diagram of eastern Gower, looking east.
(*Shading substantially as in Figure 66.*)

out as conspicuous monadnocks of nearly equal height above a smooth plateau in which the rivers have carved narrow trenches.

In many of its features the plateau surface of Gower recalls those of Anglesey and the Vale of Glamorgan; from any good viewpoint the skyline is remarkably even, the surface cutting across the edges of the upturned rocks and reflecting little of the underlying structure (Fig. 69). Large tracts at just over 200 feet and just over 400 feet may be recognised in all these areas, and it is likely that they were cut by wave action in two stages when the land stood about 200 feet and 400 feet lower in relation to the sea. The elevation of these platforms appears to have been uniform around the coasts of Wales, and accounts for the characteristic smoothness of many coastal areas.

The greater part of southern Gower is made up of Mountain Limestone, which produces, at any rate in the valleys, many of the characteristic features of limestone scenery. The narrow valley which stretches from Bishopston to the sea at Pwll du is the best known example, with a stream plunging underground as it reaches the limestone

Figure 69.—An upraised wave-cut platform; South Gower from Langland Bay.

outcrop, to rise again near sea-level; a pleasant valley of white limestone crags and rough wooded slopes. But on the plateau surface the limestone is often covered by a blanket of boulder clay, and the area is more fertile than the solid rocks would lead one to expect.

It is in its coast-line, however, that Gower is most attractive. For almost the whole distance from Mumbles Head, at the angle of Swansea Bay, to Worms Head in the extreme west (Fig. 71), are cliffs made of Mountain Limestone, cliffs which vary in form with the changing dip and structure of the rocks; where the beds are steeply inclined the cliffs are nearly vertical, where they are dipping gently seawards, as is most frequent in eastern Gower, the cliffs are more gently sloping and are there covered with great golden masses of gorse. But these cliffs always lack that smooth regularity so typical of the cliffs of the Vale, where the evenly bedded rocks of the Lias have such simplicity. At many places the rocks are broken by faults, which have enabled the sea to cut deep bays which add greatly to the charm of this pretty coast. In the larger bays are great sand-dunes, and in Oxwich Bay these have dammed up the drainage and produced a great marsh just behind the coast. Still larger expanses of marsh fringe the northern coast under Llanrhidian and Cheriton, which stand on an old cliff.

PEMBROKESHIRE

Much of south Pembrokeshire may be compared with Gower. This " Little England beyond Wales " is likewise built up of old rocks sharply folded into east-west anticlines and synclines which have been planed off by wave action to remarkably level platforms, now raised to about 200 and 400 feet above the sea. The skyline in south Pembrokeshire is if anything more even than that in Gower or in the Vale, in spite of the fact that there is a greater variety of rock types and more complication of structure than in the more eastern coastal areas. The inland scenery is for the most part sub-dued, although the rivers have cut deep but narrow notches into the generally level surface. Building it up are rocks ranging in age from Pre-Cambrian to Carboniferous, for here the coalfield is included in the low coastal plateau, but the surface ignores nearly all these differences of rock struc-ture and composition, cutting smoothly across them all. In the north of the county rise the Prescelly Hills, standing above the coastal plateau on the south as they do above the Central Wales plateau in the north. From the crest of these hills on a clear day almost the whole county is visible. Westwards they are represented by isolated rugged hills near St. David's and Fishguard which rise as monadnocks from the smooth plateau (Fig. 70).

The coalfield of Pembrokeshire shows few traces of mining activity, and its existence scarcely disturbs the pleasantness of this rich rural county. For very little coal is mined there nowadays, owing to the complexity of its structure, and the old collieries and refuse tips rarely obtrude themselves. Yet mining was carried on and coal exported from Pembrokeshire as early as the sixteenth century, for the coalfield reaches the coast both at Saundersfoot and in St. Bride's Bay, while the wide estuaries made other mines still more accessible for shipping. But with the growth of ports further east, the coal trade of Pembrokeshire has

Figure 70.—Hills north of St. David's. Monadnock rising from the coastal plateau.

steadily declined, and it remains essentially an agricultural region, green and fertile, with lovely lanes and hedgerows and many pretty villages. Although it is crossed by old roads as well as railways and has thus been more in contact with the outside world than has Gower, there are some remote villages in the south-west.

Where there is so much variety in the rocks it is not surprising that building materials are also varied in type and in colour. In St. David's the older Pre-Cambrian and Cambrian rocks have been drawn upon, and the cathedral, standing in a hollow on the seaward edge of the little town, gains a most unusual colour from the purple Cambrian sandstones. The pale grey Mountain Limestone has been freely used, especially in Tenby and in Pembroke, and Pembroke Castle seems almost to grow out of the rock on which it stands. In this fertile county there are many castles, as there are also in the coastal tracts of Carmarthenshire and Glamorgan.

But if the inland scenery presents the smooth outlines of an uplifted plain, with the different rocks having very little effect on the relief, the coast scenery is much more varied. Here differences in resistance to wave attack have led to the excavation of bays and to the isolation of numerous stacks and islands. The stretch along the south from Tenby around to Angle has much to suggest Gower, for its rocks are chiefly folded Mountain Limestone and Old Red Sandstone, and they give rise to magnificent cliff scenery. The cliffs of steeply dipping limestone in Lydstep and Skrinkle Havens contrast with the red rocks of Manorbier, while limestone cliffs again form much of the south coast around St. Gowan's Head and Linney Head, to be replaced once more by red beds near Angle and in the shores of Milford Haven. A belt of volcanic rocks (of Ordovician age, dropped by faulting among the red marls) introduces variety into the cliffs of Marloes Bay, Wooltack and Skomer Island. In St. Bride's Bay the Coal Measures have been cut back and form the dark stretch of cliffs from Little Haven northwards to Newgale, while harder and older rocks have resisted erosion along the arms of the bay. The northern arm terminating in St. David's Head includes igneous and sedimentary rocks belonging to the Pre-Cambrian and Cambrian, the varied colours of which make up an imposing array of cliffs.

One other feature of the coast scenery may be mentioned, namely the long narrow inlets, especially of Milford Haven and the branches of the River Cleddau ; one of these gives access to Haverfordwest, almost in the middle of the county, where the lowest bridge across the river into west Pembrokeshire has created an important centre. These long narrow inlets are drowned valleys or rias, formed in all probability during the subsidence (or rise of the sea-level) which affected

southern Britain in Neolithic times, matching those of
Essex and corresponding in date with the drowning of the
Wash area. The same subsidence affected the rest of South
Wales, but in some rivers, such as the Tawe, later deposits
have filled up the valley to above sea-level.

Figure 71.—Worms Head, Gower. An upraised wave-cut platform.

CHAPTER XVIII

THE BORDERLAND OF WALES

BORDERLANDS are always interesting. Where different types of country come into contact, the contrasts of scenic features and of land utilisation are often emphasised by a line of market towns where the different kinds of produce are exchanged. The Welsh borders have all these features, but they show besides a wonderful variety of scenery; where the English plain meets the mountains there are numerous castles and border ranges of no great height but of surprising daintiness; some parts of the borderland are so fascinating that they call for treatment in this separate chapter. In this, we are not greatly concerned with the present geographical limits of Wales, but propose to describe those areas of particular interest which lie immediately to the west of the Midland plain, and more or less along the line of Offa's Dyke.

SOUTH SHROPSHIRE

Among these, no region is more attractive than that around Church Stretton in south Shropshire. Here a wide range of rocks builds up a tract of extraordinary variety, where the relation of scenery to geological structure is perhaps better displayed than in any other part of Britain. Church Stretton is situated in a narrow and undulating tract of lowland by which the railway passes through the hills between Ludlow and Shrewsbury. It is a pleasant situation, with the Longmynd rising abruptly on the west (Fig. 78), and Caer Caradoc on the east. The last-named hill rises steeply from the valley in a face broken only by occasional dark crags, but its eastern face is more irregular, with ribs of ragged rock extending up its flanks. Most of the hill is composed of lavas and ashes produced by volcanoes before Cambrian times, but associated with these are other igneous rocks. The long narrow hill, running roughly north-east to south-west, is cut off by a great fault along its north-western side, a fact which accounts for the smooth face overlooking Church Stretton (Fig. 72). And in line with it are other hills of similar pattern, Ragleth to the south-west, Lawley to the north-east, similar narrow hog's backs with irregular outlines, and beyond the River Severn, about twelve miles away to the north-east, stands the

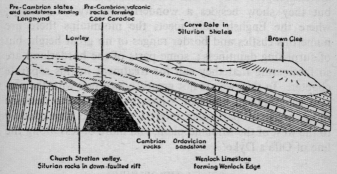

Figure 72.—A part of South Shropshire, looking north-east.

Wrekin in the same line, rising out still more conspicuously from the plain.

Across the narrow faulted trough or rift in which Church Stretton lies is the great bare mass of the Longmynd, rising even higher than Caradoc, but less impressive in its outlines, a smooth-topped plateau stretching for about six miles to the west (Fig. 78). The plateau surface is not level, but is slightly warped to north and south. Although near its borders it is deeply cut by narrow V-shaped valleys (of which Cardingmill valley is best known) most of its level upland is unbroken. Large areas on the slopes are covered with bracken, and in autumn they are a rich golden brown streaked with deep green. Like Caradoc, this plateau area is also built up by ancient rocks, belonging to the Pre-Cambrian, but they consist of slates and sandstones producing a mountain of smoother aspect than those formed by volcanic and other igneous rocks in the Caradoc range. The contrast is similar to that previously noted in Wales between the slate mountains of Denbigh, the Clwydian range and Plynlimon, and the volcanic mountains of Snowdon and Cader Idris ; the materials in these cases are different in age from those just described.

The view from Caer Caradoc eastwards looks first over

Figure 73.—Shropshire, looking north-east from Caer Caradoc. Lawley in middle distance, and the Wrekin on skyline; Wenlock Edge on right. (Compare Figure 72.)

an undulating tract of fields and woodlands, beyond the Cardington Hill mass (of material comparable with Caradoc itself) but the most impressive feature in that direction is the long straight line of Wenlock Edge, a wooded scarp running (as do so many features hereabouts and in Wales) from north-east to south-west, from near Much Wenlock to Craven Arms. This remarkably straight cliff, unbroken for many miles, is formed by the outcrop of a richly fossiliferous limestone of Silurian age, the Wenlock Limestone (Figs. 72 and 73). Underlain and overlain by shales, this limestone gives rise to one of the best known escarpments in Britain, in which the dip to the east gives rise to a distinct and smooth dip slope. Running parallel to this ridge and often less than a mile to the east is another of similar character, made by another limestone, the Aymestry Limestone. Between the two ridges is a rather discontinuous hollow, known as Hope Dale, while the Aymestry Limestone feature in turn dips down to the east and passes into Corve Dale, a beautiful valley connecting Much Wenlock and Ludlow (Fig. 72).

The limestone scarps are often wooded, with bare grey crags. These beds have been (and still are) frequently quarried. The gentler eastern dip slopes, based on the shales, are much more fertile, however, and are cultivated

Figure 74.—View Edge, a part of the scarp of the Aymestry Limestone at Craven Arms.

almost up to the crest of the scarp. Both in Corve Dale and in Ape Dale, under the scarp of Wenlock Edge, are many small villages, built mostly of the yellow-grey local stones.

The simple structure of the country formed by these Silurian limestones and shales is somewhat modified by changes in the individual scarps, for while the Wenlock Limestone diminishes southwards and forms a comparatively inconspicuous ridge near Craven Arms and Ludlow, the Aymestry Limestone scarp gets stronger in that direction, rising into the fine wooded cliff of Norton Camp and View Edge where it is cut through by the Onny at Craven Arms (Fig. 74). Near Ludlow, moreover, the escarpments lose their straightness, for the rocks are slightly folded and the structure has not the simplicity to be seen in the stretch which is so well seen from Caer Caradoc.

Rising eastwards out of Corve Dale is a great stretch of undulating country, with many fields of heavy red soil marking the outcrop of the Old Red Sandstone, while standing out above it are two flat-topped mountains, Brown Clee and Titterstone Clee, which are small outliers of Coal Measures, the latter capped by a sill of dolerite giving rise

Figure 75.—An old cottage, extended in local sandstone, Onibury, Shropshire.

to the craggy north-west face which makes the summit a prominent landmark in the country around Ludlow.

Where so many rocks are available there is naturally a great diversity of building materials. Yet old half-timbered buildings are very abundant, notably in Much Wenlock and Ludlow (Fig. 76). In the latter town the red tiles, wearing to a deeper tint than the bricks, give the dominant colour, an indication of its situation on the borders of the red marl country (of the Old Red Sandstone). But Ludlow Castle has the yellow-grey of the Silurian stones. Many villages nearer Church Stretton have also interesting stone houses,

and in the area of Soudley and Hope Bowdler, and in the
Onny valley near Horderley, much use has been made of a
local Ordovician sandstone often showing beautiful purple
and yellow-green stripes, quarried in blocks of varied sizes
and shapes.

The country west of Longmynd brings us into the actual
border of Wales and into scenery which is more suggestive

Figure 76.—Ludlow.

of North Wales, for between Montgomery and Minsterley
there are high craggy mountains and much bleak upland.
Much of this country is formed by Ordovician rocks which
differ greatly from those outcropping around Hope Bowdler,
where a series of sandstones gives rise to pleasant rolling
country; here in the west of the Longmynd the Ordovician
rocks are of Welsh type, chiefly of slates and shales but including beds of volcanic ash and lava. The great difference

is probably due to the proximity of the shore-line of the Ordovician sea, coarse sediments being laid down to the east while, in the deeper water to the west, finer muds were laid down in a sea which stretched across Wales and in which there were occasional outbursts of volcanic activity. The harder beds now stand out as ridges, running in a general north-easterly direction, emphasising the prevailing 'grain' of the structures. The most pronounced ridge lies near the western border of the Longmynd, and it is known as the Stiperstones; it is formed by a very hard light-coloured quartzite, which stands out in lofty, bare crags best known in the Devil's Chair and Cranberry Rock.

Although not the highest mountain in this region, the Corndon is peculiar on account of its shape. For while most of the high ground here, as in the Wenlock district, consists of narrow ridges or scarps following the outcrop of the harder bands, with the rivers etching out the softer groups, Corndon is a rounded cone, almost circular in plan, made up of dark grey-green rock which represents a sill of dolerite intruded into the shales; the junction of the resistant dolerite with the readily eroded shales which underlie it is marked by a distinct step in the mountainside. Corndon forms a real outpost of Wales: from its summit there is a wonderful view of North and Central Wales, while nearer at hand it overlooks the stretch of exposed moorland around Shelve, where lead mines have scarred the dreary landscape. But very little of the country in south Shropshire has been spoiled, and the varied landscape is nearly always attractive, the hills high and steep enough to be stimulating, detached enough to afford glorious views.

THE COUNTRY NEAR SHREWSBURY

Away to the north of this area the old rocks are submerged beneath the materials of the English plain, and Coal Measures and New Red Sandstone occupy great tracts beyond Shrewsbury and Wellington. Shrewsbury is really a town of the New Red Sandstone, and like Chester it has many beautiful half-timbered houses, besides having many buildings of red sandstone. Its most notable feature is its situation in a great meander of the Severn, so that the old

Figure 77.—Grope Lane, Shrewsbury.

town is almost completely surrounded, and only from the north can entrance be made without crossing a bridge. For miles up above Shrewsbury the Severn has a remarkably winding course, for although the river is mature and winds slowly through its flood plain, it is significant that its meanders in the alluvial tract under the shadow of the Breidden Hills are much smaller than the great bends near Shrewsbury. It has been suggested these latter may have been partly determined by the uneven surface on which the river began to flow again after the Ice Age had partly filled its valley with uneven deposits of boulder clay.

The valley of the Severn below Shrewsbury is noteworthy. As far as Buildwas the river flows in a wide open valley, meandering in the meadows of its flood plain, but then it enters a gorge-like valley where the river flows swiftly for several miles between steep wooded slopes, and has a much less mature appearance than higher up its valley. The gorge begins when the river crosses the line of Wenlock Edge. The river soon passes on to a tract of Coal Measures and its banks show evidence of early industrial development around Ironbridge.

This change in the character of the Severn valley may have been caused by the Ice Age. It is believed that the Severn formerly flowed northwards across the plains of red rocks to the Dee or Mersey, but that during the retreat of the ice a stage was reached when the upper Severn drainage was held up by Irish Sea ice invading the Cheshire plain; boulders from Scotland and the Lake District brought by this ice into Shropshire give some indication of its extent. Lakes were held up between the Shropshire hills and the ice front, fed by torrents of water from the melting snows and ice. As the ice retreated several smaller lakes became united, and the water spread over a great tract of country, forming a lake which has been named Lake Lapworth after the geologist who first recognised its significance. The waters of this lake rose until they began to overflow by a channel across the original watershed at Ironbridge, where a spill-way was formed and eventually became the Ironbridge gorge. The Severn has continued to use and to deepen this overflow channel even after its old course became free of ice (as did the river Derwent in Yorkshire, p. 43), and so its course shows this sharp turn southwards and its valley has the sudden change of character.

THE BORDERS OF NORTH WALES

Northwards from Shrewsbury the Welsh borders extend by Oswestry and along the Flintshire coalfield. But it is along the west of this Carboniferous tract that the most conspicuous changes in scenery occur. The Coal Measures are underlain by the Mountain Limestone which forms a discontinuous but narrow outcrop from Oswestry to the north coast; east of this lie the coalfields, with Wrexham and Ruabon, while west of it the older slates and lavas characteristic of North Wales are seen respectively in the subdued contours around Llangollen and in the more rugged Berwyn Hills. The Mountain Limestone rests unconformably on these old rocks, and the country immediately west of it thus varies in character from place to place, but the Limestone at many points stands out in a striking escarpment; in Eglwyseg Mountain the bare white crags make a strong feature facing westwards into Wales.

THE MALVERN HILLS

To the south of Shropshire the most definite scenic boundary is found in the Malvern Hills, where a north-south line may be drawn between the red English plain on the east and a series of sharp hills on the west. These hills, known from north to south as North Hill, Worcestershire Beacon, Herefordshire Beacon, Hollybush Hill, Raggedstone Hill and Chase End Hill, are built up of Pre-Cambrian rocks, but most of them are unlike the Pre-Cambrian rocks of Shropshire; the most frequent type is a gneiss, a granite-like rock in which an irregular banding has been produced by the intense pressure to which they have been subjected. The eastern face of this range is very steep and may be regarded as a fault-scarp, the fault in this case resulting from a movement which has pushed up the ancient floor and has brought Pre-Cambrian rocks against the New Red Sandstone. Between many of the hills are transverse faults running east-west, along which hollows have been eroded affording routes across the range, such as that between Hollybush and Raggedstone, and that along the Gullet north of Hollybush. These beautiful hills have much resemblance to the ancient hog's backs of Shropshire, and while their heights are little over 1000 feet they afford extensive views out of all proportion to their elevation, to the east, across the Vale of Gloucester to the Cotswolds, to the west, across the rolling country which extends to Ledbury and Hereford.

The region immediately west of the narrow Malvern ridge includes a small area of sandstone hills and shale valleys just east of Eastnor, which are based on Cambrian rocks. West of these come the outcrops of Silurian rocks (for as in much of England the Ordovician is unrepresented), consisting of sandstones, limestones and shales comparable with those of Shropshire and forming a similar series of parallel wooded ridges and fertile valleys. Dipping towards the west, these Silurian rocks disappear at Ledbury, and from that town there stretches a great expanse of undulating country of which Hereford is roughly the centre, extending northwards beyond Leominster, westwards by Hay and Brecon, southwards to Monmouth and Newport.

THE COUNTRY AROUND HEREFORD

This is the country of the Old Red Sandstone, an area of red soils and rich greens, but with undulating country rising to much greater heights than the areas formed by the New Red Sandstone. Generally these rocks are red, but they include marls and limestones as well as sandstones and conglomerates. Like the rocks of the New Red Sandstone, they probably owe their colour to formation under 'continental' rather than marine conditions, and many beds were deposited in fresh water. The presence of the sandstones and conglomerates explains the occurrence of high uplands in this tract. The most notable feature is the great escarpment of the Black Mountains on the borders of Brecknockshire and Herefordshire, which may be regarded as an easterly extension of the Brecon Beacons. Like those mountains they rise to over 2000 feet, the steep northerly scarp rising grandly above the Wye; the gentler dip slope carries them down to Abergavenny, and on this side streams have carved in the upland narrow parallel valleys much like those of South Wales.

But while there are some bare uplands and mountain pastures on the Old Red Sandstone, the greater part of the area has a rich soil, and as great areas are under the plough, this often adds deep red patches to the landscape. Seasonal changes in colouring are here very marked, for there are extensive orchards and hop gardens, especially in the east, while the masses of daffodils in woods and fields are a very delightful feature. Many of the villages and towns are of red brick, but some red sandstone is used and lovely half-timbered houses make many towns extremely attractive: Ledbury, Newent and Hereford itself.

Here and there in this wide expanse of red rocks slight folds have introduced other formations. None of these patches is more fascinating than that at Woolhope, where a somewhat dome-like anticline has brought the Silurian rocks to the surface in an area about four miles south-east of Hereford. The Silurian rocks upraised here consist mainly of limestones and shales like those of Shropshire, and the Wenlock and Aymestry Limestones give rise to scarp and dip-slope topography. Owing to the dome-like folding the outcrops are concentric circles, almost complete except along the west, and the escarpments of the limestones form encircling ridges, each with a steep dip slope facing outwards and a scarp facing inwards to the centre. Shut in by this double wall of hills it is not surprising to find that the area has remained quite isolated, its middle tract having only one village, Woolhope. The main roads skirt the area, that from Hereford to Ledbury keeping just north of the wooded dip slopes which rise so impressively; only minor roads pass through it, following the occasional gaps in the limestone ridges. Its streams have queer courses, tending to follow the shale valleys which carry them round a large part of the area until they escape through gaps such as those at Mordiford and Fownhope to join the Wye.

In the centre of the Woolhope area the oldest Silurian rocks consist of sandstones which form Broadmoor Common and Haugh Wood. The same rocks are brought to the surface again in another fold south-east of Woolhope, where they form the prominent tree-crowned May Hill, nearly 1000 feet high.

THE FOREST OF DEAN AND THE WYE VALLEY

Southwards lies the Forest of Dean, the most beautiful coalfield in England. Here the Carboniferous rocks occupy a basin embedded in the Old Red Sandstone, the Carboniferous Limestone forming a rim round most of the coalfield and extending in a broad belt beyond Chepstow. In structure and relief this coalfield has many resemblances to that of South Wales, for it is partly enclosed by border ridges of conglomerates and Mountain Limestone, and it forms a plateau-like upland in which Pennant Sandstone outcrops extensively. But the differences in scenery between South Wales and the Forest of Dean make these resemblances seem unimportant. Here at a height of 700 feet or more, dense oak forests almost hide the collieries and give to Coleford and Cinderford a setting which is unequalled in any other British coalfield.

The best-known scenery of this region is associated with the Wye valley, which between Ross and Chepstow is cut deeply into the western part of the upland. This course is the more surprising when it is recalled that a little further west there is a much more open tract, between the South

Wales upland and the Forest. The river not only takes a course through the high ground, but in its path south of Ross it recrosses the outcrops of Old Red Sandstone, Carboniferous Limestone and Coal Measures several times, and in its great loop at Symond's Yat it leaves the upland altogether only to turn back into it immediately. The river is thus unrelated both to the present relief and to the geological structure, and its course was apparently determined by other factors, at a time before the Monmouthshire plain had been lowered. Probably the river, with those of South Wales, was first developed on a gently inclined cover of newer rocks, and was later superimposed on these more complex structures.

The most remarkable features in this part of the Wye valley are the deeply incised meanders, for meanders are characteristic of mature rivers winding through broad alluvial plains, and are not usually associated with deep gorges. The Wye swings in big curves, some of them with an amplitude of three miles, and in several the river almost forms a complete loop, as in the bend at Symond's Yat already mentioned, and in the great turn under Wynd Cliff, near Chepstow. So the narrow gorge twists and turns as it passes from Ross to the sea, nearly always steep-sided and often wooded, but frequently overhung by precipitous cliffs of Mountain Limestone.

These meanders are presumed to have been initiated when the Wye, then a mature stream, flowed over a wide flood plain in an area of low relief. As the land was raised, probably in several stages, the river was enabled to cut down its bed, but there has been no time for valley widening and so its meanders are entrenched.

The gorge from Monmouth to below Tintern does not wind quite so much as at other points, and its course is followed by the road. The relative straightness of some parts of this stretch, however, is only a secondary feature, for Dr. A. Morley Davies has drawn attention to two cut-off meanders, where the river has shortened its course by finding a way over the narrow neck of the meander. At Redbrook and Newland there must formerly have been a loop like that at Symond's Yat; the old river bed now forms a channel to the east of the present river, parts of the channel being occupied by two small tributaries, the Red Brook and the Valley Brook, while the village of Newland in the dry part of the channel occupies a quite remarkable hanging valley, " with the church on its very lip ". For the floor of the channel is now nearly 400 feet above the present level of the Wye, a fact which clearly indicates that since this meander was occupied by the river the gorge has

Figure 78.—The Longmynd Plateau and Cardingmill Valley.

been cut down by that amount; it is evident, therefore, that this is a meander abandoned long ago. Farther downstream, under St. Briavel's Castle, is a wide amphitheatre east of the river, and it needs little imagination to realise that the river formerly swung under these cliffs. But since the level is little above that of the river it follows that this meander was abandoned much more recently.

Below this, where the entrance to the gorge is guarded by the grey town and castle of Chepstow, the Welsh borderlands may be thought of as ending against the widening Severn. Higher up that estuary, where the Gloucester road follows the low land beneath the slopes of the Forest of Dean, the Old Red Sandstone still influences the scenery, and such villages as Aylburton and others on both sides of

Lydney have many brown and red sandstone houses. Newnham stands just on the borders of the Old and New Red Sandstone tracts, on a line which is continuous with the front of the Malverns, but at Westbury-on-Severn the red river cliffs of Keuper Marl and the red brick houses mark the edge of the Midland plain.

CHAPTER XIX

THE BRISTOL DISTRICT AND THE SOMERSET PLAIN

ON the south-west bank of the Severn estuary and west of the oolite hills is a very varied stretch of undulating country, cut into two by the line of the Mendip Hills. Almost in the centre of the northern part stands Bristol, for long the second city in England, and still rich in old buildings and historical associations. But it is not for this reason that separate consideration is given to this quite small region, nor because the city is surrounded by some of the pleasantest country to be found near any big town, but because the Bristol district exhibits a greater diversity of scenic feature and building materials than is to be found in any corresponding area in England. This is a direct result of its structure and of the great range of rock formations which are exposed within a distance of little over twenty miles, for, excepting only the Ordovician and the Permian, there are outcrops of every main group of rocks from the Cambrian to the Chalk. In this respect, therefore, Bristol occupies a unique situation, and just as England affords more variety in its small area than almost any other country, so this district holds in still smaller miniature many of the chief features of English scenery.

Its villages show such variety of building stones that it would almost be possible to make a geological map of the area merely by noting the materials used in the cottages. Many of the tall-towered churches are built of oolite, though others take their colour from the local stones.

The best viewpoint within the Bristol district is Dundry Hill, a few miles south of the city. This hill has already been noticed as a great outlier of the oolites (p. 20) ; its slopes are occupied by Lias clays, but the summit is capped by oolitic limestones, which have been used in its cottages and in the church which forms such a prominent landmark. From the northern face of this hill a splendid view of Bristol and the areas east and west of the city is obtained. The even-topped upland of Durdham Down and Clifton is cut by the narrow gorge of the Avon (Fig. 82) and stretches thence westwards in a wooded ridge to Clevedon. From the south side of the hill there is a still wider view of pleasant agricultural country backed by the smooth lines of the Mendip range.

Perhaps the most significant feature in the area is the regularity of its hill surfaces, for in any extensive view large areas appear to be flat-topped, whatever their height may be. There are great stretches of country at more or less uniform levels; these are cut by valleys and evidently represent low plateaux in various stages of dissection. But apart from this simplicity of many of its outlines the Bristol district has an astonishing complexity of pattern. Ridges run in almost every direction and rivers seem to flow alternately in wide open valleys and in narrow gorges.

The reason for these features will best be appreciated after an inspection of Figure 79 which gives a very much simplified interpretation of the structure of the area. Two main rock groups are present. The older consists chiefly of the Old Red Sandstone and the Carboniferous, but includes also the Cambrian and Silurian; these have been intensely folded and faulted. The newer rocks, including the New Red Sandstone and Jurassic, are of much simpler structure and rest with marked unconformity on the older. The plane of unconformity is not an even plane; it was irregular when the New Red Sandstone began to be laid down, and it has been made still more irregular by such faulting and folding as has occurred since that time. The newer rocks have been removed in many places, and thus the present land surface appears as a patchwork of different rock types; rivers flow from newer rocks to older and back again to newer, generally carving gorges in the older and occupying wide shallow valleys in the newer materials, some of which are more easily worn down.

It will be seen from Figure 79 that the higher elevations are of two kinds. There are the Cotswolds and such outliers as Dundry, with a very simple structure essentially depending on a capping of oolitic limestone. Elsewhere there are elevations like the Mendips and the Clifton and Durdham

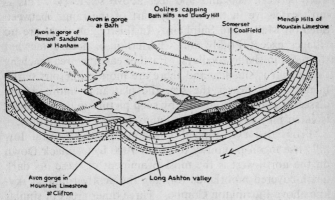

Figure 79.—The country south and east of Bristol, showing the course of the lower Avon.
Shading as in Figure 66, page 238.

Downs, made up of older rocks, mostly of Carboniferous Limestone, with varied and complicated structures. In almost all the places where Mountain Limestone occupies a large area at the surface, it forms high land.

The largest of these tracts is the Mendip Hills. Here the Mountain Limestone gives rise to an area of upland which shows typically those features already described in Chapter XI; there are grey crags above narrow dry gorges, and rather bare uplands with numerous swallow-holes. Much of the Mendip upland is a limestone plateau recalling that of the Peak District, with great fields bounded by grey stone walls.

The Mendip Hills rise from beneath the oolites at Frome and extend westwards to the sea at Weston-super-Mare, where in Brean Down and Worle Hill the steeply dipping limestone forms cliffs which at once recall those of Gower. Out at sea the rocky islet of Steep Holm clearly represents a former extension of the Mendip ridge.

In many places the Mendip plateau forms a nearly level tract between 800 and 900 feet above sea-level. This is most extensive in the westerly part of the range, between Shepton Mallet and Shipham. In this region there are no villages except Priddy and Charterhouse, both somewhat sheltered in shallow valleys. Further east the area reaching this height is smaller, and there are more numerous settlements, while nearer the sea, the plateau is more deeply dissected and is represented by such picturesque and almost isolated hills as Rowberrow Tump and Wavering Down.

From this even-topped limestone plateau several low hills rise inconspicuously to about 1000 feet. Black Down on the north-west is the most prominent of these, its dark heath-covered moorlands forming the gently rounded sky-line above Burrington Combe. Three other areas of similar character occur, North Hill (above Priddy), Pen Hill (above Wells) and Beacon Hill (above Shepton Mallet). Each of these areas coincides with an outcrop of Old Red Sandstone, exposed in the core of an anticline in the limestone. The sandstone probably projects above the limestone surface owing to its greater resistance to denudation ; in this way these higher parts of the Mendips may be compared with the more prominent monadnocks of Old Red Sandstone which rise above the plateau surface in Gower, where identical structures are found (see Figure 68).

For many people the real charm of the Mendips is to be found along their borders. On the south and west they rise impressively from the fenlands, with a chain of towns and villages occupying the narrow strip between the high-lands and the marsh, where water supplies are better than on the limestone; Axbridge, Cheddar, Westbury, Wells, Croscombe and Shepton Mallet are all attractive. But the glory of Wells Cathedral, beautiful in itself and in its setting, raises it beyond any comparisons.

Of the gorges which are incised in the Mendip borders, the finest is that of Cheddar, a narrow dry chasm cut down hundreds of feet into the upland, exposing great cliffs of grey Mountain Limestone. Evidently it is a valley cut into the hills by running water, but it was left dry when the stream found a course underground, the water now rising to the surface near the end of the gorge. The form of the Cheddar cliffs, steep in some places, sloping in others, is determined by the rock structure. The beds dip towards the south, and as the gorge runs almost from east to west, the northern face is often formed by the sloping bedding planes, while the other face, produced by rock falls along the joint planes, is frequently vertical (Fig. 80). The depth and steepness of this gorge, as of all others in the area, owe much to the uplifting of the area in relation to sea-level, which has enabled the stream to cut more rapidly. Ebbor Gorge west of Wells and Burrington Combe on the north of the hills are also immature narrow defiles making very little impression on the plateau surface.

North of the Mendips the Mountain Limestone again gives rise to Broadfield Down, with its picturesque limestone valleys of Brockley Combe and Goblin Combe, and to the wooded hill ridges of Clevedon and Portishead, while be-yond Bristol a great horse-shoe curve of low hills follows the outcrop of the limestone from Alveston to Tytherington and Cromhall and so around the northern end of the coal-field to Wickwar and Chipping Sodbury.

Within the area which is more or less bounded by these irregular limestone uplands lies the Bristol and Somerset coalfield. In many respects this is unlike most other

English coalfields, for in the Somerset part the Coal Measure rocks are rarely seen at the surface, since they are concealed beneath nearly horizontal beds of red marl (of the New Red Sandstone) and Jurassic clays and limestones. Much of the Somerset coalfield is a low plateau deeply cut by valleys, a pleasant rural area with occasional black tips

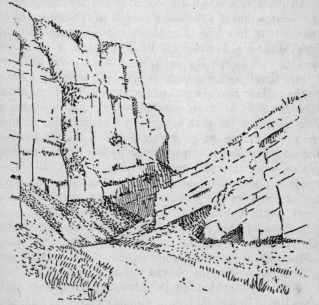

Figure 80.—Cheddar Gorge, showing the influence of dip on the form of the cliffs.

along the hillsides but with none of the grimness of most coalfields.

East and north of Bristol, however, the Coal Measures are at the surface over a much wider area (Fig. 79) and the scenery is quite different in character. Included among the Coal Measure rocks is a thick group of sandstones, the Pennant Sandstone, identical with the rocks of that name in South Wales : in the Bristol area the Pennant Sandstone generally forms low hills often quite inconspicuous and mostly flat-topped. The contrast between the elevation of the Pennant Sandstone country here and in South Wales is remarkable, for in South Wales this rock group builds much of the high plateau which so largely determines the character of that area. The difference is due primarily to the extent to which the plateaux have been raised after their formation, and if the Bristol coalfield were raised 1000 feet it would probably come to resemble much more closely that of Wales.

A greater similarity is shown by the building stones in the two areas, for where Pennant Sandstone occurs it has been extensively quarried, and many sombre villages, Winterbourne, Iron Acton and Frampton Cotterell, are largely built of the dark sandstone, besides many parts of eastern Bristol, such as Hanham and Fishponds.

The other parts of the area call for no detailed description, for they may be regarded as forming an extension of the Midland plain. Thus red marls fill many valleys and lap around the lower slopes of many of the uplands, while they underlie much of the fenland at various places along the estuary, where they have yielded rapidly to the effects of denudation. To some extent it may be said that parts of the area represent a fossil landscape, comparable with Charnwood Forest in that denudation tends to reveal the form of the older uplands as the softer marls are more quickly worn away.

Besides the red marls, the clays and limestones of the Lias occupy considerable areas, where the cottages of small blue and yellowish stones form a constant feature, especially noteworthy around Keynsham, Pucklechurch and Radstock.

THE BRISTOL AVON AND ITS TRIBUTARIES

In this rapid survey of the area no reference has yet been made to the rivers. The Avon gorge is the most impressive scenic feature in the immediate neighbourhood of Bristol, by which the river passes from the low ground south of the city through the limestone upland of Durdham Down and Leigh Woods; in the gorge the sheer cliffs are formed by beds dipping steeply towards the south, Mountain Limestone for most of its length, Old Red Sandstone at the northern end (Fig. 79). The origin of the gorge can only be appreciated when something of the history of the region is understood, for at first sight it appears surprising that the river does not keep to the left along the easy path which appears open to it through the valley at Long Ashton (Fig. 79). That it has kept to the course through the gorge, cutting its way down through hard limestone, does not seem so extraordinary when it is realised that the alternative valley probably did not exist when the river commenced to cut its gorge, and that the low district south of Bristol then stood rather higher than Durdham Downs. In short, while an observer is likely to be most impressed by the work done by the Avon in cutting its gorge, the river has actually moved much less material here than elsewhere in its course. Weathering has done little to wear down the limestone above the gorge, while it has much more rapidly attacked the readily eroded clays and marls, and has helped in the excavation of a wide valley at Keynsham. The Avon gorge, like most other great gorges, is due to a river which at that point has had little energy to spare for anything but downward cutting.

But to understand fully the Avon gorge and its relations to the river scenery of the rest of the area it is necessary to go further back along the valley, and to follow the river from Bath, where it leaves the lovely valley between the oolite hills and flows across the wide alluvial plain beyond Keynsham to enter another gorge at Hanham (Fig. 79). This is less beautiful perhaps than that at Clifton, because it is cut into the darker rocks of the Pennant Sandstone, but the sides are often wooded and the scenery is by no means unimpressive, particularly towards Conham where the river sweeps round a deeply cut meander. From this point the Avon crosses the lower ground through Bristol before entering its better-known gorge. After leaving Bath it thus flows alternately in open valleys and in narrow gorges cut into uplands of varying character and height. In these respects the Avon recalls the Wye, and it is highly probable that the later history of these two rivers has been similar. The lower parts of both river basins had probably been worn down to a fairly level plain before an elevation of the whole region (amounting to several hundred feet) gave additional cutting power to the rivers and enabled them to carve their gorges.

The rivers of the Bristol district, however, illustrate some features of their development more clearly than does the Wye system. For whereas the Wye, like the rivers of South Wales (p. 241) and of the Lake District (p. 201), is believed to have been initiated on a cover of newer rocks (now totally disappeared) and to have become superimposed on the present structures when the newer rocks were cut through, in the Avon and some of its tributaries we see a river system just in the act of becoming superimposed. In this respect it is one of the most fascinating river systems in Britain. Probably rivers began to flow across the area when it was blanketed under a thick cover of gently dipping beds, including the Chalk. Some believe that rivers may once have flowed across the present position of the Bristol Channel in a direction opposite to that of the lower Avon, but whether this is so or not scarcely affects our interpretation of the drainage; it is at least certain that rivers cutting down first through the Chalk and then the Jurassic and New Red Sandstone met older rocks more quickly in some places than in others, where these rose in elevations and the cover was thinnest. Some streams have only just cut through this cover and reached the older rocks beneath, which thus outcrop only along parts of the valley floor, as in Vallis Vale and other valleys near Frome; elsewhere rivers have not yet cut completely through the newer rocks, and will be unable to do so unless a further elevation occurs.

Some of the tributary streams show features very closely resembling those of the Avon. The Frome has attractive gorges where it cuts into the Pennant Sandstone at Stapleton, Frenchay and Winterbourne. The Chew and its tributaries are likewise entrenched near Pensford, while the Trym streams occupy astonishingly deep valleys cut in the Mountain Limestone near Westbury-on-Trym. It is clear that all these features are of similar origin, and it is fairly certain that all are to be attributed to the partial superimposing of the river system on a region of complex structure.

THE SOMERSET PLAIN

To turn briefly to that part of the Somerset plain which lies south of the Mendips, we may notice that it extends

Figure 81.—Brent Knoll, an outlier in the Somerset Fens.
The terraced slope is due to the occurrence of harder beds among the clays.

westwards and southwards to the foot of the Quantock Hills and beyond in a narrow belt to Minehead and the borders of Exmoor. Much of this country is underlain by the red Keuper Marls, which here as always form land of low elevation. Included in the area are the great flats of the Somerset 'moors', the fenlands of the west where silt and peat now fill an ancient valley. In these wide green marshes, crossed by the main road from Bristol to Bridgwater, habitations are few and are almost confined to the borders of the willow-fringed roads which are raised slightly above the field level: in many stretches of country the greatest heights are reached where bridges cross the drainage canals.

The few islands which rise out of these marshes are thus unusually conspicuous, and have been especially attractive to settlements since earliest times. The most famous among them is the lovely Isle of Avalon with the town and ruins of Glastonbury. This rises to a lofty Tor from which the most wonderful view of these fens is to be had. Further west Brent Knoll has an even greater isolation, overlooking the coast from Brean Down to Burnham and beyond.

Figure 82.—The Avon Gorge at Clifton, from the south.

Both of these islands are really outliers of Lias limestones and shales, which formerly rose out of the gentle valley whose submergence has formed the marshes. The nearly horizontal beds are traceable in the form of the hills, each harder band forming a terrace on the hillsides (Fig. 81). The Isle of Wedmore is larger, and like the hills south of Wells it is partly built of red marl, although Lias limestones form the western part.

Westwards the red marl country may be traced to the Vale of Taunton Deane, the rich agricultural region surrounding Taunton and Wellington, where villages and farms are more numerous and more evenly distributed than in the fenlands. The same red country extends by the Quantocks near the coast, but for many miles the cliffs are formed of Lias shales and limestones, which around Kilve and Watchet give rise to low blue-grey cliffs much like those on the opposite coast of South Wales, where the similar rocks in the Vale of Glamorgan emphasise again the former continuity of these regions.

CHAPTER XX

EXMOOR AND THE
NORTH DEVON COAST

THE only great tract of England which has not been described lies west of Exeter, and includes Cornwall, most of Devon and a small part of Somerset. It is a remarkably varied region, best known perhaps along its coast. The cliffs of the north are high and scarcely broken for miles, but although the south coast is quite as rocky it is not so steep and is broken by innumerable narrow inlets of great beauty. Inland there are lovely lanes between tall hedges, rich green country rising to billowing hills and to the open moorlands which occupy thousands of acres in Exmoor and Dartmoor. Much of the region is fertile in spite of its altitude; in some ways this area recalls the Welsh plateau but it is favoured by the milder climate, and much high land is ploughed.

As we have indicated, the border of this region does not coincide with county boundaries, but Exeter stands just on its margin, where the hills of the south-west pass under the New Red Sandstone. From Exeter the border runs almost due south to near Torquay, and northwards it passes by Cullompton and Milverton to trace the margin of the Brendon Hills to the coast at Minehead, only becoming a little obscure where the Blackdown Hills seem to dominate the older tract south of Wellington, and where the Quantocks stand out from the lowland near Taunton. Along the border runs the line of a great unconformity, new rocks occurring to the east of it (noticed in Chapters VIII and XIX) and older rocks to the west. These older rocks chiefly belong to the Devonian and Carboniferous, intensely compressed and folded, and forming a broadly synclinal

structure stretching east and west. In this, the Carboniferous rocks occupy the central area, with Devonian rocks
to north and south (Fig. 83).

It will be useful to approach the south-west, as so many
travellers do at present, along the north coast rather than

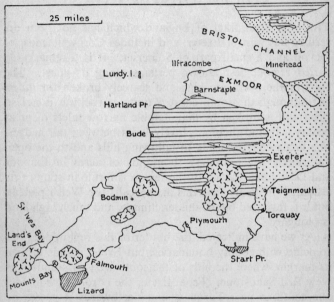

Figure 83.—A generalised geological map of South-west England.
*Serpentine and other old rocks, oblique lines; Devonian, unshaded;
Carboniferous, horizontal lines; granite, Y's; New Red Sandstone
and newer rocks, dotted.*

along the old London road which keeps nearer the south.
Beyond Bridgwater the red marls and clays give place to
Devonian slates which rise suddenly to over 1000 feet in
the narrow ridge of the Quantock Hills. The western edge
is a steep and wooded fault-scarp, but the north and east
is deeply cut by beautiful combes carved by swiftly flowing

streams rushing to the coast. Small villages are situated in some of these valleys, but the most important settlements are found where the hills meet the plain.

If the Quantocks are to be thought of as a great detached outlier of the north Devon moors, the hills between Mine-head and Porlock may be regarded as a similar but smaller and less isolated mass, on which Dunster Castle forms a prominent landmark. The low-lying valley behind Porlock Bay is underlain by the New Red Sandstone and separates Selworthy Beacon from the great tract of Exmoor. Here-abouts the red fields and brick cottages recall the Midland tract, but the famous hill out of Porlock carries the road up to the summit of the moors, well over 1000 feet high. Thence through Lynmouth to beyond Ilfracombe is one of the most impressive stretches of cliffs in England, falling almost sheer from the moorland plateau to sea-level. It is impossible to think of Exmoor apart from this line of cliffs and the incomparable views they afford across the Bristol Channel. The proximity of the coast gives character to the moor ; the sharp change of level gives energy to those moor-land streams which tumble northwards into the sea, carving dark and narrow valleys into the otherwise smooth upland.

Exmoor extends for over thirty miles from east to west and is nearly twenty miles across at its widest part. It is an area of smoothly moulded hills with little bare rock showing, the dull green plateau much resembling parts of Central Wales. Reaching a height of some 1400 feet, it preserves this level over great areas, but out of it rises Dunkery Beacon as a monadnock some 300 feet higher. This plateau, like that of Wales, cuts across beds of various types and it must be the result of either subaerial or marine action, which planed the area down to a level near that of the sea. Its present height has been determined by subsequent uplift, but of its history there is as yet little known. It may be comparable in age with the plateau of Central Wales and perhaps, like it, was raised to near its present position in mid-Tertiary times, but it is not simply an extension of the Welsh upland which, as we have seen, is tilted gently southwards. It may be that during the uplift of these two regions something happened along the belt of the Bristol Channel to disturb their relative levels. Possibly the Channel came into being at that time, and the northern coast of Devon may be in part a great fault line. However, this is all very speculative and much more evidence is required before these aspects of Devon scenery can profitably be discussed.

On Exmoor there are fields up to over 1000 feet, but much of the higher land is rough hill pasture, often very bare and desolate, bracken-covered and sometimes boggy. As in many parts of Devon, the fences are often banked on a rough wall of slates like those of Cardigan. In the sheltered wider valleys, narrow green fields run up the slopes, but the narrower valleys (especially those draining to the north coast) are heavily wooded. The valleys shelter scattered habitations; colour-washed farmsteads with slate roofs are fairly abundant, while the moorlands hold some villages, of which Simonsbath in the valley of the Barle is the most central. But in any wide view of the plateau, valleys are inconspicuous and houses are lost to sight.

The coastal border of the moor is so abrupt that there is no room for villages near the shore except on the valley slopes. Lynmouth, the only place of importance on the shore in a stretch of over thirty miles, has barely space to stretch by the road or riverside, for the picturesque wooded valleys have almost precipitous sides. Combe Martin is strung out for over a mile along the deep valley of the Umber. The growth of Ilfracombe has been controlled by the relief.

In the high cliffs the rock structure of the area is well displayed, and the diversity of rock type shows itself in the varied form of the cliffs. For although the rocks dip generally to the south, the trend or strike of the beds is not quite parallel to the coast, and newer beds form the cliffs as we pass westwards. Thus at Lynton massive sandstones form the cliff at Castle Rock, the beds and joint planes wearing out in rectangular blocks suggestive of a ruin. These bare rocks form an impressive bleak cliff, while in places farther west softer slates have been worn back to form small bays where trees creep down to sea-level, as in Woody (Wooda) Bay. Where the slates form projecting crags and stacks they have a ragged appearance quite unlike that of the bolder sandstones. The heights of the Great and Little Hangman, near Combe Martin, are due to sandstones which project as headlands owing to their greater resistance to wave advance. Along much of the coast grey slates form the irregular cliffs, but at several points the rocks are red, and the varied colours of the crags combined with the rich green of the vegetation make a coast-line of great beauty.

These rocks belong to the Devonian system (Fig. 83); they were formed mainly as deposits in a shallow sea but they have been greatly influenced by subsequent earth pressures which altered the muddy sediments into slates and contorted many beds. They are contemporaneous with the Old Red Sandstones of South Wales, and while it is thought that these latter were laid down in fresh water, the redness of several groups on the north Devon coast may indicate that these two regions were not completely separated at all stages while the rocks were deposited.

The coast west of Ilfracombe is quite different in character. Here the shore-line runs across the rock groups almost at right angles, and the harder beds project in more striking headlands than on the coast to the east, while the softer rocks have been more rapidly cut down. The contrast between these two stretches of coast is thus similar to that pointed out between the east of the Isle of Purbeck and the coast at Lulworth. At Woolacombe soft beds have been eroded to form Morte Bay between Morte Point and Baggy Point, which like the smaller rough crags under Mortehoe project westwards with the trend of the harder rocks: Croyde Bay again picks out a softer belt.

In Bideford Bay the shores are often low. The sand-dunes of Braunton Burrows, blown inland by westerly winds and banked at Saunton against the dark cliffs, have led to the formation of extensive marshes " where Torridge joins her sister Taw, and both together flow quietly toward the broad surges of the bar ". By these sheltered estuaries the picturesque towns, Bideford, Barnstaple, Appledore and Instow, are alive with memories ; in contrast with the rugged country which surrounds it, this pleasant little tract is one of the quietest and most restful places in the west.

These lovely rivers with their tributaries drain most of west Devon, but no convincing explanation is yet available of their history or their peculiar courses. The Torridge is the most surprising. Rising within a few miles of the sea, not far south of Clovelly, it flows for over twenty miles towards the south-east before turning almost completely round to flow north-west again. Undoubtedly some story of river capture is involved and it may be surmised that the lower Torridge is the poaching stream which has cut off some earlier drainage towards the east. But whatever may be the origin and early history of these rivers, some more recent uplift has led to their meanders becoming incised, a feature seen splendidly on both sides of Great Torrington, as well as in the Taw and in many other Devon rivers. The rivers thus flow on narrow alluvial plains which occupy the winding floors of their valleys.

Most of Bideford Bay is cut into the Carboniferous rocks, for the Devonian rocks which occupy north Devon dip southwards under the Carboniferous near Barnstaple. But the Carboniferous rocks are not like those of any other part of England : there is little limestone, and no tract can be likened to the Mountain Limestone areas across the Bristol Channel. The higher parts corresponding to the Coal Measures contain no important coals, but beds of culm, a soft powdery coal, occur occasionally. The Carboniferous rocks consist mainly of dark shales and sandstones, intensely crushed and folded (Fig. 84). They occupy the cliffs southwards to Boscastle in north Cornwall,

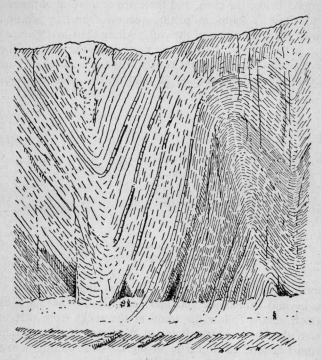

Figure 84.—Cliffs in folded Carboniferous rocks,
Hartland Quay, Devon.

for the most part a bleak and rugged coast, characteristically dark grey or brown in colour. The cliffs are never dull, however. They have such diversity of form and their dark colours react to every change in sky or sunlight, while vegetation brightens every temporary ledge.

Perhaps this coast is best known at Clovelly, on the south of Bideford Bay, where cliffs several hundred feet high form the clean-cut boundary to an undulating tract of varied fertility. As in so much of north Devon, there is little low ground below the cliffs, and there are no natural harbours, and Clovelly gains in picturesqueness from its position down the steep slope of the cliff. Along the Clovelly coast to Hartland Point the cliffs run nearly with the strike of the rocks, but from that point southwards the coast again cuts across the bedding almost at right angles. The coast of

Figure 85.—Ribs of hard rock projecting seawards,
Hartland Quay, Devon.

north Devon thus falls into four sections, that from Porlock to beyond Ilfracombe and that near Clovelly having cliffs which almost follow the trend of the rocks from east to west, that from Morte Point to Westward Ho! and that from Hartland to Boscastle having the cliffs cutting across the rock groups. These latter show the greatest diversity of pattern and the finest rock scenery. From Hartland to near Bude the harder rocks form ribs which project out at right angles from the shore, giving rise to innumerable small rough headlands, the shapes depending on the dip which varies with every fold in the rocks (Fig. 85). In places these rock ribs have been cut through along their joint planes, and portions isolated as stacks, while in the softer beds caverns have been excavated. It is a coast which is rapidly receding under the wave attack.

In places streams are carving deep valleys, usually too narrow to hold a road, but beautifully wooded and in summer full of wild flowers. Many of these little streams, which drain the land for only a few miles from the coast, form most attractive waterfalls where they reach the cliffs. The late Dr. E. A. Newell Arber made a careful study of these coastal falls, and showed how they result from the rapidity with which the coast is being worn away, truncating the valleys and leaving them 'hanging' above the shore. For at its mouth a stream will always tend to carve down its valley to sea-level, and will 'grade' its bed to that level. If, however, the coastal parts are being quickly worn away, the river is unable to attain that level before the seaward end of its valley is removed.

Such coastal waterfalls are perhaps better seen in the coast near Hartland than in any other part of England. Various types may be found. Litter Water, some nine miles south of Hartland Quay, ends in a sheer fall of seventy feet; seen from the beach it is apparent that the stream has carved a valley which makes a notch on the cliff top, but the valley is obviously hanging high above the shore, the almost vertical cliff being formed here by steeply tilted beds. In other cases the streams cascade over more irregular cliffs, especially where beds of different hardness have given rise to steps in the descent.

Most of these coastal waterfalls have been formed where valleys meeting the coast almost at right angles have been truncated by cliff destruction. Both north and south of Hartland Quay, however, are falls which have been produced when a valley running more or less parallel to the present coast-line has been cut by the sea some distance above its mouth. This accounts for the fall of Wargery Water, only a few hundred yards south of Hartland Quay. This stream flows roughly north-eastwards to the coast, and formerly reached the sea beyond the quay, flowing in a flat-bottomed valley nearly a hundred feet above sea-level. More rapid wave advance at several points has partly de-

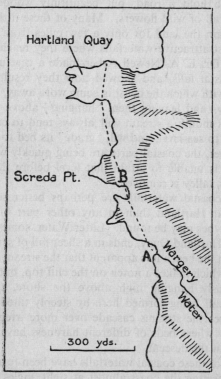

Figure 86.—Map of the coast near Hartland Quay, Devon, showing the former continuation of Wargery Water, and the present position of the waterfall at A.

stroyed the seaward side of the valley and the water now falls over the cliff at A (Fig. 86), but sufficient of the valley sides remain below that point to make the history apparent and to add still more variety to the cliff pattern.

These valleys, which have flat floors well above the present shore, suggest that this land has been raised since the valley floors were graded. But the history of its elevation is not clearly known.

Figure 87.—Exmoor and the coast of north Devon, near Lynton.

CHAPTER XXI

SOUTH DEVON AND CORNWALL

THE south Devon coast is very different from that of the north. There are no high moors near the coast, and although the great mass of Dartmoor rises behind Plymouth and Torquay, much of the coastal tract is a low plateau, deeply dissected by rivers and traversed by their long estuaries, and terminating at the coast in an irregular line of cliffs. With little variation, similar features characterise much of Cornwall. From Torquay westwards most of the coastal regions are built by Devonian rocks, which rise southwards from the great Carboniferous syncline of mid-Devon. Inland, they are broken in places by granite moorlands (Fig. 83). The Devonian rocks of this area, however, are very different in character from those of the north coast, for while they contain many slates and some sandstones, the middle part of the sequence is often made up of massive limestones, and volcanic rocks also occur. With this added diversity of rock types a still more varied coast-line has been developed.

THE COAST SCENERY OF TORQUAY

Many of the characteristic features of the irregular coast at Torquay, the amazing contrast of colour, the dainty bays and bold headlands, result from the complex arrangements of the rocks. The cliffs north and south of Oddicombe beach are of Devonian limestone, which continues by Babbacombe to Anstey's Cove (Fig. 88). Here the massive beds of limestone, grey or tinged with pink, dip at steep angles and form cliffs which in some ways resemble those of Mountain Limestone coasts. Oddicombe Bay has been cut back between projecting limestone masses along a belt of New Red Sandstone, let down by faults which almost coincide with the ends of the beach. These red beds are nearly horizontal and introduce a different type of cliff scenery, reminiscent of the coast near Dawlish and Teign-mouth.

South of Anstey's Cove the cliffs take on another form, for in Black Head dark igneous rocks, somewhat akin to basalt, give rise to a tough mass which resists erosion more

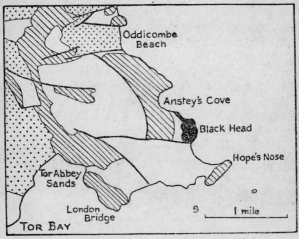

Figure 88.—A generalised geological map of the Torquay headland.
Devonian Limestone, lines; dolerite, black; Devonian slates and sandstones, unshaded; New Red Sandstone, dotted.

successfully than the tracts of slate which bound it. Hope's Nose is another headland formed by the limestones, which west of this again form the grey cliffs where the waves, working along weaker beds, have cut the arch known as London Bridge (Fig. 89). Along these miles of beautiful coast which encircle Torquay the limestone thus makes up all but one of the projecting headlands, while slates and sandstones have been carved into small bays. The same is true also of Tor Bay itself, for this repeats on a large scale the essential features of Oddicombe. Its northern arm is the complex promontory of Torquay, its southern a great tract of limestone extending through Brixham to Berry Head, while much of the bay is backed by New Red Sandstone. Low cliffs of these horizontal sandstones between Torquay and Paignton have also been worn through to

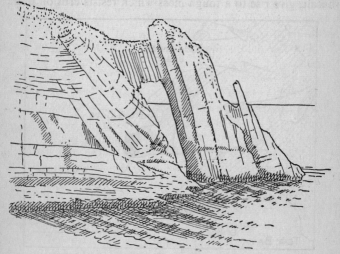

Figure 89.—Natural arch in Devonian Limestone,
London Bridge, Torquay.

form a natural arch, but in this case the erosion is along a joint plane.

Above the coast the most striking feature in the Torquay area is the even-topped plateau formed by the limestones both at Babbacombe and, more extensively, above Brixham. With a height of approximately 200 feet this plateau surface cuts across the various rocks and structures, just as do the coastal plateaux, for example, of South Wales. In a similar way, less regular hills rise out of it like islands from the sea (Black Head, Kilmorie Hill and Warberry Hill at Torquay).

It is extremely probable that like the Welsh plateaux, this surface was cut by the sea, although the evidence concerning the date of its cutting is conflicting. It would be surprising, however, if the final carving of the plateau at least were not done in late Tertiary times, contemporaneously with other wave-cut coastal plateaux. This is supported by the fact that in this plateau deep gorges such as Combe Gorge, south-east of Hele, have been carved by rivers, and these seem to be of no great age.

The Devonian limestone may be likened to the Carboniferous Limestone, for example of Gower, in its coast scenery. It shows further similarity in its solubility, leading to the formation in it of caves. Several of these have yielded evidence of their pre-historic occupants, but Kent's Cavern, Torquay, is of outstanding interest in this connection. The limestone is the predominant building stone in Torquay, as it is also in Plymouth; like the Mountain Limestone it gives rather grey effects, but it is somewhat warmed by delicate tints of pink.

THE DART VALLEY

The valley of the Dart shows several other features of south Devon scenery, particularly in its lower parts, after it leaves Buckfastleigh and Totnes to open out gradually into its narrow estuary, winding under steep wooded crags to the sea at Dartmouth. Like many rivers of the south coast of Devon and Cornwall, the Dart has been drowned by the submergence of Neolithic times, which has converted its lower reaches into a long estuary. Evidence of this lowering of the land may be found in the submerged forests of Tor Bay and many other places and in the fact that the bed of the Dart above its mouth is more than a hundred feet below sea-level. Before this submergence the valley must therefore have been even more steep-sided than at present, a deep trench in the low plateau. The influence of such long narrow inlets on communication between east and west is obvious;

the lowest bridge towns like Totnes and Truro, generally some miles above the mouths, have become of great importance while the coastal tracts between the valleys have been more isolated than would otherwise have been the case. Many unspoiled pieces of country along the coast owe much to the drowned valley mouths.

The Dart valley gains much in beauty from the fact that it cuts across rocks of several types. Between Totnes and Dittisham it flows for seven miles through a series of volcanic lavas and other igneous rocks formed during Devonian times. In some respects they resemble the volcanic series of the Ordovician of Wales, but they give rise to no outstanding surface features. In the Dart valley, however, they are responsible for much of the striking beauty of the scenery, for each igneous rock stands out in a bold wooded crag, while the softer beds give rise to more gentle slopes or are marked by the entry of small tributaries. Opposite Dittisham the river widens out still more where it reaches a belt of soft slates, but although it shortly passes off the volcanic rocks, it flows between steep banks in which much grit is present. Such tributaries as Old Mill Creek have etched out the softer beds.

THE COAST FROM DARTMOUTH TO PLYMOUTH

Along the coast east and west of the mouth of the Dart, between Sharkham Point and Blackpool Beach, are steep cliffs formed by grits and hard slates, reinforced in many places by igneous rocks. These produce wild dark cliffs much like those of Cornwall. Rugged scenery characterises the scenery west of this tract, and the cliffs near Salcombe estuary, especially those between Bolt Head and Bolt Tail and those near Start Point, are very striking. Here complex old rocks, chiefly schists of various kinds, break into rough crags and stand out in irregular rugged points. Some of these schists are green (as in part of Bolt Tail), but different shades from almost a pale yellow to a dull green, altered in places by weathering to red and brown, give a peculiar range of colour to these cliffs.

In the Plymouth district are many features similar to those of Torquay. The cliffs of Plymouth Hoe are of Devonian limestones like those of Torquay and Brixham, but most of the cliffs both east and west of the Sound are made up of slates and grits, varying greatly in colour and structure. For example, in Whitesand Bay are highly disturbed slates, pink, purple and green. For some way from the coast there is little land above 400 feet and the rivers have cut deeply into this coastal plateau.

Much of the beauty of the Plymouth district attaches to these valleys and to the long estuaries of the drowned river mouths. The Plymouth rivers reach the sea by way of narrow picturesque inlets; they are not perhaps so remarkable for their beauty as that of the Dart, but winding gracefully between green banks, the Tamar, St. Germans River and the Cattewater have many attractive old villages built above their wharves. The Yealm valley has higher banks and, though shorter, has much of the loveliness of the Dart.

DARTMOOR AND OTHER GRANITE MOORS

Both Torquay and Plymouth are so close to Dartmoor that it is perhaps suitable to turn from a consideration of the coast scenery to a brief notice of the moorland, the central mass from which the rivers of south Devon diverge. Although Dartmoor is crossed by two roads, most of the moor is trackless, and can be seen only on foot. It is an undulating country some 200 square miles in all, reaching up to 2,000 feet. There are wide areas at about 1000 feet above sea-level, from which the higher parts stand out conspicuously. Probably this high-level platform represents an early plain of erosion, as does also a similar platform at about 800 feet. The history of these surfaces is very obscure but it is unlikely that they are newer than the mid-Tertiary, when they were probably uplifted.

Much of Dartmoor is wild moorland, bleak and treeless except in the valleys; there are dark peat tracts, above which the slopes, at times purple with heather or golden with gorse, rise to bare grey ' tors '. For Dartmoor is wilder than Exmoor, and it shows more bare rock and many screes of great boulders.

Its rock of course is granite, grey in colour and coarse in grain. A typical crystalline rock, it is seen on a casual examination to consist of white crystals of felspar with

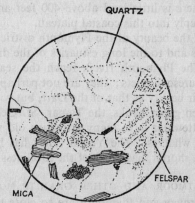

Figure 90.—Thin section of granite, Dartmoor.
Magnified about twelve times.

black and white mica and glass-like quartz (Fig. 90). Formed by the consolidation of molten material, the Dartmoor granite is an enormous dome-shaped mass or boss which was forced upwards after the Carboniferous rocks were formed and which cooled and crystallised at some depth below the surface. It has been exposed at the surface much more recently, when its cover was stripped off under the action of the weather. Owing to its hardness the granite has not been destroyed so rapidly as the surrounding slates and other rocks, so that it projects above them.

Nearly every hill has its bare tor, weathered into queer

shapes often resembling tumbled ruins. For although the granite does not occur in beds but consists of a vast thickness of almost homogeneous material, extending downward for unknown depths into the earth's crust, it is cut by regular sets of joints, some of which simulate bedding, along which it becomes worn into blocks. Such ready-made blocks of ' moorstone ' have long been gathered for building materials, and granite is the essential building stone over a wide area. Yielding great rectangular blocks, it has been used in building simple and solid churches and houses. Little decoration is possible in these granite buildings, for the material is not easily cut, but it expresses admirably the grimness of the moor.

The rivers which flow from Dartmoor—Plym, Tavy, Teign and Dart—at first occupy wide valleys on the uplands but before they reach the granite border they plunge into deep wooded gorges. Many of these are incised in the floors of wider, old valleys, marking stages in the uplifting of the region.

Numerous villages and a few towns are situated near the border and in the valleys just within the moor, Ivybridge, Shaugh Prior, Tavistock, Mary Tavy, Chagford, Widecombe-in-the-Moor and the rest, but there are few places of any size on the moor itself. Princetown is well up on Dartmoor, a grey bleak town 1400 feet above sea-level, but otherwise there are few habitations except isolated farms. Yet Dartmoor was for long a home of early man, when dense forest made much of the lower land unsuitable. Ancient stone trackways, avenues of standing stones, stone circles, barrows, hut circles, all tell of early occupants.

For many miles along both north and south coasts from Newquay to near St. Ives and from Looe to Falmouth the Cornish cliffs are mostly cut in slates, varying in colour but often dark or weathering to rusty brown. The irregular structures in the contorted rocks give rise to much variety in the cliff patterns but the close-set cleavage planes produce jagged edges on projecting points and stacks. Vegetation rapidly grows in every small crevice and though the cliffs are dark and rough, they have a richness of colour which is enhanced by the deep blue of the sea.

The slates are associated with some grits, and into these contorted sedimentary rocks, igneous rocks have been intruded. Most important among these are four large granite masses or bosses, similar in general form to that of Dartmoor. From east to west, these are the Bodmin, St. Austell, Carn Menellis and St. Just (or Land's End) masses. Each of these granite masses gives rise to moorland rather similar to that of Dartmoor, and forms an area of higher ground rising above the country formed by the slaty rocks (the Killas, as they are called in Cornwall). These latter rarely rise much above 400 feet above sea-level, and on the whole form a monotonous plateau sloping gently seawards, although of course the border of this plateau rarely coincides exactly with the margin of the granite.

As Dartmoor has just been described, it will be best to make some reference to each of these granite areas in turn, since each shows some characteristics more clearly than the others. Bodmin Moor is the highest part of Cornwall, but comparatively little of it stands above 1000 feet. From many of its western or southern hills there are splendid views across Cornwall, for the regular coastal plateau stretches for miles, embracing the whole of the peninsula save where the low granite hills stand out. Of these, seen from Bodmin, Henbarrow Down (part of the St. Austell granite mass) is most conspicuous although it only just exceeds 1000 feet.

The relief of Bodmin Moor is not very closely related to the drainage, for like Dartmoor this area is cut by two wide shelves or plateaux at heights of about 800 feet and 1000 feet above sea-level. The higher of these plateaux is seen only in isolated patches on the upper parts of the moor, but there can be little doubt that these were once connected and that the valleys have been cut down subsequently.

Seen from a viewpoint on Davidstow Moor the regularity of this surface is apparent, while in the north of the area Brown Willy and the higher tors stand out conspicuously, and obviously represent ancient monadnocks. The lower shelf is more extensive, and is easily recognised around Camelford.

The St. Austell granite is much less extensive, and although it stands out from the surrounding slate areas, it has few rugged tracts and few tors. Over much of the area there are low rounded hills, but lying half-buried on their slopes are great rounded boulders, sometimes over thirty feet in length, the weathered relics of former tors. The appearance of this upland has been greatly modified by the huge clay pits and dazzling white dumps of waste resulting from the china clay industry. China clay rock is an altered form of granite, and while some occurs on Dartmoor and on Bodmin Moor, the St. Austell district (especially the western part) has long been famed for the purity of its china clay. Although it was used for pottery as early as the eighteenth century, it has only been worked on a large scale during the past few generations. China clay rock has been derived from normal granite by a process of ' kaolinisation ', that is by the chemical alteration of its crystalline felspar into kaolin, a white clay mineral. When this alteration is complete, the other minerals present in the granite (quartz and mica) can readily be separated. There has been much discussion as to the cause of kaolinisation ; somewhat comparable changes take place in any granite as a result of weathering agents, but the great extent of the alteration of the Cornish granites, the arrangement of the altered material in parallel belts associated with fissures and the relation of these to tin veins, suggest that the origin of the china clay is connected with peculiar chemical conditions which existed during the cooling and consolidation of the granite. At that time rising vapours bearing fluorine and other gases brought about an alteration of the felspars and led to the formation of other minerals, notably tourmaline. Although simple weathering is not adequate to explain the formation of china clay rock, this material serves to illustrate very usefully the way in which granite disintegrates, more slowly, under the action of weather, to yield the sand and clay which go to form sedimentary rocks.

The Carn Menellis granite mass, with the neighbouring smaller areas of Carn Marth and Carn Brea between Falmouth and St. Ives, is still lower than that of St. Austell. Showing similar scenic features, its chief interest lies in the working of tin which has probably been carried on in the neighbourhood since the Bronze Age. Ores have also been exploited in the other granite areas, tin being the most abundant material worked, though ores of copper, lead and zinc also occur. The tin occurs in the form of cassiterite (oxide of tin), which is found in veins and lodes extending in many cases from the granite into the surrounding killas or slates. The veins in any area are usually parallel to one another, and represent fissures filled by deposits carried by vapours emanating from the granite just before its final consolidation. The vapours consisted largely of steam at high temperatures together with fluorine, boron and other gases. In some parts of most of the Cornish granite areas, tin has also been obtained from alluvial deposits in the flats of the rivers and streams. This ore, known as stream tin, represents material produced by the weathering of the veins. Many of these alluvial tracts have been dug over by tin-streamers leaving heaps of débris and water-filled hollows; such deposits were amongst the first to be worked. There are now few rich deposits of stream tin remaining unworked, and most of the mining for many years has been in the veins which run in the solid rock.

The most westerly of the Cornish granite masses is that of St. Just, which forms the coast for miles east and north of Land's End, so that the greater part of its margin is washed by the sea. Its narrow eastern edge is marked by a wide depression, connecting St. Ives Bay with Mount's Bay, which has formerly been occupied by a strait. More than a half of the Land's End area rises above 400 feet, but the highest point (Trendrine Hill) is only just over 800 feet. The coastal areas are smooth and form an extension of the low plateau which is so extensively developed in Cornwall and in south Devon. Above it the land becomes bolder and more irregular in pattern. Any distant view in this area shows a remarkable change in the form of the surface at about 430 feet above sea-level, for the smooth-topped coastal plateau often ends against a strong bluff above which the less even uplands make a more rolling skyline. The change in level is marked by an old line of cliffs, produced by the sea which moulded the plateau when the land stood rather more than 400 feet lower than at present. These old cliffs are more prominent, as might be expected, along the south and west where the wave action was most energetic.

The distinctness of the coastal plateau and the sharpness of its boundaries are the most striking features of the inland scenery of west Cornwall. In this area there is an additional interest in the coastal plateau, for its date is precisely fixed by the occurrence upon it near St. Erth of sands and clays of marine origin containing fossil shells which have enabled its age to be fixed as early Pliocene (that is as late Tertiary). It is therefore clear that the great wave-cut platform on which it rests was cut at about that time, and it is highly probable that the comparable surfaces in other parts of the south-west were smoothed down at the same time.

This plateau surface slopes gently seawards from the inner ' cliffed ' edge, and in many places it is nearly 200 feet above sea-level where it ends in vertical cliffs. The familiar cliffs of Land's End, marked by the regular jointing characteristic of the granite, have a castellated appearance (Fig. 91). At some places along the north-west coast, between Cape Cornwall and St. Ives, the cliffs are formed by hard slates and dark-green igneous rocks (known as greenstones), for there the sea has not yet advanced quite far enough to reach the granite margin. These rocks near the edge of the granite mass were baked by contact with the hot igneous material, and were thus considerably altered and often hardened. The granite and its margins have withstood wave action more successfully than the surrounding slates, and the shape of the extreme west of Cornwall is largely determined by the outlines of the granite mass.

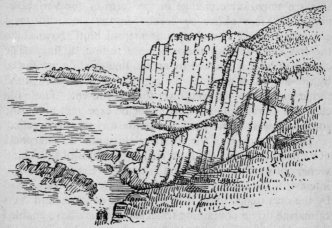

Figure 91.—Land's End. Cliffs of granite.

This is particularly noticeable on the eastern side, where there is a great hollow in the granite border; here the sea has been enabled to cut back the angle of Mount's Bay in which Penzance is situated.

Almost everywhere around the Land's End mass the cliffs are high, except where small rivers have carved deep valleys into the plateau. There are few beaches on this stretch of coast, but in the shelter of the granite cliffs both St. Ives Bay on the north and Mount's Bay on the south have areas of blown sand. The dunes on the east of St. Ives Bay are the more extensive, and though they are now fixed by the growth of vegetation, they have formerly overwhelmed much good land.

St. Ives is one of the most picturesque of the fishing towns on the Cornish coast, with delightfully jumbled groups of cottages built of massive granite blocks. For this is a stone area, and there are very few buildings which are not built of granite or other igneous rock or of the baked killas. Granite is quarried at many places and has been used for gate-posts and beams as well as for ordinary building.

One of the best-known features of Mount's Bay is St. Michael's Mount, the steep rocky islet some half mile from the shore at Marazion, with which it is connected by a causeway (Fig. 87). It is a small granite area, a Land's End in miniature, from which the sea has removed the surrounding killas on all sides but the north. Probably it has been finally detached from the mainland only within the last few hundred years, and it may formerly have been, as its Cornish name implies, " the hoar rock in the wood ".

The manner in which the granite of St. Michael's Mount has been isolated, and in which the Land's End mass has been nearly cut off by the removal of the surrounding slates, makes it easier to realise the relations of the Scilly Isles. This group consists of flat-topped granite islets, about 140 in number, apparently representing an oval area comparable with Land's End, which has been cut up by erosion and isolated by submergence.

THE LIZARD AND FALMOUTH

Projecting further south than Land's End, the Lizard peninsula differs in many respects from all the rest of Cornwall. Its cliffs have perhaps more beauty of colouring than those of any other part of England ; the lovely, rocky bays of Kynance Cove, Mullion and Coverack, backed by rugged cliffs of the richest greens and purples, are exceedingly attractive. Briefly it may be pointed out that these dark cliffs are of igneous origin and represent a complex mass of great age, possibly dating from the Pre-Cambrian. The main part of the Lizard rock is of unusual composition : it differs from granite in having no quartz and little felspar, for its minerals are more ' basic ' in composition and darker in colour. Even these, however, have been greatly altered subsequently, and the rock now consists largely of the mineral serpentine. Used extensively as an ornamental stone, this warm-toned rock was formerly sent far afield for architectural purposes. Locally it has been widely used in buildings, for it has the advantages that it is extremely durable and can easily be trimmed. The villages thus acquire a rather sombre green tint, but some of the churches are built of light-grey granite. Most of the area lies between 200 and 300 feet above sea-level, and it clearly forms a part of the coastal plateau. Inland, therefore, the scenery has less attraction, the soil is thin and often poor, supporting a characteristic flora which includes the Cornish heath (*Erica vagans*).

In the shelter of the Lizard is Falmouth Bay, cut back like Mount's Bay into slaty rocks. But the rivers entering Falmouth Bay are more considerable than those farther west and their drowned valleys form long estuaries much like those described in the Plymouth area. The winding branches of the river Fal extend far inland ; the banks are wooded but lack the rocky crags of the Dart valley, for there are few igneous rocks in this tract. Truro has acquired a nodal importance from its position where routes cross the estuary, and above it the river flows on its alluvial plain. Nearer the sea, the wide deep inlets shelter many attractive villages, St. Mawes, St. Just and Mylor.

In spite of the great difference in geological structure, there are remarkable resemblances in general relief between south-western England and the coastal parts of South Wales. Low plateaux near the coasts truncate the sharply folded rocks of both regions, and deprive them of much of

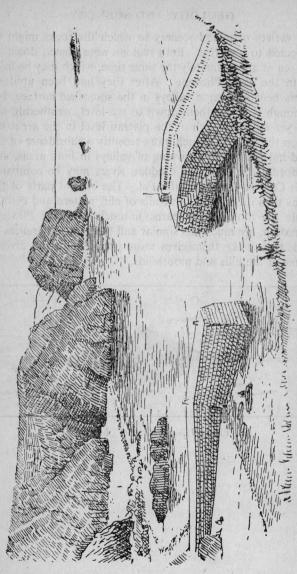

Figure 92.—Mullion Cove, Cornwall. Cliffs of Serpentine.

the variety of inland scenery to which the rocks might be expected to give rise. Both regions were planed down by the sea at approximately the same time, which may be fixed as in the early Pliocene. After they had been uplifted, rivers began to carve valleys in the smoothed surface, but although they cut them down to sea-level, weathering has not yet reduced much of the plateau level in the areas between the valleys. Much more recently a subsidence of the land has led to the drowning of valleys in both areas, and Milford Haven and the Cleddau rivers may be compared with Carrick Road and the Fal. The coastal parts of the areas thus differ most in details of cliff pattern and colour, while the more inland parts, untouched by the Pliocene planation, are much less similar and the great differences of rock type make themselves more apparent in the diverse forms of the hills and moorlands.

Figure 93.—St. Michael's Mount.

CHAPTER XXII

THE CHRONOLOGY OF THE CHANGING SCENE

MANY of the features in English scenery which have been described are of great antiquity. Geological history covers exceedingly long periods of time, however, and it is important to recognise that there are great differences in the dates of origin of these ancient features. Some reference has been made to the relative ages of the different rocks, of plateaux and of river valleys. In this chapter an account is given of the sequence of the chief events in the geological history of Britain, in order to make possible a better appreciation of these degrees of antiquity.

In this account little reference is made to periods of years, although the age of the earth has necessarily interested geologists a great deal. It would be impossible, however, to find agreement in the placing of the sequence of events alongside a table of dates, even an approximate table showing only tens of millions of years, and there is no need to attempt it at present. Geological time is more conveniently divided into periods, the order of which is well established; the history of some of them is known in great detail. Our present position regarding the chronology may be likened to a knowledge of history in which all the important periods such as Norman and Tudor are well known, but in which no dates are fixed, though the approximate duration of each can be estimated fairly closely.

The approximate minimum age of the earth is well established from evidence obtained from the study of the radio-active minerals in rocks of the earth's crust; it is not less than a thousand million years, and possibly twice that amount.

The history of the earth can be divided into two parts, and it may be said at once that we know comparatively little of the earlier (and longer) portion. The events of the later part of the earth's history are more completely known, however, and that division of time may be subdivided into a sequence of periods which are named in Figure 94. In this figure the space given to each period is very approximately proportional to its duration.

The chief reason for the greater confidence with which these groupings are made, as compared with the vagueness in the earlier part of geological time, is to be found in the occurrence of fossils. Little reference has been made to fossils in the preceding chapters, but it must be emphasised that practically all determinations of the ages of rocks and their grouping into periods is based on the fossils found in them. Any systematic interpretation of geological history or comparison of the rocks in different areas must have reference to their fossils, for the nature of animal and plant life on the earth has of course changed throughout geological time, some forms becoming extinct and new forms being evolved. It is not the purpose of this book to trace this organic evolution, but it may be pointed out that in the more ancient rocks practically no fossils are found, perhaps partly because no life existed in the earliest times, partly because the first forms of life had no skeletons which could be preserved as fossils. Many of these old rocks, moreover, have been exposed to very great increase of temperature and pressure, and have been much modified since the time of their formation.

Thus while it is known that in Pre-Cambrian times there were periods of igneous activity, with volcanoes ejecting ash and lava, and that there were periods of quiet sedimentation when sandstones and muds were laid down, it is not possible to give a satisfactory account of the sequence of these events. Pre-Cambrian rocks occupy great areas in the Highlands of Scotland but they do not contribute greatly

QUATERNARY		These periods are shown in fuller detail on Figure 114
TERTIARY		A widespread uplift.
CRETACEOUS	CHALK GREENSANDS, GAULT, Etc.	Marine deposits in a sea covering much of England.
JURASSIC	OOLITES LIAS	Fresh-water deposits in South-East England. Marine deposits of limestone and clay.
TRIAS	KEUPER BUNTER	The New Red Sandstone formed mostly in inland lakes.
PERMIAN		A period of mountain-building and rock folding.
CARBONIFEROUS	COAL MEASURES MILLSTONE GRIT	Deposits mostly in shallow water.
	MOUNTAIN LIMESTONE	Limestones formed in a sea covering much of England.
DEVONIAN AND OLD RED SANDSTONE		Marine deposits in Devon and Cornwall, red beds in fresh-water in Hereford and South Wales.
		A period of mountain-building and rock folding
SILURIAN		
ORDOVICIAN		The rocks of Wales and the Lake District were formed, mostly as marine deposits. In Ordovician times, much volcanic activity.
CAMBRIAN		

This line represents a time at least 500 million years ago.

PRE-CAMBRIAN OR ARCHÆAN	This period may have lasted for at least 500 million years. During this time the old rocks of Anglesey, Shropshire and the Malverns were formed.

Figure 94.—A chronological table of the main episodes referred to in the growth of England and Wales.

to the present surface of England and Wales : they are found chiefly in Wales (in Anglesey, Carnarvonshire and Pembrokeshire) in the Welsh borders (in Shropshire and the Malverns) and more rarely in the Midlands (notably in Charnwood Forest).

Since the Pre-Cambrian there have been several periods when most of Britain has for long been beneath the sea and has received deposits which record the changes taking place. At other times our area has been upraised and mountain chains have stretched across it ; then deposits have been formed only, if at all, in small areas, filling lakes and basins or valleys with material worn from the mountains.

With the Cambrian began the first great marine episode of which detailed knowledge is available. It was introduced by the submergence of a land area which had been carved from the ancient rocks, and in the newly developed sea the Cambrian, Ordovician and Silurian rocks were deposited. Most of these rocks consist of sandstones and shales or slates (originally deposited as muds), but there are some thin limestones, especially in part of the Silurian. The sea in which these rocks were laid down varied somewhat in its extent, but through most of the time it covered the whole of Wales and stretched northwards over southern Scotland. The position of the shore-lines varied, and the rocks in these areas show the greatest diversity in their sequence, the Ordovician rocks being the least widely distributed. During the Ordovician also there occurred a series of volcanic outbursts, especially affecting the areas where North Wales and the Lake District are now situated, when lavas were poured out from numerous submarine vents.

But these volcanic episodes were followed by a further period of tranquil deposition on a subsiding sea floor, and it was not until the end of the Silurian that the essentially marine conditions were brought to an end by a great revolution caused by the upraising and compression of this thick

mass of sediments. This mountain-building period probably lasted for a long time, but its chief effect was to produce
an entire change in the aspect of Britain. The area where
there had been sea became a great range of mountains, the
folds of the rocks trending north-east to south-west, a
direction which is still the dominant ' grain ' of the structures
in the Lake District and in North and Central Wales.

In Devonian times the only area where marine sediments
were laid down lay to the south of these mountains, occupying what is now Devon and Cornwall. Here marine
muds, sands and limestones were laid down to form the
rocks now seen in north and south Devon. Over the rest
of Britain the newly formed mountains were subjected to
rapid denudation and the only deposits were formed in more
or less isolated inland basins, mostly of fresh water, on the
flanks of the mountain ranges. These rocks are mostly red
in colour, and constitute the Old Red Sandstone; they are
of the same age as the marine Devonian but are of quite
different appearance.

With the beginning of the Carboniferous there was once
more an invasion by the sea, which spread northwards
across England and submerged all but a few areas. The
Carboniferous or Mountain Limestone was therefore deposited over most of England and a good part of Wales;
in some places it was laid down upon the Old Red Sandstone, but as the latter was very limited in its distribution,
the limestone in many areas overlapped it and came to
rest directly on the older rocks, giving the striking unconformity which was described in the Lake District (Fig.
55 A; see also Figs 38 and 50).

The Carboniferous deposits accumulated to a great thickness and spread over an even wider area as time went on.
Increasing amounts of sediment were carried into the sea
to form the deltas which make up much of the Millstone
Grit. Later, the area became one of predominantly fresh
water, with shallow lagoons and swamps overgrown from

time to time by dense vegetation, and in these conditions the Coal Measures were formed.

Once more the end of a long period of steady accumulation of sediment was brought about by earth movements, and pressure, this time from the south, bent the newly formed rocks into a series of folds trending east to west. The effect of this pressure was most marked in the south, and the complex folds seen in Cornwall and Devon testify to its intensity (Fig. 84); the east-west trend of the structures and of many surface features in the south-west of England, in the Mendips and in South Wales is due to this folding. Further north the rocks were much less disturbed (Figs. 38, 50).

Once more the earth movements produced an entire change in the aspect of the region which became chiefly an area of desert-like conditions with small patches of water in inland basins or in nearly isolated arms of the sea. Here again red beds were laid down, forming the New Red Sandstone. As the mountains were worn away the area receiving deposits increased, and the sediments came to lie unconformably on Carboniferous or older rocks, as in the area near Bristol (Fig. 79) and in Charnwood Forest (Fig. 22).

When a wide tract of desert and salt lake had been established and much of the mountain country had been brought down to a common level, the sea invaded the area. Most of England and South Wales then received deposits of mud and limestone, the Jurassic rocks, in a sea of wide extent. At times there were changes in the position of the shore-line, but a much greater change occurred towards the end of the Jurassic when an uplift of western England and Wales restricted deposition to a small area in the south and east; here the Purbeck and the Wealden beds were formed in a freshwater lake. At that time the upraised Jurassic rocks, tilted gently to south-east or east, were exposed to denudation and were rapidly removed, so that when the sea once more spread over the whole region, as it probably did when the higher Cretaceous rocks were laid down, these came to rest on Jurassic and other rocks of various ages.

The Chalk represents a deposit which was formed slowly in a sea of clear water. Over a considerable area the conditions seem to have been remarkably uniform, but the deposition of the Chalk was brought to an end by the rising of the sea floor. The uplift was probably greatest in the west but was sufficient everywhere to convert practically the whole British area into dry land.

It will be useful to consider the probable appearance of England and Wales at that time. It must have been essentially an area of very subdued relief, gently sloping towards the east and south-east. Over the greater part of it there can have been little variety of rock type, for the newly formed Chalk certainly had a greater extent than at present. It has been thought that it completely buried most of Wales, with Snowdonia and a few other peaks rising above its surface, but even if it were not so extensive and if much of Wales had remained above sea-level during the time the Chalk was deposited, it is most likely that this land had been planed down by weather and rivers almost to sea-level.

In the succeeding periods of the Tertiary some deposits were formed in parts of Britain, but these occupy relatively small areas, and the sea did not again cover much of England and Wales. Thus in the early Tertiary, Eocene and Oligocene rocks consisting mostly of deposits of sand and clay were laid down in a sea or estuary which extended over south-eastern England; these rocks are now found in the London and Hampshire basins. But elsewhere in England and Wales this period was one of denudation, during which rivers flowed down the dipping surface of the Chalk into this sea and its extensions. Of the effects of this denudation there is little precise knowledge, but it is extremely likely that during this part of the early Tertiary the land was planed down very considerably, and it has been supposed that several plateaux represent uplifted portions of a peneplain which was formed at that time. The Chalk and the Jurassic rocks (being the uppermost in many areas) were no doubt greatly denuded, and older rocks which

	Subsidence and drowning of valleys.
PLEISTOCENE	The Great Ice Age.
PLIOCENE	} Uplift of several hundred feet. Deposition of gravels, etc., in East Anglia. Formation of peneplanes.
MIOCENE	Folding in Southern England. Uplifting of peneplanes.
OLIGOCENE	
EOCENE	Deposition of sands and clays in South-East England. Elsewhere denudation leading to formation of extensive peneplanes. This represents a time about 50 million years ago.
	Uplift of sea floor with Chalk deposits.

Figure 5.—A generalised chronological table of the more recent episodes in the growth of England and Wales.

had been buried beneath them were once more exposed at the surface in some places.

In northern Ireland and western Scotland this was a period of volcanic activity, but although some igneous rocks were then intruded in parts of the north of England it does not appear necessary to deal with these events here.

There are no Miocene deposits in England. This period marked the climax of the folding of the Alps and this mountain building had great influence on Britain. In the south-east, the folds of the Weald, the Isle of Wight and the London basin can be attributed to this period (Fig. 23). Elsewhere the effects of the Miocene movements are not so easily traced, but probably they were of much importance, and many faults may have been formed (or movements may have taken place along old fractures) at this time. It is believed that the Lake District finally received the domed form on which its rivers were developed, and that early Tertiary peneplains were uplifted to form the high plateaux, although these must have been still further elevated at later dates.

Indeed the Miocene saw Britain assume essentially its present structures. Most of its river systems then began to develop along the lines they occupy at present, and the Thames drainage was collected into the newly formed trough. Probably many east and south-east flowing rivers were longer at that time, and river capture has since modified many courses, new tributary streams etching out the strike of softer beds and so developing such escarpments as those of the oolite and Chalk.

Most of the scenic features of England and Wales have thus developed since the Miocene, but their pattern was determined by events of much greater antiquity. In the case of the high plateaux, however, many of the features may be more ancient, dating at least from the early Tertiary, while to some extent late Tertiary denudation has unearthed landscape features which had long been buried under other sediments.

During the Pliocene, England was still joined to the Continent, and received deposits along the East Anglian coast on the shores of the gulf which occupied much of the area of the North Sea. At that time most of England and Wales was lower by several hundred feet in relation to sea-level than at present. A wave-cut platform, especially well seen around the Cornish coasts, in South Wales (Figs. 69, 71) and in Anglesey, marks this stage of Tertiary history, and testifies to the considerable length of time during which these conditions remained stable. The position of sea-level controlled river erosion also, and many rivers reached maturity and carved wide plains sloping gently to the sea.

These nearly level platforms, whether cut by one agent or the other, have subsequently been uplifted, probably in several stages, and now are the most striking features in the landscape in many areas. Following their elevation, rejuvenated rivers have once more been enabled to cut vertically and have incised new and deeper valleys in them. As a result of this elevation, many meanders such as those of the Wye became incised and many other gorge-like valleys were formed.

The next phase in geological history, representing some hundreds of thousands of years and ending only a few thousand years ago, was the Great Ice Age of the Pleistocene. The effects of the ice sheets which at times covered nearly all Britain north of the Bristol Channel and the Thames valley have already been described. They produced many changes in the scenery, although some of them are quite superficial. The form of valleys was greatly modified, especially in such mountainous country as the Lake District and North Wales; in the lower parts of valleys and on the plains great masses of ice-borne material were left, altering the character of many areas and adding new land around some coasts. The formation of lakes, sometimes very temporary features, and the cutting of overflow channels, were other results of the Ice Age, and in many respects the scenery of Britain was considerably changed at this time.

As the ice disappeared and the climate improved, vegetation spread northwards across England, and much of the country was covered by forests. During this period the land sank (or sea-level rose) and valleys were drowned near their mouths, forming narrow inlets such as Milford Haven and the mouths of the Fal and Dart. Where valleys were wider the drowning gave rise to wide shallow bays like the Wash, and the silting up of such areas has lately made them land again.

It is interesting to note that from mid-Tertiary times England has for the most part been rising in relation to sea-level. Whether such a change of level is properly to be attributed to the rising of the land or a withdrawal of the sea is not always clear, for the effects will naturally be similar. Many changes were, however, probably the result of the movement of the land; for example, in the Pliocene the effects were not uniform in different parts of England, as they would have been if brought about by a fall of the sea-level, which must necessarily be similar at all parts of the coast. Thus while parts of southern England were raised several hundreds of feet, East Anglia was raised very little. The drowning of valleys after the Ice Age, on the other hand, affected many parts similarly, and it is probable that it resulted from a rising of sea-level, perhaps consequent on the melting of the ice and the return to the sea of water which had been ' locked up ' on the land.

Man has probably been living in England since Pliocene times but it was not until the close of the Pleistocene that he began very greatly to affect the landscape. With the establishment of settlements and the clearing of forests, the spread of cultivation gradually altered the aspect of the country. But man's activities in the last 150 years have produced vastly greater effects and man may now be regarded as an important agent of geological change. It is at least a gain that his appreciation of the beauty of his surroundings is increasing while much that is lovely remains.

GLOSSARY OF
SOME TECHNICAL TERMS

Agglomerate: A rock of volcanic origin, composed of irregular blocks of various sizes, comprising solidified lava and fragments of the rocks through which the volcano has broken. Met with mostly in the pipes or necks of volcanoes.

Anticline: An arch or upfold in the rocks, generally produced by the bending upwards of the beds under lateral pressure. Anticlines are structurally weak, and the upper part rapidly becomes worn away (see Figs. 27, 43).

Basalt: A dark lava of basic composition, containing the minerals felspar and augite, and sometimes olivine. Mostly crystalline but of fine grain.

Boss: A large mass of igneous rock, intruded into and disrupting other rocks. Generally nearly circular in plan; often of coarse-grained rock such as granite (see Figs. 83, 90).

Cassiterite: Oxide of tin; occurs in square prisms capped by pyramids. Commonly blackish-brown to black.

Cirque (Corrie or Cwm): An amphitheatre or armchair-shaped hollow, usually excavated on a mountain-side; the slopes are precipitous, the floor nearly level. Due to glacial erosion. In Britain are commonest on north-facing slopes, especially in Wales and the Lake District.

Conglomerate: A rock which consists of an aggregate of pebbles or boulders in a matrix of finer material: a pudding-stone. Formed by rapid streams and powerful currents.

Consequent stream: A stream which flows in the direction of the dip of the rocks on which it was initiated; the direction of the stream is a 'consequence' of the original inclination of the surface (see Fig. 7).

Dip: The inclination of a bed of rock; measured in degrees from the horizontal (see Fig. 7).

Dolerite: A dark-coloured igneous rock, basic in composition and resembling a basalt, but composed of rather larger crystals. Generally occurs in a small intrusion such as a dyke or a sill, where it crystallised from a molten state.

L

Dyke: A more or less vertical wall-like mass of igneous rock, which cuts across the rocks into which it is intruded. Dykes vary greatly in width and in horizontal extent. They may project at the surface or may be hollowed out, according to the relative resistance of the dyke rock and the rocks bounding it.

Fault: A dislocation in the rocks, where one side has moved relatively to the other. Many fault planes are nearly vertical, others inclined at small angles. Faults have been produced by a variety of causes: some are due to intense lateral pressure, others to differential uplift or to tension (see Figs. 38, 50).

Felspar: A mineral group comprising various complex silicates of alumina and potassium, sodium or calcium. Abundant constituents of most igneous rocks.

Flint: A siliceous rock, grey or black; composed of very minutely crystalline silica. Occurs mostly as nodules in the Chalk.

Gneiss: A metamorphic rock, crystalline and coarse-grained, somewhat resembling a granite but showing a more or less banded arrangement of its constituents.

Granite: An igneous rock, composed of crystals of quartz, felspar and mica, of coarse grain. Results from the slow cooling of a large molten mass.

Grit: A rock much like a sandstone, composed mainly of grains of quartz. The grains are either more angular or larger than those in a sandstone.

Igneous rock: A rock formed by the consolidation of molten material. The characters of the rock depend mainly on the composition of this material, and on the conditions under which it cooled. Material ejected as lava generally cools quickly, material intruded in small masses less quickly, and material in large masses very slowly: the quickly cooled material may be glassy or very finely crystalline (*e.g.* basalt); the slowly cooled material is coarsely crystalline (*e.g.* granite). Thus most igneous rocks are crystalline.

Joints: Divisional planes which traverse rocks, cutting them in different but regular directions and allowing their separation into blocks. They are due to movements which have affected the rocks, and to shrinkage or contraction on consolidation.

Marl: A calcareous clay.

Metamorphic rock: A rock which may originally have been either igneous or sedimentary but which has undergone such changes since the time of its formation that its character has been considerably altered : in extreme cases it may be difficult to ascertain its original nature. Heat and pressure are the chief agencies of metamorphism. The commonest rocks of this class are gneiss and schist.

Mica: A mineral group comprising complex silicates of iron, magnesium, alumina and alkalies. Several different types can be recognised. Mica can be split into exceedingly thin, flexible plates. An important constituent of granite and other igneous rocks, and of some sedimentary rocks.

Mineral: A constituent of a rock, either an element or a compound of definite chemical composition. Mineral as used here has not the same meaning as the ' Mineral Kingdom ', which principally includes rocks : the latter are aggregates of one or more minerals and usually occur in large masses or extend over wide areas.

Monadnock: An isolated remnant (often of more resistant rock) projecting from a peneplain (name from Mt. Monadnock, U.S.A.). The name is used in this book for any hill rising conspicuously from a planed surface, whether the planation is the result of river erosion or wave action (see Fig. 70).

Oolite: A limestone of marine origin, composed of more or less spherical grains, each with concentric layers of calcium carbonate, usually formed in shallow water ; probably the grains are of chemical origin.

Peneplain (or peneplane): A land surface of low relief, worn down by prolonged weathering and river erosion ; the final stage in a Cycle of Erosion. An extensive peneplain needs for its formation a considerable time during which sea-level remains practically stationary. It is often difficult to distinguish in any given plain whether part of the planation has resulted from wave action during times of slight submergence.

Quartz: One of the commonest minerals in the earth's crust. Composed of silica (oxide of silicon). A constituent of granite and sandstones. Crystals are hexagonal prisms terminated by pyramids.

Quartzite: A highly siliceous sandstone. A rock composed mainly of quartz. Breaks with rather a smooth fracture. Usually very tough.

Rejuvenated stream: A stream which has received added power to cut vertically into its bed, usually owing to the uplift of the land, after it has reached some degree of maturity.

Sandstone: A sedimentary rock composed mainly of sand grains, chiefly grains of quartz, cemented together by some material such as calcium carbonate.

Schist: A metamorphic rock composed of one or more minerals, which appear to be squeezed out into lenticles, giving the rock a flaky appearance. Mica is a very common constituent of many schists.

Sedimentary rock: A rock consisting of sediments laid down either in water or on land. Usually stratified or bedded. Includes sandstones, clays, limestones, coal, etc.

Serpentine: A massive rock consisting largely of the mineral serpentine; a very basic igneous rock of coarse grain, originally made up principally of the mineral olivine, subsequently altered by contact with water.

Sill: An intrusive sheet of igneous rock, more or less following the bedding of the rocks it invades, but occasionally changing its position among the beds (*e.g.* the Whin Sill).

Slate: An argillaceous or clay rock which breaks along planes (cleavage) produced by pressure. The cleavage planes rarely coincide with the original bedding and may obliterate it almost completely.

Strike: The direction of a horizontal line on a dipping stratum; level-course of the miner. The strike is at right angles to the dip. The strike direction is generally the trend of the outcrop of the stratum (see Fig. 7).

Subsequent stream: A stream tributary to a consequent stream or originally so, following the strike direction. Generally along the outcrop of a less resistant bed (see Fig. 7).

Syncline: A trough-like fold in the rocks, generally resulting from lateral pressure. In some cases (*e.g.* the London basin, Fig. 24) the surface reflects the structure, but owing to the wearing of the rocks on either side, many synclines ultimately stand out as hills or mountains (*e.g.* Fig. 60).

Tufa: Material deposited by calcareous springs; usually white or yellowish. Sometimes soft, sometimes hard enough to form a building stone.

Tuff: A rock composed of the fine-grained material ('ash') ejected by volcanoes. Often arranged in beds or layers which have accumulated under water.

Unconformity: The relation of rocks in which a sedimentary rock or group of rocks rests on a worn surface of other rocks (sedimentary, igneous or metamorphic). Frequently the plane of unconformity separates rocks of vastly different ages and the rocks beneath the unconformity are of more complex structure than those above (see Figs 38, 55, 79).

Weathering: The general result of meteoric action on the exposed parts of rocks. Rain, frost, wind, and changes of temperature tend generally to help in the disintegration of the surface rocks.

ON MAPS AND BOOKS

THE reader interested in any special regions will no doubt have made himself familiar with the Ordnance Survey maps of the area. He may also feel the need of geological maps. A coloured geological map of the British Isles (25 miles to 1 inch) published by the Geological Survey at half a crown, is excellent for many purposes. For greater detail he should obtain the quarter-inch maps (mostly three shillings per sheet, twenty-three sheets covering England and Wales) or the one-inch maps (New Series, mostly two shillings per sheet, but not all areas are covered) These maps may be obtained from agents in all large towns.

The Geological Survey also publishes memoirs descriptive of the areas shown on many of the maps, but the general reader is likely to find more interest in the Regional Handbooks (published at two shillings and sixpence) dealing with various larger areas of Britain. Many of these are very suitable for readers wishing to follow up the study of any region, for in most cases they give some references to other literature.

Many of the pamphlets which are issued by the London Geologists' Association also give clear and simple accounts of certain areas, and the reader who wishes to extend his opportunities for acquiring geological knowledge is strongly advised to get in touch with the Hon. Secretary of this Association (care of Geological Society, Burlington House, London, W.1) or with other local geological and natural history societies.

For more general reading on geology the following are recommended:

Fearnsides and Bulman, *Geology in the Service of Man* (Pelican Books).
Trueman, *An Introduction to Geology* (Murby).
Leitch, *Geology in the Life of Man* (Thinker's Library).
Wills, *Physiographical Evolution of Britain* (Arnold).
Steers, *The Coastline of England and Wales* (Cambridge Univ. Press).

INDEX

I

L

A New Penguin Series

*

THE BUILDINGS OF ENGLAND

NIKOLAUS PEVSNER

Slade Professor of Fine Art at the University of Cambridge

This series is being launched to meet a growing demand from
students and travellers for more detailed information about the
history and architecture of the buildings they visit. It will provide
a complete and authoritative introduction to the churches, monuments, and large houses, in fact to every structure of interest in a
county, from prehistoric remains to the latest building of note,
treating them village by village and town by town, and in the case
of churches describing not only the exterior but also the furnish-
ings, such as pulpits, roof-bosses, plate, and rood-screens. Each
volume will contain a long general introduction to the architectural history of the county, a map, and a large section of
illustrations. The first three volumes, at three shillings and sixpence each, are *Cornwall*, *Nottinghamshire*, and *Middlesex*. *North
Devon*, *South Devon*, and a volume on *London (except the City and
Westminster)* will follow early in 1952.

*

'Inventories these books are, and wonderfully detailed ones. But
they are much more than that. On every page one is continually
made aware – sometimes by a sentence of comment, sometimes by
as little as a single word, sometimes even by what isn't said – of
learning, intelligence, and taste of work, placing, testing, and
assessing. So far as architecture is concerned, this series will rele-
gate most other guides to the status of picture books.' – *Architects'
Journal*.

Pelicans

*

MINERALS IN INDUSTRY
W. R. JONES
A 123

A concise account of the many minerals and mineral products – such as gold, copper, zinc, and salt – employed in modern commerce, describing their nature, where they are found, and their various uses and importance to man. (1s 6d)

THE ENGLISH VILLAGE*
VICTOR BONHAM-CARTER
A 241

An informative survey of the English village as a place and as a community, describing its history, analysing its various elements – physical, industrial, administrative, religious, and human – and outlining its probable future. The author is well known as a farmer in Somersetshire, a popular broadcaster on country matters, and an author and journalist. (2s 6d)

METALS IN THE SERVICE OF MAN
W. ALEXANDER AND A. STREET
A 125

How metals are obtained and worked, and the part they play in modern life, illustrated with sixteen pages of photographs and many drawings. A revised and enlarged edition is now available. (2s 6d)

PREHISTORIC BRITAIN
JACQUETTA AND CHRISTOPHER HAWKES
A 115

'An astonishingly vivid and circumstantial picture of the pre-Roman inhabitants and immigrations of the British Isles.... A fascinating human study.' – *Spectator*.
'Covers an astonishing amount of ground with admirable clarity and brevity, ranging from apemen to Anglo-Saxon.' – *Observer*.

* *Not available in U.S.A.*